W9-CKI-486

In Trout Country

IN TROUT COUNTRY

Edited and with an introduction by

Peter Corodimas

Illustrated by Leslie Morrill

A SPORTS ILLUSTRATED BOOK

LITTLE, BROWN AND COMPANY · BOSTON · TORONTO

LIBRARY OF CONGRESS CATALOG CARD NO. 79-143713

T 03/71

FIRST EDITION

Sports Illustrated Books
are published by
Little, Brown and Company
in association with
Sports Illustrated Magazine

Published simultaneously in Canada
by Little, Brown & Company (Canada) Limited

PRINTED IN THE UNITED STATES OF AMERICA

ACKNOWLEDGMENTS

"Opening Day" by Jack Gilchrist. Reprinted by permission from *The Georgia Review,* Spring 1964. Copyright © 1964 by the University of Georgia.

"The Cleveland Wrecking Yard" and "The Hunchback Trout" are reprinted from *Trout Fishing in America* by Richard Brautigan. Copyright © 1967 by Richard Brautigan. A Seymour Lawrence Book/Delacorte Press. Used by permission. First published by Four Seasons Foundation in its writing series edited by Donald Allen.

"Mine Enemy, the German Brown" from *The Sweet of the Year* by R. Palmer Baker, Jr. Reprinted by permission of William Morrow and Company, Inc. Copyright © 1965 by R. Palmer Baker, Jr.

"In Praise of Trout—and Also Me" by Paul O'Neil. Reprinted by permission from *Life* magazine. Copyright © 1964 by Time Inc.

"Portrait of a Worm Fisherman" by Lynn Montross. Reprinted by permission of *Esquire* magazine. Copyright 1936, renewed © 1964 by Esquire, Inc.

"The Werewolf" and "Perfidia" from *Bright Salmon and Brown Trout* by Dana S. Lamb.

"The Cutthroat Trout" reprinted from *One Day at Teton Marsh* by Sally Carrighar by permission of Alfred A. Knopf, Inc. Copyright 1946, 1947 by Sally Carrighar.
"Something Was Fishy About Stonehenge" by Ed Zern. Reprinted by permission of *Sports Illustrated* magazine. Copyright © 1966 by Time Inc.
"The Intruder" from *Trout Madness* by Robert Traver. Reprinted by permission of St. Martin's Press, Inc. Copyright © 1960 by Robert Traver.
"Along A Trout-Stream" by L. F. Brown from *The Speckled Brook Trout* edited by Louis Rhead, published by R. H. Russell, 1902.
"The Old Crawdad" from *The Big Ones Get Away* by Philip Wylie. Copyright 1939 by Philip Wylie, Copyright renewed. Reprinted by permission of Harold Ober Associates, Inc.
"The Big Brown Trout" by Robert Travers. Copyright © 1966 by Robert Travers. Used by permission of the author.
"Crocker's Hole" by R. D. Blackmore from *Tales From the Telling-House* Sampson Low, Marston & Co., Ltd., 1896.
"Don't Fish While I'm Talking" by Robert Manning from the *Atlantic Monthly*. Copyright © 1967 by the Atlantic Monthly Company. Reprinted by permission.
"Pool Number 37" by Donal C. O'Brien, Jr., from *American Trout Fishing*, edited by Arnold Gingrich. Copyright © 1965 by the Theodore Gordon Flyfishers. Reprinted by permission of Alfred A. Knopf, Inc.
"Turn Left at the Porcupine" by Jack Olsen. Copyright © 1970 by Time Inc. Reprinted by permission of the author and the author's agent, Scott Meredith Literary Agency, Inc.
"The King" from *No Life So Happy* by Edwin Lewis Peterson. Copyright 1940 by Dodd, Mead & Company, Inc. Copyright renewed. Reprinted by permission of the publisher.
"The Sun Stood Still" from *Where Flows the Kennebec* by Arthur R. Macdougall, Jr. Copyright 1947 by Arthur R. Macdougall, Jr. Reprinted by permission of the author.
"John Monahan" by Paul Hyde Bonner from *Aged in the Woods*. Copyright © 1958 by Paul Hyde Bonner.
"The English Exposure" from *Fresh Waters* by Edward Weeks. Copyright © 1968 by Edward Weeks. Used by permission.
"The Fisherman" reprinted from *Sir Pompey and Madame Juno* by Martin Armstrong by permission of A. D. Peters & Company.
"A Fight with a Trout" by Charles Dudley Warner from *In the Wilderness*. Houghton, Osgood and Company, 1897.
"Big Two-Hearted River: Part II" is reprinted with the permission of Charles Scribner's Sons from *In Our Time* by Ernest Hemingway. Copyright 1925 by Charles Scribner's Sons; renewal of copyright 1953 by Ernest Hemingway.
"Trout Widows" by Corey Ford. Copyright 1936, copyright renewed. Reprinted by permission of Harold Ober Associates, Inc.
"The Trout" from *Fishes, Birds and Sons of Men* by Jesse Hill Ford. Copyright © 1961 by Jesse Hill Ford and Sarah Davis Ford and Katherine Kieffer Musgrove, trustees.

For my father, Nicholas, who taught me how to fish for trout;
And for my little ones — Kathy, Keith, Deirdre, and Jennifer —
whose hooks always seem to need baiting.

Glory be to God for dappled things —
For skies of couple-colour as a brinded cow;
For rose-moles all in stipple upon trout that swim.

Gerard Manley Hopkins, *Pied Beauty*

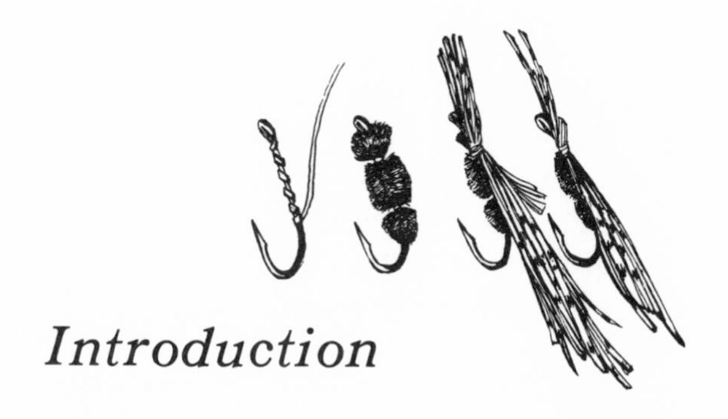

Introduction

For reasons best known to trout fishermen, the trout is the most idealized fish that ever swam. No fish has captured the imagination of so many people; no fish has been celebrated in as many books, including at least one novel completely about trout fishing (*No Life So Happy* by Edwin Lewis Peterson), nor in as many essays, short stories, and poems. In 1819 Franz Schubert composed his lovely Trout Quintet; how many fish have enjoyed a similar distinction? William Butler Yeats's poem "The Song of Wandering Aengus" describes a Celtic god who hooks a berry to a thread, drops it into a stream, and catches "a little silver trout." Later, the trout changes into "a glimmering girl / With apple blossom in her hair," who calls out to him and then runs and fades "through the brightening air." To understand how idealized the trout has become (and to spoil the poem), try substituting another fish for Yeats's trout. A little silver shiner? A little yellow perch? A little green pike? A little copper bass?

By allying himself with the trout, the trout fisherman has prospered beyond his wildest dreams; indeed, no other fisherman has made out half so well. The very expression "trout fisherman" conjures up an almost archetypal image: wearing waders, a plaid flannel shirt, and a beat-up old hat dotted with tied flies, he is standing in a fast-moving stream, white water, with some rocks above the surface; in his mouth, a pipe; and on his face, contentment, serenity: "I saw Eternity the other night / Like a great ring of pure and endless light."

It wasn't always like this. For the most part, the trout fisherman had to wait until the last two centuries before he could enjoy his new status. But even a glance at the history of angling literature reveals a slow process of idealization in which, over the centuries, both fish and fisherman emerge as something more than just fish or fisherman.

An Egyptian wall painting dating back to around 2000 B.C. assures us man has fished with a rod and line for at least four thousand years. He has been trying to beguile fish with artificial wet flies for nearly half that time; as early as A.D. 200, for instance, Macedonian fishermen were using flies tied with red wool and rooster feathers. Several venerable antiquarians, including Plato and Aristotle, have remarked on fishing. In the third century B.C., Theocritus wrote one of the earliest "fish stories," in which a fisherman dreams of having caught an enormous golden fish. Plutarch went on record cautioning fishermen in search of materials for braided horsehair lines to avoid the urine-weakened tail hair from a mare. To Plutarch also goes the credit for preserving a fine anecdote involving Antony and Cleopatra on a fishing excursion:

> He [Antony] went out one day to angle with Cleopatra, and, being so unfortunate as to catch nothing in the presence of his mistress, he gave secret orders to the fishermen to dive under water, and put fishes that had been already taken upon his hooks; and these he drew so fast that the Egyptian perceived it. But, feigning great admiration, she told everybody how dexterous Antony was, and invited them next day to come and see him again. So, when a number of them had come on board the fishing-boats, as soon as he had let

> down his hook, one of her servants was beforehand with his divers, and fixed upon his hook a salted fish from Pontus. Antony, feeling his line give, drew up the prey, and when, as may be imagined, great laughter ensued, 'Leave,' said Cleopatra, 'the fishing-rod, general, to us poor sovereigns of Pharos and Canopus; your game is cities, provinces, and kingdoms.'

Antony, the rumor goes, managed to retain some of his fishermanly pride by insisting he had at least caught the oldest fish of the day.

Unfortunately, such glimpses are infrequent. With few exceptions, classical writing offers little imaginative insight into the world of fishing — which is understandable, since, from the beginning, man has fished primarily to feed himself, and has carried on his occupation with the aid of a gorge, a handline, a spear, a net, or some such pragmatic instrument virtually light years away from a 3X tapered leader.

For centuries, angling literature remained basically a how-to-do-it literature which viewed fishing as work rather than as sport or recreation. Aelfric's *Colloquy on the Occupations,* a product of the tenth century, is perhaps one of the best examples of the purely instructional attitude earlier writers held toward fishing. Although Aelfric was the outstanding scholar and teacher of his century, his deadly serious approach to fishing is less than inspirational. Not until the fifteenth century did the classical angling tradition receive new life and direction — curiously enough, from an English prioress of a Benedictine nunnery, Dame Juliana Berners, who almost single-handedly changed the course of angling history. Her pioneering work, entitled *A Treatyse of fysshynge wyth an angle* (1496), contains copious advice on matters ranging from rod making to bait selection. But more important, it manages to rise above the relentless didacticism of much previous angling literature. Reading the treatise, one immediately senses Dame Juliana's deep love for her subject. For her, the ideal fisherman knew his craft completely; he could construct his fishing materials, rods, horsehair lines, hooks, flies, almost from scratch. He was, as well, a nature lover and a philosopher, a gentle but active man who abided by certain rules of angling conduct — restraint in taking fish, respect for the property rights and fishing rights of others. The act of fishing, as Dame Juliana envisioned it, involved the entire man physically and spiritually. For the first time in angling history, the fisherman was not merely a fisherman, but Man fishing. Dame Juliana praised many kinds of fish (and recommended, besides several kinds of bait, twelve different wet flies); in her hierarchy of desirable fish, however, the trout ranks very high, second only to the salmon.

If by touching on the delights and pleasures of fishing and by defining, in a rudimentary sense, the character of the fisherman Dame Juliana opened up new imaginative possibilities for angling literature, Izaak Walton's *The Compleat Angler* (1653) extended and refined these possibilities into the first indisputably great work in the entire history of angling literature. Craftsman, artist, gourmet, lover of nature, poet, entomologist, meteorologist, philanthropist, philosopher, theologian, Walton's angler is even more "compleat" than Dame Juliana's; and he is more fully realized as a man actually performing his multiple roles. To Dame Juliana's conventions Walton applied the indispensable techniques of dialogue and anecdote. In the transformation, Walton's pace becomes more leisurely than Dame Juliana's, his mood more literary and idyllic. In the tableau-like atmosphere of *The Compleat Angler,* there is more time for conviviality; time for admiring cowslips and water lilies and lady's-smocks; time for listening to a milkmaid's song; time even for setting down phrases which continue to delight generations of fishermen: "Indeed, my good scholar, we may say of angling, as Dr. Boteler said of strawberries, 'Doubtless God could have made a better berry, but doubtless God never did'; and so (if I might be judge) 'God never did make a more calm, quiet, innocent recreation than angling.' " Whereas Dame Juliana generalizes about a trout, content, for example, to describe the fish as "dainty," Walton instinctively turns to loving portraiture: "Come, my friend Coridon, this trout looks lovely; it was twenty-two inches when it was taken! and the belly of it looked, some part of it, as yellow as a marigold, and part of it as white as a lily; and yet, methinks, it looks better in this good sauce."

With the new techniques in upstream fishing, the renewed

interest in entomology, and the invention of the dry fly, the nineteenth century witnessed a revolution in trout fishing. A complete list of works written in the century would be impractical, but one should include Alfred Ronalds's *The Fly-Fisher's Entomology* (1836), George Philip Rigney Pulman's *The Vade Mecum of Fly-Fishing for Trout* (1846), William C. Stewart's *The Practical Angler* (1857), Thaddeus Norris's *The American Angler's Book* (1864), Frederic Halford's *Floating Flies and How to Dress Them* (1886), Mary Orvis Marbury's *Favorite Flies and Their Histories* (1892), as well as the pioneering work of Theodore Gordon, the father of American fly fishing; of G. E. M. Skues in the championing of nymph fishing in Great Britain; of men like George La Branche and Edward R. Hewitt, and a host of other important angler-writers who have increased and multiplied over the past several decades.

Much of the work has been primarily instructional and anecdotal — occasionally argumentative. Good trout stories have been less abundant. Several fine stories were written in the nineteenth century, two of which are included in this anthology, but the trout story really seems to blossom in the twentieth century. Some reasons are perhaps obvious. The literary short story was principally a mid-nineteenth-century discovery; it had to exist before many of the stories in this collection could exist. Moreover, the brown trout was not introduced into American waters until the last quarter of the nineteenth century. The native brook trout, in spite of its loveliness and delicacy, has inspired fewer stories and essays than the craftier, more temperamental brown trout.

Although several centuries removed from Dame Juliana Berners and Izaak Walton, all of the trout pieces contained in this volume owe some portion of their existence to the Berners-Walton tradition. "Crocker's Hole" fits so comfortably in the tradition that one would hardly guess any centuries had elapsed between it and *The Compleat Angler*. Published in the eighteen-nineties it remains one of the permanent splendors of trout literature. What future trout story can ever hope to approach it, or to duplicate the rush of joy that characterizes its final sentence?

The debt to the Berners-Walton tradition is also reflected in the ritualization that occurs in practically all the stories, even in pieces as diverse as "Along a Trout Stream" (1902) and "Big Two-Hearted River: Part II." The former is a prose hymn, unabashedly sentimental at times, to a trout stream, while the latter is a low-keyed, objectified celebration of the immediate pleasures of trout fishing. Style aside, both pieces share much common ground: a joy in the myriad details that often cluster around fishing — eating flapjacks with apple butter, setting up a rod, approaching a stream, watching a trout dimple the water — joy in the simple facts of existence. Ritualization appears in various forms, depending on the story, but the reader is certain to recognize it. Often it appears in the releasing of a trout by a fisherman who feels no need to keep the fish, since it already has given the best of itself before being landed. The ritual appears, too, in the trout fisherman's fascination with what is difficult, in the satisfaction he takes in setting up barriers to catching trout. Why else would some fishermen use 6X tippets with size twenty hooks, and seek out treacherous water with overhanging trees that are greedy for lines? For the same reasons, probably, that a tightrope walker uses a wire rather than a board, or that a poet elects to write a sestina rather than a commercial jingle. "In Praise of Trout — and Also Me" deals with this phenomenon, and a story like "Portrait of a Worm Fisherman" takes the phenomenon to task.

Many of the stories, of course, depart from the Berners-Walton tradition in a variety of unique ways; apparently the tradition of imaginative trout literature has a great deal of life in it yet — which bodes well for the future. At least two stories, "The Werewolf" and "Pool Number 37," challenge the view that expert trout fishermen are generally "compleat" men. Is the process of idealization finally beginning to break down?

Practically all of the comic pieces included here have abandoned Izaak Walton's quiet humor (which has exerted a deadly influence on many lesser writers) for a broader comic range. "A Fight with a Trout," the oldest story in the collection, describes with deadpan irony a mock-epic struggle to land a "giant" trout. Its author, Charles Dudley Warner, a few years earlier had collaborated with Mark Twain on *The Gilded Age,* and one suspects Mark Twain's humor may have been contagious. "The Cleveland Wrecking Yard" is a splendidly offbeat satire on purchasing a used trout stream which has been disassembled and shipped to the Cleveland Wrecking Yard from Colorado. The usual comic fish story about the big one that gets away is, I am happy to report, absent from this collection. On second thought, not entirely absent. But the plot receives new vitality from several gifted writers. In the hands of Ed Zern ("Something Was Fishy About Stonehenge") it takes on a stiff jolt of black humor; in the hands of Dana S. Lamb ("Perfidia") it is muted by the pangs of adolescent love.

A fair percentage deals with confrontation, the major theme of angling literature. But the varieties of confrontation! "Opening Day," "Mine Enemy, the German Brown," "The Intruder," "The Old Crawdad," "The Big Brown Trout," "The King," "Trout Widows," "The Trout," and several others are confrontation stories of one kind or another; beyond that point, however, simple classification breaks down, for the stories display an astonishing range of mood and theme. The object of confrontation may be the trout; but the fisherman may actually be confronting himself, his wife, another fisherman — perhaps some dream of perfection, as in the delightfully mystical story entitled "The King." In "The Old Crawdad," an aging trout fisherman must confront the distasteful business of saltwater fishing in Florida. And, speaking of confrontation, who would expect the themes of unrequited love, husband-snatching, or latent racism to appear in a trout anthology?

Why does a person fish? What alchemies exist between the trout and the trout fisherman? The stories explain — dramatize — better than any introduction can. That is the reason for this book's existence. To my knowledge, this is the first anthology of stories devoted exclusively to trout (I have been using the word "stories" loosely to include the literary short story, of which there are many here, as well as the yarn, the tale, and the narrative essay). Apart from the unavoidable element of personal taste, my principle of selection has been that of excellence. Each of the stories is a carefully wrought work of art; each, it seems to me, contains that indefinable element (empathy?) which makes a story work and which immediately transports a reader into another world. Whether the world is real or imaginary is not quite as important; that can be for the reader to decide, although I suspect that if the reader is also a fisherman he will gladly suspend his disbelief in the presence of a well-told angling story .

PETER CORODIMAS

At the edge of a trout stream

Contents

In Trout Country

Opening Day

Jack Gilchrist

The air hung heavy with the chilly dampness of a frosty spring morning. Light of another day played tag with shadows of the forest and wisps of fog resembling miniature cyclones curled up slowly from quiet spots on the face of the stream.

The man in the water crouched low as if hiding. Chest-high rubber waders protected him from the dampness. The khaki shirt he wore blended almost perfectly with the color of the waders and a wide-brimmed hat of almost the same neutral tan shielded a face that bore the pallor of indoor confinement and office employment. A willow creel hung at his left side and in his right hand he carried the slender, flexible length of a fly rod.

Progressing gently, the stranger placed each foot forward with care as he waded silently and steadily upstream in the shallow water. Slowly and ever so quietly, his eyes focused on a bend in the stream ahead, he moved in his creeping crouch, pausing occasionally for long moments as if time were endless and this day forever.

Gaining his objective, the bend in the stream, the wilderness intruder straightened behind the concealing screen of a rhododendron bush. Carefully, as if fingering the delicate web of a spider, he parted two frost-laden branches of green and peered through to survey a deep wide pocket of water that escaped silently but swiftly from the churning base of a crashing waterfall. Nothing missed his scrutiny as he surveyed the pool . . . his attention eventually focusing on a large boulder that rose from the water near the head of the pool but some fifty feet to his right of the falls.

Estimating his distance from the boulder the man's experienced eye judged what needed to be done to accomplish the mission that had brought him some one hundred fifty miles during the early hours of predawn darkness. His objective was a fish. Not just any fish but one single, solitary fish; to him the only fish in the world. A beautiful creature of iridescent colors with a blood-red band lining each side. A trout. A rainbow trout. The largest he had ever seen and the largest he could ever hope to catch.

Thoughts of the fish filled him with impatience and a burning desire to get on with the job at hand. But thoughts of two previous meetings with the beautiful creature of the hidden pool filled him with a wariness and a caution. Twice before, during his first two years of fly fishing apprenticeship, he had hung this wonderful fish. Twice before, in the early part of the two past seasons, before warming weather brought out novice fishermen to tramp the tender fern on the banks of the stream and muddy the quiet pools, he had met the fish in combat. And in his inexperience he twice had lost. Now for the third time and in the third season he would try again.

Crawling silently beneath trailing branches of the rhododendron bush, he waded cautiously into the shallow end of the pool barely disturbing its surface. Still crouching and pausing long moments between each step he moved so slowly that the surface of the water softly hugged his rubber-clothed legs and finally his waist as the ocean of morning mist hugged the tops of the Georgia mountains towering to either side. After many long minutes he had moved less than fifteen feet from the bend in the stream and the concealing screen of rhododendron that had guarded his approach to the pool.

Eventually reaching a location he deemed suitable for his work, the fisherman paused there for a long moment and then, turning, carefully appraised the terrain to his rear to make certain his back cast would not flick a leaf or nick a twig. Satisfied he quietly committed himself to the moment. Breathing deeply he summoned all his skill, all his planning and all his patience to the meticulous task of placing the delicate fly lightly on the water in an exact spot some thirty feet away and not more than two feet past the boulder.

Lengthening several feet of leader and line through the guides of the wispy rod the fisherman stretched the bamboo before him and then raised it sharply but smoothly, sending the line backward in one long continuous flow. As it straightened, he flicked the rod forward changing the direction of the line 180 degrees while feeding excess line through the guides with his left hand to get more distance. As the line completed its first roll before him he brought his right forearm back a second time, reversing the direction of the line again, and as the added length completed an arc and tugged gently with its backward motion, he drove the rod forward for the last time, with power and yet grace in the movement.

The lengthening line shot forward. As it straightened and flew past the boulder, he lowered the rod tip slightly and then raised it deftly to settle the fly on the surface of the water with the barest whisper of disturbance.

Completely absorbed in the rhythmic ritual, the fisherman noted with satisfaction the location of the fly some few inches short of its goal but sufficiently past the lair of the trout to insure a proper float. The muscles of his arms and shoulders tensed expectantly as the bit of camouflaged steel swirled gently in a slight cross current then began the journey that would carry it to the base of the boulder.

Although it took only a moment for the short drift it seemed to the fisherman an endless moment. His brow furrowed and crow-foot wrinkles of concentration deepened at the corners of his eyes as he projected himself thoughtfully to the drifting fly and the creature that lay watching it from the depths of the pool below.

The artificial insect sailed lazily toward its destiny, then brushed the face of the boulder, and the surface of the water dimpled deeply as the trout took.

The fisherman's strike came at the same instant . . . so quickly and efficiently and yet so gently that any casual onlooker would have sworn the fisherman could see the fish and thus know the exact moment it sucked the fly into its mouth.

At the first solid tug of resistance the fisherman struck a second time but with more power and less delicacy. As the point of the hook followed by its sharp engaging barb dug into the jaw of the trout the surface of the quiet pool shattered like a breaking mirror and with a mighty surge the great fish began its fight for life.

The trout dived for its hideaway beneath the boulder and the fisherman raised his rod to apply firm line pressure and halt the surge. Fearful of abrasion from the rock that could easily weaken the delicate leader but mindful of the power in his adversary, he fought to keep the fish away from the rock and in open water.

Responding to the pressure the fish jumped again, leaving a momentary spray-filled hole in the middle of the pool. Then as its strong sleek body crashed back into the water the trout propelled itself across the pool toward the boiling froth at the foot of the falls seeking refuge and help in the cascading force.

Once again the fisherman raised the rod and applied line pressure to turn the fish, but he had underestimated its strength and before he could turn it, the trout reached the churning water. Suddenly tautness left the line and a sickening feeling clawed at the heart of the man in the pool.

Had the great fish escaped? Had its strength, aided by the thundering water, torn the hook from its mouth? Quickly the fisherman raised the slender bamboo higher with arms reaching skyward and stepped back to get better leverage on the rod. Then again he felt the resistance, the power and the strength that would test his own, and panic subsided as thoughts once again turned to his strategy for the battle that still lay ahead.

He did not try to sting the fish into moving out from under the falls immediately. Knowing that the buffeting water was forcing the fish to exert itself against the tension of the rod, he was satisfied to keep pressure on and let the fish sap its own strength.

Gradually the great trout began to yield. Its continued pull against the strength of the line and the tension of the rod began to lessen. With pectoral fins fanning gracefully, the fish floated out from under the falls slowly as if undecided what action to take next. Gradually it began to move rapidly. It exploded on the surface for a third time and then began circling the pool as if seeking a watery side door through which to escape. For better than ten minutes the fish canvassed the pool as if caged in a strange and unknown world.

Finally, with ebbing strength and in fearful panic of approaching death, the trout made one last great effort to get away. Sweeping across the pool in a renewed surge of action it turned sharply and directly toward the fisherman, seeking access to the stream that flowed from the trail of the pool. Borne on the wings of fright it shot toward the shallow water as if to crash through the legs of its tormentor and into the neck of the stream by force. The bullet-shaped missile of color sped toward the freedom gate, and for the first time since it had taken the fly the fish was free from the pressure of the rod and line.

The sudden and increasing slackness in the line as the fish approached made it impossible for the fisherman to force line pressure control on his adversary. Once again panic gripped his mind and fear crawled through the alley of his imagination as thoughts of losing the fish spurred him to action. Abandoning caution in a desperate attempt to halt the rush of his quarry and turn it back into deeper water, he knelt and then sprawled his length across the mouth of the small stream, blocking exit from the pool.

Frightened by the disturbance in the shallow water and finding its escape path blocked the great trout turned and bore back toward its lair under the boulder. The fisherman struggled quickly to his feet and rapidly gathered slack line until he could once again feel the tautness of the connection between himself and his opponent. Wet, with waders full of water and hat floating out of sight downstream, he was oblivious to all but the soul-satisfying thought that now he had the battle nearly won.

The fisherman continued to play the fish gently, feeling its strength and power bleed slowly through the line and rod. The growing weakness of the fish served as a transfusion of strength to him, and his growing confidence lifted him on wings of exhilaration.

What a stir he would create at home. This should rank as one of the finest trout killed in the state in years. He could envision the shine of enchantment in the eyes of his nine-year-old son at the telling of the story of the fight, and in his imaginings he could picture the creature mounted in a curving leap, positioned on a rustic plaque and hanging on a wall at the office.

Now the job was done. The dark broad band of red lay exposed on the face of the pool as the spent creature floated on its side almost as motionless as the misty dampness that hung suspended in the air of the close mountain valley. Firmly but with great care the victor steadily drew line in through the guides of the rod and as he did so the lifeless bulk gradually approached. He had done his job well. As he quit gathering line and raised the rod to float the fish into the shallow water at his feet, the creature came in with hardly a stir, its gills pumping gulps of oxygenated water but its broad, powerful tail virtually motionless.

Stooping quickly the fisherman inserted his thumb into the mouth of the big trout, grasping the lower jaw firmly between thumb and forefinger. Rising he lifted his arm up and forward and in almost unbelieving awe inspected his prize. Never could he have imagined capturing such a trout.

Suddenly, as if on command, a bolt of sunshine pierced the gray mist of early morning and focused itself on the drama. The red band extending full length on each side of the great fish captured the bright ray to glow like wired neon tubing, and speckled blotches of color that bordered its back and sides flickered and glimmered with the fire of diamonds, rubies, and emeralds. As if imitating the beauty of the trout, a rainbow formed in the waterfall beyond, and as the sun's rays fought through the fog of morning, its reflection danced on the surface of the pool.

The fisherman stood briefly as a frown of contemplation replaced the smile of victory on his face and then suddenly, as if obeying an order he could not refuse from a voice he could not deny, he knelt in the shadows and lowered the trout into the pool. With a firm but gentle grip he released the barb from its lip, and holding the creature upright moved it to and fro in the water until its gills stroked firmly. He then released his hold, and with a weak wavering motion of its broad tail the fish moved slowly away from him until it disappeared beneath the sunlit surface of the pool.

For a long, long time the fisherman knelt there in the shallow water and the warm sunshine and gazed into the heart of the pool where the great trout had disappeared.

The Cleveland Wrecking Yard

Richard Brautigan

Until recently my knowledge about the Cleveland Wrecking Yard had come from a couple of friends who'd bought things there. One of them bought a huge window: the frame, glass and everything for just a few dollars. It was a fine-looking window.

Then he chopped a hole in the side of his house up on Potrero Hill and put the window in. Now he has a panoramic view of the San Francisco County Hospital.

He can practically look right down into the wards and see old magazines eroded like the Grand Canyon from endless readings. He can practically hear the patients thinking about breakfast: *I hate milk,* and thinking about dinner: *I hate peas,* and then he can watch the hospital slowly drown at night, hopelessly entangled in huge bunches of brick seaweed.

He bought that window at the Cleveland Wrecking Yard.

My other friend bought an iron roof at the Cleveland Wrecking Yard and took the roof down to Big Sur in an old station wagon and then he carried the iron roof on his back up the side of a mountain. He carried up half the roof on his back. It was no picnic. Then he bought a mule, George, from Pleasanton. George carried up the other half of the roof.

The mule didn't like what was happening at all. He lost a lot of weight because of the ticks, and the smell of the wildcats up on the plateau made him too nervous to graze there. My friend said jokingly that George had lost around two hundred pounds. The good wine country around Pleasanton in the Livermore Valley probably had looked a lot better to George than the wild side of the Santa Lucia Mountains.

My friend's place was a shack right beside a huge fireplace where there had once been a great mansion during the 1920s, built by a famous movie actor. The mansion was built before there was even a road down at Big Sur. The mansion had been brought over the mountains on the backs of mules, strung out like ants, bringing visions of the good life to the poison oak, the ticks, and the salmon.

The mansion was on a promontory, high over the Pacific. Money could see farther in the 1920s, and one could look out and see whales and the Hawaiian Islands and the Kuomintang in China.

The mansion burned down years ago.

The actor died.

His mules were made into soap.

His mistresses became bird nests of wrinkles.

Now only the fireplace remains as a sort of Carthaginian homage to Hollywood.

I was down there a few weeks ago to see my friend's roof. I wouldn't have passed up the chance for a million dollars, as they say. The roof looked like a colander to me. If that roof and the rain were running against each other at Bay Meadows, I'd bet on the rain and plan to spend my winnings at the World's Fair in Seattle.

My own experience with the Cleveland Wrecking Yard began two days ago when I heard about a used trout stream they had on sale out at the Yard. So I caught the Number 15 bus on Columbus Avenue and went out there for the first time.

There were two Negro boys sitting behind me on the bus. They were talking about Chubby Checker and the Twist. They thought that Chubby Checker was only fifteen years old because he didn't have a mustache. Then they talked about some other guy who did the twist forty-four hours in a row until he saw George Washington crossing the Delaware.

"Man, that's what I call twisting," one of the kids said.

"I don't think I could twist no forty-four hours in a row," the other kid said. "That's a lot of twisting."

I got off the bus right next to an abandoned Time Gasoline filling station and an abandoned fifty-cent self-service car wash. There was a long field on one side of the filling station. The field had once been covered with a housing project during the war, put there for the shipyard workers.

On the other side of the Time filling station was the Cleveland Wrecking Yard. I walked down there to have a look at the used trout stream. The Cleveland Wrecking Yard has a very long front window filled with signs and merchandise.

There was a sign in the window advertising a laundry marking machine for $65.00. The original cost of the machine was $175.00. Quite a saving.

There was another sign advertising new and used two and three ton hoists. I wondered how many hoists it would take to move a trout stream.

There was another sign that said:

THE FAMILY GIFT CENTER,
GIFT SUGGESTIONS FOR THE ENTIRE FAMILY

The window was filled with hundreds of items for the entire family. *Daddy, do you know what I want for Christmas? What, son? A bathroom. Mommy, do you know what I want for Christmas? What, Patricia? Some roofing material.*

There were jungle hammocks in the window for distant relatives and dollar-ten-cent gallons of earth-brown enamel paint for other loved ones.

There was also a big sign that said:

USED TROUT STREAM FOR SALE.
MUST BE SEEN TO BE APPRECIATED.

I went inside and looked at some ship's lanterns that were for sale next to the door. Then a salesman came up to me and said in a pleasant voice, "Can I help you?"

"Yes," I said. "I'm curious about the trout stream you have for sale. Can you tell me something about it? How are you selling it?"

"We're selling it by the foot length. You can buy as little as you want or you can buy all we've got left. A man came in here this morning and bought five hundred sixty-three feet. He's going to give it to his niece for a birthday present," the salesman said.

"We're selling the waterfalls separately of course, and the trees and birds, flowers, grass and ferns we're also selling extra. The insects we're giving away free with a minimum purchase of ten feet of stream."

"How much are you selling the stream for?" I asked.

"Six dollars and fifty cents a foot," he said. "That's for the first hundred feet. After that it's five dollars a foot."

"How much are the birds?" I asked.

"Thirty-five cents apiece," he said. "But of course they're used. We can't guarantee anything."

"How wide is the stream?" I asked. "You said you were selling it by the length, didn't you?"

"Yes," he said. "We're selling it by the length. Its width runs between five and eleven feet. You don't have to pay anything extra for width. It's not a big stream, but it's very pleasant."

"What kinds of animals do you have?" I asked.

"We only have three deer left," he said.

"Oh. . . . What about flowers?"

"By the dozen," he said.

"Is the stream clear?" I asked.

"Sir," the salesman said. "I wouldn't want you to think that we would ever sell a murky trout stream here. We always make sure they're running crystal clear before we even think about moving them."

"Where did the stream come from?" I asked.

"Colorado," he said. "We moved it with loving care. We've never damaged a trout stream yet. We treat them all as if they were china."

"You're probably asked this all the time, but how's fishing in the stream?" I asked.

"Very good," he said. "Mostly German browns, but there are a few rainbows."

"What do the trout cost?" I asked.

"They come with the stream," he said. "Of course it's all luck. You never know how many you're going to get or how big they are. But the fishing's very good, you might say it's excellent. Both bait and dry fly," he said smiling.

"Where's the stream at?" I asked. "I'd like to take a look at it."

"It's around in back," he said. "You go straight through that door and then turn right until you're outside. It's stacked in lengths. You can't miss it. The waterfalls are upstairs in the used plumbing department."

"What about the animals?"

"Well, what's left of the animals are straight back from the stream. You'll see a bunch of our trucks parked on a road by the railroad tracks. Turn right on the road and follow it down past the piles of lumber. The animal shed's right at the end of the lot."

"Thanks," I said. "I think I'll look at the waterfalls first. You don't have to come with me. Just tell me how to get there and I'll find my own way."

"All right," he said. "Go up those stairs. You'll see a bunch of doors and windows, turn left and you'll find the used plumbing department. Here's my card if you need any help."

"Okay," I said. "You've been a great help already. Thanks a lot. I'll take a look around."

"Good luck," he said.

I went upstairs and there were thousands of doors there. I'd never seen so many doors before in my life. You could have built an entire city out of those doors. Doorstown. And there were enough windows up there to build a little suburb entirely out of windows. Windowville.

I turned left and went back and saw the faint glow of pearl-colored light. The light got stronger and stronger as I went farther back, and then I was in the used plumbing department, surrounded by hundreds of toilets.

The toilets were stacked on shelves. They were stacked five toilets high. There was a skylight above the toilets that made them glow like the Great Taboo Pearl of the South Sea movies.

Stacked over against the wall were the waterfalls. There were about a dozen of them, ranging from a drop of a few feet to a drop of ten or fifteen feet.

There was one waterfall that was over sixty feet long. There were tags on the pieces of the big falls describing the correct order for putting the falls back together again.

The waterfalls all had price tags on them. They were more expensive than the stream. The waterfalls were selling for $19.00 a foot.

I went into another room where there were piles of sweet-smelling lumber, glowing a soft yellow from a different color skylight above the lumber. In the shadows at the edge of the room under the sloping roof of the building were many sinks and urinals covered with dust, and there was also another waterfall about seventeen feet long, lying there in two lengths and already beginning to gather dust.

I had seen all I wanted of the waterfalls, and now I was very curious about the trout stream, so I followed the salesman's directions and ended up outside the building.

O I had never in my life seen anything like that trout stream. It was stacked in piles of various lengths: ten, fifteen, twenty feet, etc. There was one pile of hundred-foot lengths. There was also a box of scraps. The scraps were in odd sizes ranging from six inches to a couple of feet.

There was a loudspeaker on the side of the building and soft music was coming out. It was a cloudy day and seagulls were circling high overhead.

Behind the stream were big bundles of trees and bushes. They were covered with sheets of patched canvas. You could see the tops and roots sticking out the ends of the bundles.

I went up close and looked at the lengths of stream. I could see some trout in them. I saw one good fish. I saw some crawdads crawling around the rocks at the bottom.

It looked like a fine stream. I put my hand in the water. It was cold and felt good.

I decided to go around to the side and look at the animals. I saw where the trucks were parked beside the railroad tracks. I followed the road down past the piles of lumber, back to the shed where the animals were.

The salesman had been right. They were practically out of animals. About the only thing they had left in any abundance were mice. There were hundreds of mice.

Beside the shed was a huge wire birdcage, maybe fifty feet high, filled with many kinds of birds. The top of the cage had a piece of canvas over it, so the birds wouldn't get wet when it rained. There were woodpeckers and wild canaries and sparrows.

On my way back to where the trout stream was piled, I found the insects. They were inside a prefabricated steel building that was selling for eighty cents a square foot. There was a sign over the door. It said:

INSECTS

Mine Enemy, the German Brown

R. Palmer Baker, Jr.

The fly fisher loves the brook trout for the beauty of its colors and the remoteness of its habitat. The rainbow trout he loves for its strength and speed, the way it leaps against the pressure of the line. But the brown trout, the German brown, is his ultimate adversary, the final test of his skill in presentation and his knowledge of the stream.

Nowhere is this testing more rigorous than on my favorite Vermont river, a lovely but overfished and moody stream. For this is truly brown trout water. Take two good fish from it and you have had a banner day. More often than not they will refuse to rise — and then, if they rise, more than often refuse to take. But it is for these reasons, surely, that their pursuit is so rewarding.

One evening in early June I saw a skilled angler who spends a week each year on this fascinating stream go to work in a manner that was a tribute to its fish. My wife and I had arrived the afternoon before at the country hotel that he made his headquarters and had been shown three of his fish in the icebox, still marked with the vermilion spots and lovely yellow cast of the wild German brown. The trout weighed upward of three pounds each and represented three days of fishing; the sight of them was enough to get us promptly out on the stream.

In the late afternoon there was a mixed fly hatch, and we had a good time as the small trout went on the feed. After supper we strolled along the village sidewalks and lingered on a bridge that crossed a tributary stream. A few trout were showing, but life was so pleasant that the idea of getting back into waders hardly seemed worthwhile.

It was after dark when our fellow guest returned to the hotel and we introduced ourselves. This time he had no trout. Something had gone wrong. Maybe it was the fly, he said, or perhaps the leader had dragged on the current. Or perhaps it was just the fish, a big one, a surly German brown that had refused his fly.

The following afternoon I met him on the stream. He did not have his rod with him. He was sitting with his back against a maple tree, watching the far bank.

"See," he said; "there he is. A good trout, going on the feed."

A little dimple appeared where the smooth-flowing current was broken by a snag close to the bank.

"With luck I might take him at nightfall. He'll feed steadily now, as long as the flies keep coming. He's in the surface mood."

I asked the angler why he did not have his rod with him.

"This time of year," he said, "in daylight, you ought to spend your time walking along the banks of the stream. If you're looking for big browns, avoid temptation: leave your rod behind. If you cast over the fish before dusk, you'll only put him down."

He got up. "Why don't you try for him after supper?"

The invitation was as serious as it was generous. However, I had the good sense and grace to refuse. What I should like, I said, was to see him finish the day's campaign. He kindly agreed to the suggestion, and we walked together back to our cars.

After supper we returned leisurely to the same location on

the stream. On the far side there were willows and alders, their roots giving protection to the daylight lie of the trout. We approached carefully, by the maple tree.

"Ah, good!" said the angler. "Look at that fish!"

A swirl appeared at the same place by the snag.

This time the angler was fully equipped, in fishing jacket and waders, carrying his rod. But the selection of a fly was yet to be made.

What, I asked him, had he decided?

This time of year, he said, the usual choice would be a little fly. Maybe an olive. Probably an eighteen. Finally, he decided, over a first-class fish, at this late and dusky hour, the choice would be a white-faced spider.

We waited for another twenty minutes, almost until dark. Meanwhile the angler had waded quietly into position. Again the trout dimpled.

On the first cast the fly landed too far out in the stream but directly in line with the snag and the lie of the fish. The second cast was right. The fly landed cocked on its hackles, close to the snag, floated six inches, and was engulfed. I had the pleasure of netting the trout, about fifteen inches and well over a pound.

"A handsome fish," the angler said; "but let's leave him for another year."

With a vicarious sense of virtue, I released the fly, which was like a white rosette in the trout's upper jaw, held the fish steady in the water for a moment, and then watched it swim off. I thanked the angler for my evening of pleasure and the lesson learned.

On the same stream, a month later, my wife and I met another brown trout fisherman who in his way was equally skillful and whose task, because of the later season, was probably more difficult. In the afternoon we had been fishing the dry fly without success down where the stream crosses the state line and becomes a river. The water was low, no trout were rising, and none was going to show. Then I saw a fisherman in the pool above me land and release a small trout.

When we met, he told us that he had fished this valley every summer for thirty years. His home was in the Middle West, so these were journeys of devotion. "I love this valley," he said, "and here is where I meet mine enemy and friend, the German brown."

There were two ten-inchers in his creel. He showed me the green-bodied nymph which had taken them, and I knew that he must have been handling it in the most subtle and accomplished manner. Gently he disclaimed the ability to catch a sizable fish. "If you could only have seen the fifteen-incher that was caught here last night," he said. "A lovely fish—what a lovely fish!"

The sight of one of these big browns can inspire a single-minded determination on the part of the angler and often a campaign against the quarry that may last a season or more before coming to a conclusion. Such fish acquire individual reputations and personalities and sometimes even names. Kneeling on the bank of the little but marvelously rich Letort in Pennsylvania, the angler sees a two-foot fish swim up the channel between the weed beds, seemingly unconcerned. Above the old dam at Arlington in Vermont a heavy fish feeds steadily on the hatching Hendricksons and then, almost as though sensing the approaching angler, disappears. These are fish like Trout Jonathan, killed on a streamer in the Schoolhouse Pool of the New York Ausable, and there are counterparts in every brown-trout water. One late summer evening, near a bridge crossing a nondescript cow-pasture stream, I met two boys carrying an enormous brown trout between them. "Mister," they said, "this is the trout from the Dutchman's Hole" — and I realized they were speaking of a celebrity.

Because of its appetite and capacity, one of these trout can just about eliminate all other fishing on a stretch of stream. Along one of the smaller Catskill rivers there is a mile of lovely water that a family has owned and fished for generations. Within sight of the farmhouse a favorite pool has always carried a stock of fair-sized fish. Most of the pool is shallow, but under one bank there is five feet of water, in which the trout lie during the daytime. At dusk they enter the shallows to feed.

This is a good pool early in the season, but once there was an April when it produced scarcely a fish. In May, when the water cleared and warmed and the flies began hatching and the trout were on the feed all up and down the stream, only an occasional fish showed itself, by dimple, splash or swirl. A few of these were caught, and they were of a somewhat better size than usual.

The general opinion was that the pool had been fished out by poachers. This was not a very satisfactory opinion, owing to the nearness of the pool to the house, but there was no fair alternative. The presence of a big fish, a cannibal, would have provided an explanation, but it was obvious that no such fish had its hold there. Late in May the young heir to this stretch of river and his brother-in-law explored the pool carefully with underwater goggles. They saw only one trout of ten inches and a few chubs.

A decision was made to restock the pool. Several dozen trout, from eight to ten inches long, were purchased from a nearby commercial hatchery and deposited in the pool and the riffle above it. Three evenings later, on the Friday before Decoration Day, the surface of the pool was dimpled and broken by feeding fish.

At mid-June there were still a number of fish showing in the pool, but they were oddly wary and difficult to catch. By the end of the month only a few were rising in the evening. Evidently the rest of the stocking had migrated to other parts of the stream. Something had happened to the pool. At any rate, it was no longer the good holding water it once had been.

In July the daughter of the family and her husband and two little children came to the farmhouse for a holiday. Wading, swimming, and frogging took the place of fishing in the pool. Soon there was no sign of trout, but that was not thought to be very odd. No doubt the constant presence of the children had driven out the last of them. In any event, it was late in the season.

Then the daughter saw the fish. While bathing in the stream before breakfast, she stepped into the sluicelike run of water at the tail of the pool just as the first rays of the morning sun were striking its surface. As she did so, a tremendous fish, the length of her arm, came over the lip of the pool and shot past her downstream. She could clearly see the configuration and colors of a brown trout.

"Dear," she said when her husband came downstairs for breakfast, "there are cannibals in these hills, and I met one this morning." She described the fish to him, and the campaign was on.

Plainly this trout had its hold somewhere downstream and at night came into the pool to feed. Like the overconfident skipper of a wartime submarine, it had finally stayed, open to view, a little too long.

This happened on a Monday. Every night that week, until Friday, the girl's husband spent an hour or two fishing the pool. He did not see, hear or feel any sign of the trout. Then on Friday night at about eleven o'clock the fish struck. The angler was casting a trace of two wet flies, letting them swing with the current, retrieving them slowly, and casting again. At the end of the swing he felt a tug. He tightened on the line, and there was the surge of a big fish.

This was the trout, the cannibal brown. It stayed and fought in the pool for fifteen minutes. In that interval, meanwhile, the angler's brother-in-law had arrived for the weekend. He walked down in time to witness the fight.

"Stay at the tail of the pool," the angler shouted. "Maybe you can turn him if he tries to go downstream."

The trout did exactly that, but the attempt at turning was not successful. The trout made one wild circle of the pool, leaped once, and went strongly over the lip of the pool into the fast water. The leader snagged on an underwater boulder and the trout was free.

Two weeks later the cannibal was hooked again, this time at dawn, on a bucktail fly fished in the current at the head of the pool during a violent summer freshet. It was the daughter, not her husband, who struck the fish on this occasion. She was using her two-ounce Leonard, a rod equal, though not accustomed, to such work, and she almost succeeded in killing the fish; however, two hundred yards downstream, in a narrow run of water, it eluded her net, swam under the bank, and broke away.

But now she knew where the trout had its hold: under the bank, protected by a dead elm and by willow roots, a hard place to fish, bypassed by most anglers. It was a fine place for an old brown trout, tired of foraging in the big waters of the lower river, to make its home.

The girl now wanted to take this fish. July was almost at an end, the water was low and warm, and there was not much chance of success. Still she was going to try in the ten days of vacation left to her, and her husband and her brother agreed not to interfere.

The level of the stream had dropped so that the trout could no longer forage upstream into the pool. The big fish could feed now, almost entirely after dark, only in the narrow run where its hold was located. What kind of fly would it take? How should it be presented? The lady angler was confronted, to an intense degree, with all the classic questions. Yet she had one vital advantage. She knew precisely where the trout lay and where it would have to feed.

Her conclusion was that the trout would drop down to feed at the lower end of the run. Here, also, she would be able to make an effective cross-stream cast, from a reasonable distance, with low bush willows to screen or break her silhouette. This choice dictated the type of fly. Neither a streamer nor a wet fly could be effective in this narrow water. She would have to use the dry fly, imitating the caddis or the night-flying moths — or suggesting them. The big spider fly does not look like an insect to the angler. To the brown trout, however, the drop and float of this fly and its action on the water are more suggestive after sundown than the most precise of imitations. The lady angler selected her fly accordingly.

On four successive evenings, at dusk, she forsook friends and family to wait for the trout to go on the feed. Carefully she took her station by the bush willows, with the rod by her side, and watched the water as darkness came on. She did not return from her vigil — in each case unsuccessful — until well past nine o'clock.

On the fifth day something happened to the weather. There were thundershowers. The wind came out of the south and then shifted from one compass point to another. During the afternoon the girl's husband and brother caught a few trout, their first successful venture of a fortnight. Grasshoppers, beetles, honeybees, and a myriad of smaller terrestrial insects were blown onto the stream. Before supper, the husband and brother drank an extra cocktail each, told the girl to keep in training, and wished her luck.

The thrilling part of this evening for the girl was that she could see the trout when it moved from its hold and finned slowly backward down to its feeding station. In the evening light, polarized by the mist and thunderheads, every pebble in the waters of the run was visible to her. She could observe every movement of the trout.

A lesser angler would never have resisted the temptation to try for the fish at once. Like her senior on the Vermont river, however, the girl kept her station until dark. Then, with controlled excitement, she made her cast — and the fish took.

Feeling the iron and the pressure of the line, the trout leaped in the shallow tail water, then quieted and swam slowly up the run to its hold. For a smaller fish this maneuver would have meant freedom. The fish would have twisted and broken the leader among the willow roots. The cannibal, however, was too big to do this. It responded to the pressure of the rod and moved into the open water. The girl had hoped for such a reaction. She thought her only hope of landing the fish was to wait it out.

At half past nine, when she had not returned, her husband and brother came down to the stream. Along the way her brother noticed a pitchfork that had been left out near a hayrick in the meadow and picked it up to return it to the barn.

"Hey!" he said. "I've come to your rescue." And then he saw that she was indeed playing the trout.

"You two get away from here, go away!" she shouted at them. "If I lose this fish while you're here, I'll never forgive you."

Reluctantly they left her and walked back into the meadow. But they could not keep away. A few minutes later they returned just as the trout, in a change of mood, moved down and began thrashing the shallow water at the tail of the run. This was too much for the angler's brother. He grabbed the pitchfork, jumped into the water, and with a mighty thrust impaled the trout and heaved it onto the bank, where his brother-in-law fell on it.

The girl, who had been standing on the bank about fifty feet upstream, ran down to them, crying in a mixture of rage, relief, and excitement.

"Oh, why did you do it?" she cried. "That was my fish. I wanted to land him myself." And then she said, "But I'm glad you came back. I thought I'd lost him. I was sure I'd lost him."

"Relax," said her brother. "All I did was gaff the fish for you. That was the least you were entitled to."

When the three of them looked at the fish by flashlight they experienced the feeling of admiration and then the slight sense of regret which attend the angler's greatest moments of triumph. Yet these feelings were momentary. Back they went to rouse the household and celebrate.

The trout weighed five pounds and three-quarters. It was a male with a hooked jaw like a cock salmon, an old cannibal and yet a riser to the fly, a difficult, surly, and rewarding German brown.

In Praise of Trout— And Also Me

Paul O'Neil

Angling for the noble trout with an artificial fly is widely defined in literature as an exercise in contentment — a process hardly less stupefying, apparently, than an overdose of goof balls. Bait fishermen consider the practice effete, like tennis as it was played by young females in 1890. Bartenders, undertakers and other sentimental kibitzers assume it denotes high purpose, since fly fishermen — ah damned fool expression! — are alleged to be purists. Fishing experts, and particularly those who write for sporting publications, make fly fishing sound like lion hunting. Experts never have a moment's doubt as to what fly pattern to use, never cast over a trout weighing less than two pounds and never fail to bring the monster to net after 1) a thrilling battle, which went on long after night fell over the clear pool, or 2) a very short tussle, really, due to the fantastic skill with which the quarry was played.

During my twenty years of fishing with a fly, each and every one of these assumptions and definitions has caused me vague but recurring unease and guilt — the sort of fleeting pangs a second-story man with a hangover might experience at the sound of a Salvation Army band. It seems impossible that there could be a grain of truth in any of them, but the fisherman's handmaiden, alas, is doubt and he is often impelled to ask, "Why am I not a better man?"

The maniac who engineered my worst August afternoon — this was five years ago, but I will remember it if and when I am ninety — typifies the sort of phenomenon which occasions such self-analysis. My first response to his appearance was simple astonishment. He held a wobbling glass rod high in air and, as he lurched slowly downstream, he jiggled and jerked from ankles to head and plucked at his monofilament line — thus activating the lure tied to its end — like Billy Sunday's own bull-fiddle player. The man never stopped; he must have trained for his performance as Dempsey trained for Willard or Hackenschmidt trained for Gotch.

"How ya doing?" he cried as he sloshed up, still jerking spastically, to my side. "No good," said I. "Ought to use a minnow," said he, pointing with his chin to his own line. He then shut off his engine for a moment and opened his creel. "Five," said he.

He lied. There were only three. But each beautiful trout was fifteen inches long. I felt — I cannot deny it — like an orphan child at the wading pool.

It was a moment in which it was impossible not to wonder — even though one could pick no worse time for fishing a fly than an August afternoon — whether a real expert would have been standing there, as was I, with an empty creel and an emptier expression being patronized by an inartistic and greed-riddled bait-using cretin. It was also impossible not to wonder, once the first awful shock had passed, whether I would not have reacted more charitably if I had been truly dedicated, truly sporting and pure. I was privy, after all, to fresh air, sunlight, the sight and sound of running water, the loom of green and gentle Catskill heights and the chance to speak generously to a fellow sportsman — all of the ingredients of contentment, certainly, if man ever possessed them. It did no good. I waited, steaming with avarice, until the interloper vanished from view and then attached a streamer fly which imitated the minnow he seemed to have used and did my fruitless best to ape his curious style. Ninety per cent of fly fishermen, in my opinion, would have fallen prey to the same lamentable instincts (and would doubtless have failed, as did I) provided they, too, evaded observation by their peers.

It would be incorrect to say that the fly fisherman never enjoys tranquility, never appreciates nature or is incapable of high purpose — even to the point of freeing the trout he has hooked for the masses to snaffle. All are possible as long as the trout are decent enough to rise to the angler's fly in the first place. These conclusions are based, I must confess, on personal speculation, as is my conviction that fly fishermen tend to be competitive, status conscious and crafty types skilled in the low arts of gamesmanship.

I was enormously encouraged in these views, however, by a recent visit — my first — to the gambling hells of Las Vegas. I was startled out of my wits by the boiler factory din — the crash of slot machines, the cries of crap shooters, the sound of music — in which I was enveloped at an hour when most people are eating breakfast. But, for all that, the unlikely scene was instantly familiar. Everyone in the big casino — from the old ladies yanking away after jackpots to the high rollers at the dice tables — betrayed that complete obliviousness of all other humans and wore that look of mingled cupidity and resignation I had seen on scores of dry-fly pools.

My own case may very well be worse than the average. I not only bear the scars of a thousand old frustrations and anticipate a thousand more but must admit, after a score of years spent flailing away at streams, that intolerance and prejudice have encroached on my mind as mildew does on last year's cantaloupe. I would rather catch an eight-inch trout than an eight-pound bass. I am incapable, in fact, of understanding why anyone wants to fish for bass in the first place — or for perch, or for muskellunge, or for pike. Ted Williams seems, at least from afar, to be an absolutely splendid fellow. What impels him to pursue the tarpon — a piscatorial slob with a cheap suit of theatrical armor and a mouth like a vacuum cleaner? Trout, si! Salmon, si! You can make fishmeal of the rest for all of me.

I am against roads. I am against detergents. I am against insecticides. I am against logging. I am against flood control. I am not against golf, since I cannot but suspect it keeps armies of the unworthy from discovering trout, but I pity them for playing it when they could be putting a fly on the water.

I have been brought to this condition not only by the beautiful, the disconcerting, the succulent trout, but by the Catskill stream in which I have wooed it — come heat, cold, high water, low water, mud, bulldozers, the New York City Board of Water Supply and locals bent on dumping used tires and old tin cans — for lo these two decades. Esopus Creek is a famous Catskill trout stream; not so famous as its sisters, the Beaverkill and the Neversink, but famous enough, thanks in good part to the fact that fishing writers, like many other kinds of writers, tend to live in New York and to find life there far more significant than life in Colorado, Minnesota or Oregon.

The Esopus rises as a trickle of cold, clear water on the shady slopes of Slide Mountain, the Catskills' highest (4,204 feet) elevation, and ends up, after enduring many lesser indignities, in the faucets, sinks and fire hydrants of the Bronx, Manhattan, Brooklyn, Staten Island and Queens. My addiction to it, nurtured perhaps by some inner masochism, stems from this contrast between promise and fulfillment.

It is a lovely little river. It runs north, then east, then southeast in a twenty-five-mile circle around a cluster of green, ledge-scarred little mountains — Panther, Wittenberg, Terrace, Garfield, Romer, Cross, Pleasant and Cornell — before its broadening valley angles off, still into the east, to blend after another twenty-five miles with the great valley of the Hudson. Its fall is gradual and it presents, mile after mile, that orderly succession of gentle riffles, noisy, boulder-strewn rapids and long, slow pools in which both trout and fisherman are most likely to prosper. It gathers size and authority from two main tributaries as well as from dozens of little hollows, cloves and kills; and these brooks — Woodland Valley Creek and Stony Clove Creek — are pleasant trout streams in their own.

The Esopus is an old American landmark. Henry Hudson

paused just off the gates of its valley — as he sailed up the Hudson River — in 1609, and there were Dutch and eventually British settlements there from 1614 onward despite bloody raids by the Sopus, a collection of river Indians from whom it got its name. The centuries have left their imprint. State Highway 28 parallels it along the route of an ancient wilderness path and the roadside is littered, between stretches of farmland, with houses, motels, gas stations, stores and little summer resorts. Hamlets with dusty memories — Phoenicia, Boiceville, Shandaken, Allaben, Big Indian — toe up to the highway for the motorist's dollar. But the towns are quiet, comfortably weatherworn and resigned. The summer boarding houses doze amid weedy lawns. Tree-edged meadows often intrude between road and wandering river. The soft mountains, which rise abruptly and overlook all, are clothed in unbroken wilderness.

One can drive from New York City to Phoenicia in just two and a half hours, but deer drink in the mist-hung stream at dawn and the fisherman can wade all through a weekday morning in midsummer and never see another soul. At humid dusk, with the last shine of light on the water, he can fancy that he and the angler silhouetted just upstream are alone on the continent. The Esopus nevertheless can drive him out of his mind. It is victimized so steadily by both man and nature that its wounds, illnesses and distortions of personality, its slow recoveries and its sudden relapses gradually become the major preoccupation of his existence; and he finds himself — even on those rare occasions when the creek is clear, its temperature normal and its water level perfect — cringing in sure anticipation of horrors to come.

The Esopus is tortured by weather. The unprecedented series of hurricanes which belabored the East Coast between 1938 and 1955 almost wrecked its whole system. Tropical deluges accompanied these great storms and roaring, mud-colored floods rolled great boulders down the streambeds, toppled trees, ate out of banks, scoured away insect life and killed thousands and thousands of trout. The scars are still evident along all the creeks. Winter clogs them annually with ice; the snow melt of early spring makes them frigid torrents, and the sun of July and August leaves them appallingly low and warm.

Man, meanwhile, labors cheerfully to further the damage. Trout streams are treated with reverence in England and men devote their lives to the art of managing them. But in the U.S. streams are fair game for any lunatic with a bulldozer. Roads are more important. So is a fallacious theory of flood control by which wandering, rock-blocked sections of brooks and rivers — the very sort of water that trout need for their survival — are straightened and flattened into sluices which speed up flow and cause worse damage farther on.

The fisherman can do little in response but fulminate. The creek's torturers are all men of goodwill and are equipped, each and every one, with valid and logical reasons for the depredations—just as were the early tanners who razed the valley's original hemlock forests in the half century after the War of 1812. Only the bark of these great trees was used; the bare hills were left littered, as by endless acres of great bones, with their rotting trunks. New forests of beech, maple, oak and other leafy trees have mercifully replaced them in the last century, but the beds of the streams are given scant chance to recover from the steam shovels and bulldozers of road builders and flood control engineers.

But if the Esopus is endlessly put upon and lamentably accident prone, it has one even more exasperating quality. It is loaded with trout and, though it often makes the fisherman's life a living hell and often seems on the verge of disintegration, he simply cannot — or at any rate *I* simply cannot — walk away and leave it to its own fiendish devices.

The New York City Board of Water Supply dammed its lower valley in 1912 and formed the Ashokan Reservoir, a wide twelve-mile lake into which the stream now empties. In so doing, it inadvertently provided Esopus trout with their own little ocean: a deep, feed-rich haven from which huge rainbows and browns launch themselves, the first in the spring and the latter in the fall, on salmonlike spawning runs to the farthest kills and hollows and to which they return, their genetic duties accomplished, to shelter during the rest of the year. Despite its difficulties, thus, the river stocks itself naturally with wild trout and these progenitors of the big brood fish valiantly defy man's best efforts to eradicate them.

They are benefited, in the process, by the Shandaken Tunnel, an eighteen-mile aqueduct which runs north beneath the hills to tap another Catskill reservoir and which feeds extra water into the Esopus and thence, eventually, into New York's hydrants and dishwashers. This enormous conduit, known locally as the "portal," makes the river unique.

In drought season, when every other Catskill stream — including the upper Esopus and its tributaries — is dreadfully low and warm, the lower river is kept high and cool by the flow from the tunnel mouth. It is kept so high for long periods that, in fact, it can hardly be fished at all; the water department, naturally, is more interested in shooting 500 million gallons a day toward the Bronx than in an angler stranded at streamside by raging rapids. The portal water does ease off in August, it is true, often bringing the fisherman negotiable riffles and slow, gliding pool surfaces. But it brings in late-season silt as well, so that the tantalizing stretches of water, rendered more turbid day by day, are usually the color of bad coffee by the end of the month.

In moments of understandable despond I sometimes think desperately of other trout water — crystalline, virginal, shadowed — and particularly of a little lake hidden high on the northwest's Mount Rainier which I once found by dint of secret directions an old friend cunningly extracted from a knowledgeable ranger. I was the fourth human to fish it. It was rimmed by fir, reflected the great, white dome of the peak like a mirror and, more delightful yet, attracted swarms of flies and bugs from a green marsh which bordered one area of its shoreline. The dry-fly fisherman wants his trout near the surface and I could not see but, in the absolute stillness, could hear the fish splashing away at their insect banquet. They were lovely creatures — a species of cutthroat known as Montana black-spotted trout — with scarlet fins and bellies tinted softly with old rose. But they were also, alas, without discrimination; they took any fly I offered.

There was no trail to the lake. I scared myself half to death working up through vertical cliffs to find it and suffered more grievous fright on the way down; for I was privileged, during the latter process, to look past my shoes at treetops two thousand feet below. But the fishing in itself was simply too easy and, even in memory, does not compete with the Esopus — which not only justifies greed and other less admirable human qualities by its own displays of temper, but makes any minor victory a Roman triumph and provides a steady atmosphere of awful suspense. I could easily drive to the Schoharie, the Beaverkill or the upper Delaware from the rambling and rickety summer house I inhabit in Woodland Valley, but in the last two decades, no matter how disappointing the local fishing, I have never gambled a day on trying them. I have invested so many hours of frustration in the Esopus and its tributaries that the prospect of losing even one unlikely dividend because of absence is more than I can quite bring myself to contemplate.

Water constitutes only one part of the puzzle a fisherman is eternally trying to solve. The other part, of course, is the fish he is trying to extract from it. A trout is not, to put it mildly, gifted with intellect; one would be impelled to say, after the most cursory inspection of his mental apparatus, that he is downright stupid. A great many non-addicts, as a result, find the angler a hilarious spectacle. There he stands, draped in more equipment than a telephone lineman, trying to outwit an organism with a brain no bigger than a breadcrumb, and getting licked in the process. But the fisherman is engaged — or he should be — in a far more complex sort of reasoning. He is trying to understand the trout's environment and to predict the trout's response to it. The trout, if stupid, has his own low cunning — or is equipped, at any rate, with a subtle set of instincts — and he responds to what is happening around him with amazing accuracy. In thus interacting with the stream in which he lives, he creates the illusion of enormous wisdom and instills a sense of gloom and mental inadequacy in his pursuer.

He is both wary and greedy, and the pull of these two aspects of his nature makes him subject to startling alteration of behavior. When the water is full of feed, as during a big hatch of mayflies, nature seems to bet that the benefits of a full stomach far outweigh any danger which may be encountered in achieving it, and the trout will roll and splash recklessly within a yard of a fisherman's waders.

But when he is feeding heavily, he also becomes fantastically selective. He will stuff himself on insects, sometimes so small that they can barely be seen with the naked eye, until he bulges like an Indiana hog, and he will go right on choking them down as long as the supply holds out. Since nature does not want him to waste energy capriciously, however, he will ignore the biggest and most delicious bugs and flies of other species while he is concentrating on the predominant insect of the moment. He will ignore even the tidbits on which he is feeding, if they do not wash almost directly into his mouth and will hardly move an inch, right or left, while doing so.

When such a big drift of feed ceases, however — and it is a phenomenon which can tail off in a matter of seconds — the trout's *modus operandi* changes completely. As far as the fisherman is concerned he simply seems to vanish, since his natural sense of alarm reasserts itself and he either takes cover behind rocks or in the depths of pools or beneath the distorted light of riffles, or flashes away to such shelter at the first tiny change in the pattern of light or shadow on the water above him. Having retreated, however, he drops his fastidious airs and gulps anything edible which comes his way.

Each of these manifestations of the trout's personality confronts the angler with dilemma. But each presents him, simultaneously, with glorious opportunity. When a trout is feeding selectively, he will refuse any artificial fly which does not duplicate the size, the color and, in an impressionistic sense, the shape of the type upon which he is dining. Give him that, though, and he will grab it with suicidal joy — and so, on the next cast, will the trout who was feeding only a few feet from him. All sorts of little things will disturb him when he is skulking behind a rock; but if he is convinced that he is not being gulled, he will often sip in any old fly the angler puts over him. The practice of fly fishing is based on these twin revelations, and the hopes, the dreams and built-in despondency of the fly fisherman revolve around them.

There are hundred of fly patterns, large and small — dry flies, which float on top of the water, and wet flies and imitations of nymphs, which are induced to wash along under the surface.

If a fisherman were able to choose just the right imitation and present it at the right place at the right moment in the right way, he could hook a trout on every cast. He cannot do it. He could not do it with the aid of an IBM computer. But once in a while he can feel himself on the verge of it. If he labors to understand the entomology of streams, keeps notes, memorizes miles of water, always casts with care, fishes continuously and is lucky, he will enjoy occasional brief but dazzling moments of absolute triumph — moments in which he can believe he is the reincarnation of Attila the Hun and the possessor of a mind as penetrating as that of Sherlock Holmes himself. If he enjoys this sort of self-image — and, personally, I find the role of Attila rather attractive — he will be addicted to the fly forever.

He prays for a big hatch of aquatic insects. In the Northeast this usually means a hatch of mayfly, a little creature obviously invented for the fisherman's special benefit. The mayfly spends most of his life as a nymph — an ugly little underwater bug which lives, depending variously on his type, on almost every variety of river bottom. During this phase he does his poor best to keep the trout from eating him. He is finally moved, however, to splendid self-sacrifice. He rises to the surface and changes, in a few seconds, into a dun — a delicate and beautiful little fly with four upright wings, two or three tiny tails and a slender body. The dun bobs on the current like a little sailboat, flutters and, if he is still undevoured, flies slowly upward and away.

In so doing, the mayfly performs several wonderfully unselfish functions. There is no point in fishing a dry fly — or a wet fly either — if no trout can see it; when fish are feeding on the bottom, an angler can beat the water into a froth without attracting their attention. As the nymphs rise, however, the trout rise with them, eating them en route like peanuts. At the surface the fish begin sucking in the floating duns — and are thus positioned to suck in a dry fly which imitates them.

The mayfly is kind enough to engage in these rites on a schedule the fisherman can often anticipate. *Epeorus pleuralis* (often known as Iron Fraudator), the blue-gray mayfly which is first of the species to appear in the spring, may be expected on the water at one o'clock, E.S.T., during the last week in April and the first days of May. The fisherman who is equipped with a dry Quill Gordon, size 12 or 14, can expect to slay trout with ease and precision for fully forty-five minutes.

The Esopus watershed is inhospitable in late April; the hills are rust brown under bare trees, wet snow falls with the rain, and the streams are often too high, too cold or discolored. I find it beautiful. A fly fisherman should think of insects rather than fish, for it is they — since the trout merely respond to their presence — which are the real key to a full creel. The knowledge that Iron Fraudator is absolutely bound to hatch during the week, and at an hour which allows a long, leisurely breakfast, is as bracing as possession of a chart indicating buried treasure.

But the season's exasperations begin in April too. Early mayflies are enormously obliging, but they do not appear simultaneously on the whole river and the fisherman can slop along from pool to pool, maddened by the certainty that duns are appearing somewhere along the stream, and yet never find them — or rising trout — at all. Subspecies of the wonderful insect appear, one after another, through May, June and early July, changing in color from iron blue — through subtle shades and blendings of gray, olive and brown — to creamy yellow forms. Famous old dry fly patterns imitate all the important types; the Hendrickson, the Red Quill, the Grey Fox, the March Brown, the Light Cahill were all invented to match specific mayflies and to take fish when they are hatching. But as the season progresses, the fisherman often finds several different sorts on the water at the same time and can be moved to borderline neurosis while attempting to discover which one predominant insect the trout are actually eating at the moment he casts a fly over them.

There are works of practical entomology (*Matching the Hatch* by Ernest G. Schwiebert, Jr., *Streamside Guide to Naturals and Their Imitations* by Arthur B. Flick) which provide him with thorough background; but he is often balked, nevertheless, as he stands in midstream glaring wildly around him, for clues as to what is going on in the water. Some forms of mayfly — and the artificial flies which imitate them — are remarkably alike. The

Hendrickson and Red Quill, in fact, are exactly the same save for the winding on the shank of the hook. But the trout will take one and refuse the other. They not only refuse the fly, they insult the fisherman. A trout will rise within a quarter inch of a fly which is too big or admits light improperly or is slightly off shade and will contemptuously splash water on it. He will jump clear of the surface and land on the other side of it. There are times when he seems to spit on it. But he will not touch it. And he will refuse a fly which matches the emerging duns in every respect if he has decided, for reasons known only to himself, to keep feeding just below the surface on the supply of rising nymphs.

Nature, it must be admitted, has provided the baffled angler with certain helpful signs and portents. A trout usually rises gently if he is feeding on the surface, but tends to splash and roll if he is feeding on nymphs or spent insects floating just beneath it. There are experts who maintain they can identify sixteen different kinds of rises (amongst them the sip, the slash, the double-whorl, the suck, the pyramid, the bulge and hump, and the spotted ring) and instantly announce just how the fish is feeding by noting the way he disturbs the water. But if a man can see dozens of rising trout and cannot make them pay the slightest heed to his artful casting, he has a tendency to quit thinking. Usually he takes refuge in trial and error and begins changing flies at random — a process which involves juggling his rod, a knife, a fly box and a bottle of dope in which he dunks each successive lure to make it float, and doing it all while up to his hips in a turbulent creek.

If he enters into this rigmarole at dusk, he must eventually ask himself an awful question: if he cuts the fly off the end of his leader, will there be light enough to allow his replacing it with another pattern? He can see dim, aluminum-colored flashes where fish are rising in the dark pool. He takes the course of courage and boldness. He cuts. He instantly regrets it. Swarms of no-seeums sift down and bite him like clouds of red-hot pepper. He cannot swat. He is standing motionless, holding a No. 16 Light Cahill toward the dim sky with one hand and trying to poke the invisible end of his synthetic gut leader through its invisible eye with the other. He grunts and sweats. He may even make small moaning sounds. But eventually he admits the cruel truth. He is disarmed. He turns, disconsolately, to wade ashore. At this moment he is subject to a final indignity and, if he is truly unlucky, he will be claimed by it. He slips in the darkness, lurches wildly, tumbles arse over tea kettle. The vehemence, the utter foulness of the profanity which can be induced by this common, even comic little accident is shocking, and the witness who laughs does so at his peril.

But the angler needs more than a knowledge of entomology — although this is a first requirement — to attack trout successfully on streams as cranky as those of the Catskills. He must do more than cast well, too. The fly must be presented correctly, but casting is simply a means to an end and is a far simpler process than is generally believed. After a few months of practice, any fool ought to be able to put a fly within a couple of inches of his target; he should be able to avoid getting hung up in trees and have mastered the trick of dropping loose line on the water to compensate for the drag of current. This is not to say there are no difficult casts. If an angler sees a big fish rising under an overhanging branch and has to reach out to the limit of his rod's power to deliver his fly, there is a very good chance he will manage any number of embarrassing mistakes. But on most water the long, difficult cast is seldom necessary. It is my opinion that motivation is more important than technique and that the successful fisherman catches trout when others do not because he possesses sneaky and atavistic instincts which heighten his perception and his ability to concentrate, and make him respond to all sorts of unkind little signals from his subconscious mind.

Something of this sort occurs in my own case, I believe, out of simple hunger. A great many fishermen are uninterested, or at least profess to be uninterested, in small trout. But in most streams — and certainly in the Esopus, save for the preseason and postseason spawning runs — there are very few fish of any other kind.

I am an eight-inch trout fisherman. I must admit I enjoy being an eight-inch trout fisherman. I sometimes keep seven-inch trout. A nine- or ten-inch trout looks like an absolute leviathan to me. I admire their beauty. I like the bulge a collection of them makes in my wet canvas creel. I am grateful to them for the fact that they are as selective, if not always as wary, as big trout and that the intellectual problems and gratification involved in luring them to the fly has little to do with their size or weight. But essentially, I like the way they taste and, when I wade into the stream, I am after something special to eat.

This does not mean that I am insensitive to the social delights of landing a big fish. A few big brown trout do skulk in deep holes or beneath boulder-studded white water during the summer and a few more seem to begin their autumnal spawning runs as early as August. These monsters — anything longer than sixteen inches or heavier than two pounds is a monster in the Esopus — may rise to the surface for a few minutes during really big spring fly hatches, but mostly they stay deep and invisible, think dour thoughts and eat such minnows and small trout as incautiously invade their lairs. The chances of hooking one of them on a fly are remote in the extreme despite the experts and their interminable creeds about casting. But if the angler wants to be considered absolutely compleat and even perhaps occult — and a fly fisherman would not be a fly fisherman if he did not welcome such rumors — he simply has to produce a monster at least once.

Between May and September real, live, exciting news in Phoenicia concerns only one topic: trout. John McGrath and Joe Holzer who preside over its two grocery stores are fishermen. The Folkerts brothers, Herman and Dick, who run its social center — a combined tackle and gun shop, soda fountain, newspaper stand, bus stop and sporting goods store — are consummate anglers. So is Fred Muehleck, whose racks of ancient Payne, Leonard and Hardy rods are wondrous to behold. So also is Phil Halzell, his Woodland Valley neighbor and streamside companion of thirty years' standing. Half the inhabitants, in fact, are fishermen and the other half cannot avoid listening to them. Let someone — anyone — catch a monster by whatever means (a construction stiff once lifted a big brown out of Woodland Valley Creek with a clamshell power shovel) and the news flashes up and down the valley roads with the speed of light.

Three summers ago, after going year on year without even seeing a monster, I caught two of them in one three-week period — a two-pounder of 17 inches and a three-pounder which measured 20⅝ inches. I am willing to admit that I took each of them into town, lugged them through the crowd of people waiting for the Pine Hill–Kingston line bus and thence into Folkerts' tackle shop to be measured, weighed and admired by hangers-on from the soda fountain. While nobody has since spoken of me as a veritable artist with a fly rod, I have reason to believe that I am no longer considered a mere dilettante from New York. I have, in fact, heard several generous remarks about my prey, and one man, whom I did not discourage, seemed to be under the impression that I was able to track down monsters at will.

Honesty compels me to say that I hooked both of them by accident. In each case, a stray current sucked my wet fly down deep beside a sunken boulder and presented it to the fish, whose presence I did not remotely suspect, in a completely natural way — an effect no one could have achieved otherwise in a month of trying. Both leviathans, I am sorry to relate, acted like Bowery drunks after I put the iron to them. A three-pound trout, of course, will put a splendid arc in a four-ounce rod, but neither of my fish seemed to have any concept of the thrilling fight which was expected of them. The bigger one ran out of steam after half stranding himself in a shallow riffle while I was trying to lead him into a quiet pool for the big battle. I simply fell on him, wrestled him two out of three falls and carried him ashore. And though both were wrapped in cheesecloth and lovingly poached in a court bouillon, neither of them, alas, tasted very good.

Smaller trout — if they are fat, wild and freshly caught — are something else again. The prospect makes my entire endocrinological system thump, palpitate and clank like a houseful of old-fashioned steam radiators on the first day of winter. It has been my privilege to sample the haute cuisine of Paris, New York, San Francisco and New Orleans, but neither Maxim's nor Le Pavillon have offered me anything to match the tender and delicate taste of these lovely fish. They should, to my mind, be rolled in corn meal, sizzled for four or five minutes in bacon fat (better, for reasons I do not understand, than butter) and served with a fresh green vegetable or salad, a baked potato, or macaroni with a bland cheese sauce. The exterior of the trout, properly done, is crisp and gold; the interior, white, moist and of a flavor, subtle but poignant, as to pierce the very soul. If the air of the dining room is faintly perfumed by fireplace wood smoke, the fish will taste better; and if one drinks a clear, icy martini while they are cooking and a half bottle of well-chilled Moselle while they are being consumed, he will find himself, when all are gone, sitting mindlessly, happily motionless while his inner being relives and resavors the sensations which have been visited upon it and congratulates itself upon a turn of fortune too splendid to be quite believed.

My memories of such orgies and my unbridled appetite for more of them have a great deal to do, I am convinced, with what successes I may manage in my contest with the Esopus. There are days when some curious perceptiveness — stimulated, I can only assume, by messages from my digestive tract — allows me to strike at the split second a trout takes my sunken, drifting nymph, although I can neither see nor feel the fish before it is magically hooked. I am incapable of remembering telephone numbers or even, at times, the names of people I have known for years, but I can visualize miles of stream in infinite detail. The Esopus has its obvious and easily remembered water: the Greeny Deep, Twin Rocks, the Spanish Farm, the Pool-in-Front-of-Bill-McGrath's-House and a succession of noisy cascades known, simply, as Down at Elmer's Diner. But I know hundreds of minor riffles, rock-divided eddies and patches of slack water; I know how they change at various river levels; I remember how fish behave in them and I remember when shadow, if any, falls on them, morning and evening.

The Catskill fisherman needs such information just as the prospector needs an understanding of rock formations — not that the knowledge is likely to produce riches in either case, but because it keeps hope alive. He needs a very good, very expensive fly rod for the same reason, even though in nine hundred ninety-nine out of a thousand situations one can fish just as well with a cheap glass rod.

A fine rod is made of a particularly hard and resilient cane from North Vietnam's Tonkin region. Its delicate sections are machined to tolerances of a thousandth of an inch to produce a specific and particular bending mode or "action." It is simple, exquisitely balanced and beautiful to see — at once an efficient tool and a work of art. The very process of removing a good rod (in my case an eight-foot Orvis) from its aluminum case, of jointing it up and carefully attaching an English reel (no others click so satisfyingly when spun) does something to the spirits comparable, I imagine, to climbing into the cockpit of a Spad or polishing up a set of safecracker's drills. When the fisherman's hand closes on its smooth, cork grip he is armed as Arthur with Excalibur and anticipates triumph almost automatically as he wades into a stream.

Once in a while, furthermore, even on streams as exasperating as the Esopus or its feeders, he will win an enormous victory. I cannot help but feel that my own performance during the hurricane of 1955 was absolutely brilliant. On considering it in retrospect, in fact, I am able to discover in myself qualities so admirable that I would be inclined to discount them were it not for the penetrating, even pitiless, honesty with which I have reviewed the episode. I will go so far as to say that I rose as a phoenix from the ashes of defeat and that I hoped and was rewarded while all others were cast down by despair.

The hurricane and its accompanying deluge made a horrible mess of our Catskill streams; they poured down their valleys under opaque curtains of rain in roaring, muddy floods. It made a mess of my house, too. The roof leaked, and when I put pans under the drips, I was impelled to endure something very like a xylophone concert. Forced into the open by this ungodly racket, I took my rod, drove five miles to the end of the Woodland Valley road and began walking upstream under the trees. I was as wet, in five minutes, as if I had fallen into a swimming pool; but I pressed sternly on and, after two miles, came upon the splendid and gleaming phenomenon I had hoped but not actually expected to find.

Under normal conditions Woodland Valley Creek betrays itself at this high point of its valley only in little skeins and trickles of water among shadowed, mossy rocks. But now it was ten feet wide and, since there were no clay banks to discolor the water, it ran clear as crystal. The native brook trout of the Northeast had been extinct in ninety-five per cent of the Esopus system for a long time — very probably since the tanners cut the hemlocks more than a century ago. But brookies, which had somehow endured year after year in the shadowed trickles of water here, were feeding voraciously in the swollen creek. They were absolutely beautiful fish with a sheen of electric blue, white piped fins, mottled backs and crimson spotted sides. I hooked them for two hours, released all but five of the handsomest, since even a hungry man could hardly deny they had earned the right to freedom, and splashed back down through the rain feeling as though I had discovered the Mother Lode.

Despite such bagman's satisfactions, however, I must confess that my pursuit of artistry, restraint and purity of purpose has progressed very slowly, if at all. But I strive. I have a model: an erect, wispy and grave old gentleman whom I encountered at midday on the Esopus above the portal five years ago and have admired, wistfully, ever since.

The sun was bright. The stream was low and clear. It was not a time to fish at all, for any movement sent trout flashing to cover in the still, brilliantly lighted pools and I was carrying a rod only as insurance against some unlikely opportunity. As I strolled along inspecting a stretch of water I had not seen for a long time, I became conscious of the old gentleman only when I saw him bend, perhaps seventy yards below me, and then straighten, net in hand. But in that instant, even at that distance, I saw that the net contained the dark, curved form of a very big trout — a monster, or, at the very least, a monster junior grade.

When he came slowly upstream, minutes later, I began to understand what a feat he had managed under those absolutely impossible conditions. He did not show me the fish or even allude to it. He had wrapped it in newspaper and had contrived to get most of the resulting package into his creel. If I had not had that glimpse of it in his net, I might not have known he had a fish at all.

He must have been eighty; I doubt if he weighed much more than a hundred pounds and he walked slowly and with care.

But I could only assume that he had come to the river with his sheets of old newspaper because he expected to stalk that one particular fish and that he had fully expected to land it. He nodded to me, glanced at my rod and, after reaching into a pocket, produced a roll of leader so fine that it was almost invisible. It must have tested less than a pound. He snapped off two feet of it simply by breaking the fragile stuff between his fingers. "Use this as a tip," he directed. Then he pulled out a plastic box, removed a tiny, curiously bedraggled black fly and handed it to me as well. "Try this," he said. "I tie them during the winter."

This was the fly and this was the weight of leader with which, quite obviously, he had subdued his thick, heavy trout. He had been forced, on such water, to take a long, long, almost impossible cast to avoid frightening his quarry. In teasing up such a fish, indeed, he had very probably had to drop the fly again and again, and each time as lightly as thistledown. And having hooked the monster, he had played it coldly and delicately at the end of that gossamer tip, knowing one slightest false move would lose him the game.

He fixed me with a stern eye until I had tied on his contributions and then, apparently satisfied that he had prepared me, too, for higher things, nodded and turned away toward the road. I knew better — that he had only prepared me for a few fruitless casts on such a day. But I got down on my hands and knees, for all this, to approach a pool formed by the confluence of a little side stream called the West Kill and then, sitting up slowly to avoid alarming its inhabitants, I looked carefully for evidence of opportunity.

The pool was deep, blue and still, but there were gnats dancing over the faint currents at its head and I felt that I saw an occasional tiny disturbance on its surface. I lighted a cigarette, and then made a long cast and promised myself that I would let my fly lie on the quiet water until I had finished smoking. But impatience and lack of faith were soon my undoing. I yanked the line off the water in dissatisfaction after three puffs and cast a foot to the right of its first position. As the line was still in the air, the biggest brown trout I have ever seen broke water like a runaway torpedo and fell back with a shattering splash. "Good Lord!" I cried in astonishment and cupidity — I talk to myself considerably when fishing — and, moved to mindless activity, made still another frantic cast. And this time I saw that my little fly was gone and realized what I had done. The big fish had sucked it in at the split second I had retrieved my line and I had broken off the hairlike leader without the slightest sense of having done so. The monster had jumped because my hook was imbedded in its lip. Had I concentrated, had I waited one second longer . . .

Ah, well. I will, given a bit of luck, be eighty years old myself one day and I like to think a certain improvement in both skill and moral tone will have become evident at that point and that the Esopus — or what is left of it — will yield to the superior man. And, if one matures late, one can always look forward to ninety.

Portrait of a Worm Fisherman

Lynn Montross

If an angleworm had ever invaded the Parmachene Club the shock might easily have been fatal to some of the more devout members. They were of a high-blood-pressure age and income, and as certified sportsmen they believed only in fly fishing — preferably with dry flies. Their twelve-acre artificial pond, resulting from a cement dam across Owl Brook, was stocked each spring with expensive eight- and ten-inch squaretails from the State Hatchery; and memberships in Parmachene were as limited as they were costly.

On the other hand it would have been hard to find a blacker sinner than old Ned Putney, who chewed twist tobacco and brazenly fished with worms. But he was the only workman left in the countryside who could still swing an artistic adze, and Parmachene needed him in the remodeling of the clubhouse.

My part was that of the go-between, hearing both sides of the story. Coming originally from the city, I spoke the language of the summer residents who made up the club's membership; and having spent several winters in my New England home, I was so accepted by the local Yankees that they charged me no higher prices than they paid themselves.

Yet at my first interview, the old man was as obstinate as one of the oxen he drove behind a bright blue yoke. The tiny veins in his face — case histories of many an ancient hard-cider bout — sprang into fiery outline.

"Godfrey Mighty!" he roared, full-throated. "They ought to known better'n send you — the dum fools, I told 'em they didn't *need* no beams in that clubhouse. It ain't that kind of a house, can't they understand?"

I saw the point. What he meant was that the modern clubhouse was held together by nails. But the ancient Cape Cod type of dwelling, such as old Ned inhabited, was built from top to bottom of heavy, hand-hewn timbers of "pumpkin pine" interlocked at the ends and secured with wooden pegs. At the end of the eighteenth century neighbors helped one another to put up these houses, using few tools and "leveling by eye." The first overhead beam became the "rum pole," and the host kept a two-gallon jug of rum or brandy hanging from it. With such a gallant impetus, the massive framework went up in a few days of hand-labor; yet it was built to last for a few centuries, since a strain against any one beam is met by the united resistance of all the others.

"It's only for the *looks* of the thing," I explained again. "Sure, the clubhouse doesn't *need* overhead beams, but they'd look good lit up by the flames from the big field-stone fireplace, wouldn't they?"

Ned snorted like an aged stallion. "How could they look good if they wasn't needed?" he demanded fiercely.

Here was a principle of architecture that applied to modern skyscrapers as well as Cape Cod houses, so I retreated to the safer ground of economics. "What do you care? They're willing to pay well, you know, and you're the only one around here who can swing the job."

He still shook his head stubbornly, but I had a fifth ace up my sleeve. "I don't blame you, Ned," I said, beginning the exit from his front yard that horse-swapping craftiness demanded, "I suppose it's almost impossible to hollow out those timbers without splitting — "

"Hah!" he muttered. "So *that's* what they think?"

He was shrewd enough, of course, to scent my obvious trap; but he was utterly unable to resist any such compelling bait as a doubt of his craftsmanship. His adze was one of the very few things left on earth which the Machine Age couldn't challenge, and he was one of the last good adze-men left in all New England. "You go tell 'em," he said in a thick voice, "that I'll yoke up Dave and Diamond and be down after them timbers this afternoon."

As the faithful go-between I reported back to the clubhouse and was asked to lunch with the Committee on Remodeling, consisting of Mrs. Brantome (laundry machinery, Newark), Mrs. Soames (wholesale groceries, Worcester), and Mr. Bugby (paper towels, Brooklyn). The committee was jubilant at the good news I brought. It seemed that when the clubhouse was first built, only comfort and utility had been considered by its masculine membership. The architecture, if such it could be called, had been shaken up like a cocktail: one part bungalow, two parts barracks, with a dash of log cabin. But as Parmachene prospered, and as trout-fishing became fashionable, the wives took a sudden and alarming interest. No Eden without its Eve, of course, and the middle-aged ladies of the club decided that only a thorough remodeling along colonial lines would do.

The question of overhead beams had been a poser until the architect had suggested that old timbers be hollowed out for lightness, and suspended from concealed steel plates, thus reversing their usual role of helping to suspend the house itself. "Can't you just see the lounge-room when it's done?" exclaimed Mrs. Brantome, half closing her eyes in facile ecstasy. "Pine-paneled walls and Revere lanterns wired for electricity and overhead the stained beams with the dimpled, hand-hewn marks on them?"

I replied that I could indeed vision the splendid effect. Meanwhile I squeezed more lemon juice on a broiled trout which tasted faintly of the chopped liver which had reared it to maturity at the State Hatchery. "It's a Jock Scott — the one you're eating," remarked Mr. Bugby, his round features lighting up with pride. "I tried him first to a Silver Doctor but he wouldn't rise to it."

At that moment there was a sound as of mild thunder outside, punctured at intervals by lightning-sharp commands: "Dave! *You,* Diam'! . . . Hoosh, g'long, both of you!"

Old Ned Putney had come for the beams.

"A worm fisherman," observed Mr. Bugby with distaste. "But nothing can change those mule-headed old natives, I suppose."

He went out to give directions while I trailed along in the rear. The beams were piled near the water's edge: immense slabs a foot in diameter and twenty feet long; solid and knotty pine a century old, with the bark still on. The club had bought them when an ancient barn was torn down, for it would have been impossible to find new timbers of such impressive dimensions.

"I should think," said Mr. Bugby, echoing my own thoughts, "that you'd bring your adze *here* instead of — "

"I'm taking the timbers *there,*" said Ned testily, "because I want that I should work in peace without a raft of women around." He paused to glare pointedly. "I aim to show you the best adze job this country ever seen."

A bit mollified, Mr. Bugby still yearned to be constructive. "Those things must weigh a quarter of a ton apiece — won't you need somebody to lend you a hand?"

The old man was all of seventy-five years old, crippled by rheumatism in spite of his powerful build, but he snapped, "I brought my pry bar along, didn't I? . . . Dave, Diam' — *hoosh, g'long!*"

The oxen surged ahead with the calm insolence of the irresistible force approaching the immovable object.

By this time I realized that I was not only a witness but an umpire to the strange clash between two schools of art. For it was no coincidence which caused Mr. Bugby to be fishing on that particular side of the pond when Ned returned for a second load of timbers. It is doubtful, in fact, if Mr. Bugby would have been fishing at all in the middle of a hot afternoon except for a purpose. The truth is that Mr. Bugby was proceeding to put a worm-fisherman in his lowly place; and any trout which might have succumbed as a result would have suffered the usual fate of the innocent bystander.

A tiny flash of crimson, as frail as hope straining against space, described an ever widening arc at the end of the tapered line until the Ibis finally settled toward the water with an artful little flutter. Whisked out almost before it was wet, it took wings again at the command of Mr. Bugby's plump hands; and this time, with minute allowance for trajectory and windage, it was wafted down within an inch of a half-submerged log some forty feet away. The afternoon was blazing, but no aesthetic trout could have failed of response to such talent — the water boiled and the tip of the rod went up.

A bald little man in his late fifties, Mr. Bugby had the air of a Buddha as he played his victim. With the same delicate touch he used in casting, he offered just enough resistance to persuade but never to manhandle a gallant foe. One did not need to be told that he had fished waters as exotic as those of Scotland and Norway when at last he netted a fifteen-inch beauty and allowed it to slide gently off the barbless hook into the bottom of the boat.

My admiration was so intense that for the moment I forgave Mr. Bugby the nonabsorbent qualities of his famous paper towels. I foresaw that I would emerge from gents' washrooms the rest of my life surreptitiously using my handkerchief to finish drying my hands, but without bearing Mr. Bugby any further grudge.

Ned was speechless. His jaws worked a long while before he made the only comment left in him. He spat — and on an alder twig twelve feet away a drenched dragon fly scuttled off in alarm.

At the explosive sound Mr. Bugby glanced up as if he had just noticed spectators on shore. He smiled with bland innocence, nodded, lit a cigarette and picked up his oars for the perfect exit.

Ned eyed me with sudden and grim resolve. "How," he demanded, "would you like to go fishing with *me* tomorrow morning? Fishing, I mean, and not crocheting?"

It would have been cruelty to refuse, even though I held to the fly-fishing school of ethics. At sunrise, when I drove into the old man's front yard, the first thing I saw was a large tin can with a flaming red label — obviously a can of worms shouting in defiance to the world. Beside it on the door step was a short bamboo pole with a cotton line.

But Ned was nowhere in sight and I found him in one of the woodsheds which trailed out behind the house toward a barn bringing up the rear like a caboose. Chips were flying as the old man swung his adze, and an extinguished lantern hinted that the work had been going on since earliest dawn. The hoe-like tool, whetted to razor sharpness, rose and fell in easy rhythm; now gouging out a chunk which landed with a *thwack,* now taking off a sliver so thin that it floated to the floor. "By Godfrey!" grumbled Ned. "If they think I can't — "

"Oh, no!" I hurried to reassure him, suspecting that I had gone too far in my well-meant challenge. "Why, the Committee on Remodeling even sent me over with a little present for you. It's imported Irish rye — "

The cantankerous old fellow uncorked the bottle and sniffed. "Guess I'll take it over to Grandma Binns for cough syrup," he remarked, unimpressed. "Come on in and we'll have a drink."

The mysteries of "Forty Below" were cleared up by his fond description as he set out the jug on the kitchen table. This beverage was the final product of a barrel of hard cider left outdoors on a sub-zero night until all had congealed except a few gallons at the core released by means of a red-hot poker. The more icy the weather, of course, the more fiery and vehement is the product. "Freezes the meekness out of it," Ned explained, the tiny veins in his nose already brightening with anticipation.

Although his bachelor kitchen was spotless, he blew politely in my teacup to reassure me against dust before filling it to the brim. I took two sips and the reaction was instantaneous. For if wine could be said to sing within the human system, or gin to set up a sharp yelping noise, the effects of Forty-Below could only be compared to a pipe organ, with all stops out, playing "Yankee Doodle!" Great, crashing chords thundered through one's very soul and ended in tingling notes as far away as the toes, while in response millions of hormones joined hands and began a sprightly dance around the spinal column.

"Warming, ain't it?" remarked Ned, noting with approval the tears which coursed down my face. He wiped his mouth with the back of his hand and refilled our cups. "We'll take some along for bait."

As we scrambled through thickets on our devious way up Hump Mountain, the old fellow wistfully told me his side of the story. It seemed that he nursed no bitterness toward fly fishing. On the contrary he admitted with tart justice that it was an art which might take several years in the learning.

What he objected to was not the fly-fishing itself but the vulgar class of people it had attracted to a sport once remarkable for exclusiveness.

Indeed it had been a rare distinction in Ned's day to be recognized as one of the died-in-the-wool fishermen of a community. Only a very few loafers, drunkards or wife-beaters had any chance to qualify in the long run, since fishing at its best permitted no outside interests. Work of any sort, physical or mental, was especially apt to blunt the keen faculties required for perfection; and nothing must be allowed to interrupt the persevering apprenticeship of decades.

Thus it was that a finished worm fisherman of the Golden Age seldom arrived in less than half a century to that intuition and generalship which, more than mere mechanical skill, constituted the glory of an authentic master.

Ned only claimed to be a likely journeyman himself, having devoted so much time to the adze, but he had known giants in his day. In contrast the crass intrusion of a paper towel manufacturer was shocking and inconsistent, for how could one pretend to be a genuine fisherman while still bowing to the half-gods of respectability! Such an imposter could only hope to become one of the eager amateurs who have always been shunned by the true artist; and as for women trifling with a sport which has ever been their deadliest enemy, Ned found the idea too revolting for words.

After several perpendicular miles through second growth and wild blackberry bushes I was bleeding from a dozen wounds, but a few gulps of Forty Below served as an anesthetic. At the same time it didn't blind me to the fact that there was no brook yet to be seen.

"Seen?" growled the old man. "When you can *see* a mountain brook you know it's no good. You *listen* for real trout water and *smell* out the big ones in it, understand?"

Hugging this reprimand, I stayed in the background while he "wormed up" and spat on his hook. Dropping to his hands and knees, he edged into a thicket which completely hid the brook. Each move was painfully stealthy as he gave his worm a deft flip and eased it down through a funnel of twigs.

Before it had time to touch the water there was a splash as sudden as a gunshot and the tip of the rod jerked sidewise. Fractions of an inch became miles as the old man began to play his fish, sight unseen. Even an unguarded twitch counted in such close quarters, yet the writhing trout soon began its spiral ascent, scarcely touching a leaf as it emerged into the clear and flopped to the grass.

Ned crawled to reach the next bend. Then he reared up on one elbow as he cunningly worked his worm past twig after twig. The landing of a trout out of such a jungle constituted an engineering feat, but the old fellow made it appear easy.

I was encouraged to wet a line myself — and spent the next five minutes untangling it from the branches.

For reasons unaccountable, Ned would pass up a long stretch of brook, then take several whoppers in succession from a spot which appeared no better. Perhaps he really did "hear" and "smell" his way upstream! Finally I creeled a mere seven-incher, my only prize of the day, after rescuing it from a choke-cherry bush where the leader had become looped around a bird's nest. By this time Ned had enough trout for both of us and Grandma Binns. He tenderly covered them with ferns, after lining his basket with snow from a gorge which the sun never touched all summer.

More than a week passed before I saw him again and I could not help noting a vast change. He looked tense and preoccupied. He was about to pass me up in the village without recognition when I touched him on the shoulder and he started as if rousing from a sleep-walking dream. It was plain that the adze job had become an obsession amounting to temporary madness. I had heard of sculptors or painters going into such a frenzy while in the throes of creation, and I felt guilty for my part in inciting it.

The neighbors had become curious after remarking a lantern gleam in Ned's woodshed until late hours of the night. They guessed that something extraordinary must be forthcoming, especially since the old man would allow nobody a preview of his handiwork. The ancients of the community began to discuss great adze jobs of the past, and it was agreed that Uncle Johnny Caldwell was best qualified as final critic.

Aged ninety-six, he had made a study of the adze since and including President Polk's administration; and though he was practically on his deathbed from a recent "stroke," he got up as if by a miracle and put on his clothes. The last genuine masterpiece Uncle Johnny had seen was exhibited in 1859, but the artist had been killed at the Battle of Fredericksburg, and no other local talent had ever risen to the same heights.

The atmosphere of tense expectation communicated itself to the Parmachene Club, where the lounge-room was now complete except for the rough-hewn beams. Paul Revere lanterns, old flax wheels, hooked rugs and pewter sconces had crowded out the stuffed and varnished trout which once served as adornments; and only the ceiling lacked that quaint touch of antique handcraft.

When the day finally came, a large audience was on hand as suddenly as if it had sprung from the earth. The club members grouped themselves on one side and the natives on the other, both factions staring in solemn anticipation as Ned's oxen thundered up the driveway. The day was cloudless but he had covered his beams with patchwork quilts in protection even from the June sunlight. Looking tired and haggard, he began to unfasten the wrappings while the crowd waited with the hushed air of people watching for the unveiling of a statue.

As he threw off the last quilt and stood aside with dramatic calm, I glanced first at the faces of the audience. Uncle Johnny Caldwell uttered a squeak of astonishment and his eyes protruded so far that another "stroke" seemed imminent. Mrs Brantome, of the Committee on Remodeling, appeared equally agitated but in quite another direction — she gasped, turned pale and shuddered from the very depths of her aesthetic and antiquarian soul.

The reason was apparent when I looked at the beams. For they had been finished with such perfection that any hint of a "dimpled and hand-hewn" effect was entirely eliminated. Each one had been hollowed out into a thin shell through which the sunlight glowed with rosy splendor: and only a microscope could have detected the adze-marks on a surface as smooth and polished as a plate-glass window.

"Goddamighty!" croaked Uncle Johnny at last; and then in an awed, quavering voice he paid the highest tribute of a century's criticism, "Why, you'd swear it'd been done by *machine*."

The Werewolf

Dana S. Lamb

Mrs. Barker's cousin was a werewolf. This was quite generally known in Upper Jay, and even as far away as Wilmington. Scarcely credible to you perhaps but we who live in Essex County know that werewolves are quite common. Or perhaps I should say, since this phenomenon is not exactly common, that the incidence in this locality of the loup-garou is not unusual. As a loup-garou Mrs. Barker's cousin was, however, quite unusual. Instead of a nocturnal transfiguration when the moon was in the proper quarter, Mrs. Barker's cousin became on occasion a veritable wolf in sheep's clothing. His appearance, save in the matter of adornment, changed not at all when he entered the wolf phase; the devil entered into him by day as well as by night, and his seizures might last not for one night only but for the better part of a year.

Like many of his kind, Mrs. Barker's cousin was, in what we like to think of as his normal state, a noble, generous, easy-going fellow whom everyone liked and who was full of good deeds and kind words for all the neighbors roundabout — especially for the youngsters. Many a day I have seen him up on Byron Conway's barn roof, when Byron was busy with plowing, doing a bang-up reshingling job. If one of the housewives whose husband was lying up there in the graveyard beyond the orchard was in some trouble and needed a man's strong arm on the farm, she needed only to drop the merest hint to have Mrs. Barker's cousin help out in almost any fix. He was the man that introduced seven-man football to Jay and Wilmington and down to the Forks and bought the uniforms for all three teams.

Best of all, you'd see him out back of Mrs. Barker's garden digging worms and picking up nightcrawlers after a rain so he could be ready to take the local boy scout troop up to the headwaters of the West Branch on holidays and Saturday mornings and bring them back at evening proud as punch with a gunnysack half full of beautiful brookies in the back of the car, and an ice cream cone in each and every grubby, freckled hand.

After these youngsters that he liked so much got older he started them fishing in the river, teaching them how to drift worms as gently and realistically as though no leader tied it to a line. And when his pupils discovered the superiority of this as sport to dunking bait in still water straight down, he introduced them to the bucktail and the streamer, flies wet, then dry and, as their skills increased, to nymphs and wet flies fished upstream.

After a couple of weeks of visiting Mrs. Barker or boarding at Ben Straw's, folks forgot that Mrs. Barker's cousin was a werewolf. Wives let their husbands go with him to fish the Saranac or watch the ball team at the Forks; mothers smiled to see their youngsters cruising in his wake, realizing there would be no mischief for that day at least, and horny-handed deer hunters were well pleased to have their womenfolk ask him to come in for doughnuts and a cup of coffee.

But let us not forget that the awful curse of the loup-garou can only be temporarily sidestepped. Sure as shooting there always came a time when all his virtues soured and although the casual observer could not see the slavering jaws, detect the hairy pointed ears or feel the fearful repulsion consequent upon meeting the baleful glance of those erstwhile soft brown eyes, the man was no longer man but wolf.

Director of the Casham Bank with more than half the stock in his safe-deposit box, he'd suddenly change from the friendly, understanding, cooperative family banker to a policy of steely-eyed ruthlessness, calling a widow's mortgage without a day of grace, letting the grocery store or lumber mill or automobile agency go under for lack of credit and ending up with the whole thing in his own hip pocket; moving coolly away from his boyhood friends and former happy haunts to an exclusive club or expensive inn as though to de-emphasize his connection with his old friends and neighbors and to disavow his relationship to Mrs. Barker.

At such unfortunate times his skill as an angler curiously enough was never more apparent. Unhindered by his barefoot cohorts and schoolboy learners, unmindful of the obvious interest of local youngsters getting ready to go off to college who might, if taken at this magic moment, be made into stalwart conservationists, he fished either alone or in the company of fashionable, famous and fortunate chauffered gentlemen who came up from Rolling Rock and the South Side and the Wyandanch and Clove Valley or the Tuscarora to see what was going on in what they called "the sticks." No longer did he carefully and gently release the lovely native trout to leave a heritage for those who would come after. Rather he seemed bent on accumulating evidence that he could catch more pounds of fish than the next man; that his technique and methods, elegant and well thought out, were better than the best.

Now his dusty station wagon was replaced by a foreign sports car; now he hourly sought phone booths from which to telephone New York; now his accent once straight, honest upstate New York, became as nearly as possible that of the British aristocracy; now he headed back for the city and for months was seen no more.

At first we thought that these fashionable gentlemen whose arrival generally presaged in Mrs. Barker's cousin the emergence of the werewolf were themselves a subtle breed of loup-garou. But evidence piled up that they were nothing of the sort. In fact they seemed to see the loup-garou in Mrs. Barker's cousin and to dislike what they saw. As years went by they seemed more and more to shun his company and even to avoid the river if it was necessary in order to fish it to associate with Mrs. Barker's cousin.

Time passed and when the evil was upon him he fished now avidly and all alone, attempting by his daily kill, to amass statistics readily substantiated which might when mailed to the Racquet Club or Union serve to humiliate his fishing friends and show them the error of their ways in not joining him on the Ausable.

They say that water seeks its own level. Eager to bring in really big ones Mrs. Barker's cousin began to fish the Bush country in the late evening and at night. And here on the rivers' dusky banks he at last encountered his brothers of the tribe of loup-garou. Hairy and horrible, fanged and frightening, runners, in packs or all alone, along the lonely moonlit ridges. Here at last he felt at home; here at last he reached his goal so normally abnormal that he quickly lost the key of re-entry to the world of being Mrs. Barker's cousin.

Thus it is that now on summer nights when cannibal trout minnow in the moonlight shallows above Slant Rock or when winter comes, against a silent snowy background, the carcasses of the gutted deer hang freezing by the campfires the folks who live in the village of Black Brook hear him howling in the woods each evening before the moon comes up over the jet-black hills; hear his horrid, haunting agony each eery, misty, moon-sad hour before the mountain dawn.

The Cutthroat Trout

Sally Carrighar

Only a sharpened, seeing look in the Trout's eyes proved that he had wakened. No shift of the eyes had flashed their crystalline shine. The wrongness of some sound had roused him. He peered from his nook along the west shore of the pond; was there a glisten of wet fur in the polished darkness? Or did he see the pale clouds hung in the water, moonlight, which had turned to luminous froth the bubbles clinging to the underwater plants?

His shelter was a groove among the sticks of the beaver house. He was holding himself as still as the sticks, so quiet in their tangle that a slippery ooze had grown upon them. His breathing lightened until the water drained through his gills with no perceptible beat, no pulse to send its circular waves out through the pond, revealing that he lay at the center of them.

From the edge of the Beaver's sunken pile of aspen boughs a string of small globes, faintly silver, smoked to the top. Some animal must have touched a branch and rubbed out air that was held within its fur. The water swayed; the creature had begun to swim. Its stroke was not familiar to the Trout, not one of the rhythms that he knew as harmless or a threat. It had more pulse than the Beaver's paddling or the striding of a moose. It was rougher than the swimming of a fish and heavier than a muskrat's sculling. At first the Trout must steady himself with his fins to keep from being slapped against the sticks. But the underwater waves diminished. The last of them struck the shores and clattered back, a liquid echo. The only motion in the pond then was its regular mottling flow, a current from the brook to the beaver dam.

The surging had torn the film of sleep from a thousand little minds. After it ceased, constrained breaths made the pond seem lifeless. But hunger was a danger too. It rose above the fear of the animals, one by one — of the smallest first. Soon the twinkling prowls of the mayfly nymphs, the quick strokes of the water boatmen, and the foraging of even tinier creatures mingled in a hum like that of insects in the air, but louder. The lightest sounds were wave beats in the pond. To the Trout's ears came the twanging of minute activity.

Night was nearly over. The Trout knew by the brightening of the water, by his hunger, and the stiffness in his muscles. He saw the webs of the pelican start to push the bird's breast over the top of the pond. Its wingtips dipped in the water, the webs were shoveling back with greater vigor, the breast was shrinking upward. Only the kick of the feet now broke the surface. When the bird was gone, the fin on the Trout's back stood a little higher, and a ripple scalloped from its front edge to the rear.

The Beaver swam to the entrance of the house and climbed in onto the floor. His angry voice came through the wall. He was driving from his bed the muskrat he allowed to share his home. The feet of a mother moose and her calf had waded off the bank. They dragged their splashes down the shore to a patch of horsetail. The big soft muffles plunged beneath the surface, closed around the plants and pulled them dripping from the water. Even yet the Trout would not risk showing himself. He was the wariest of all the animals in the pond.

Beside the stranger's threat, a more familiar danger kept

him hiding. Three times a day the Osprey dived in the pond for fish. The Trout's good time-sense held him under cover when its strike was due: at dawn, as soon as the hawk could see its prey; at noon; and at sunset, with the first receding wave of light. Most mornings the Trout went out for an early swim, returning to his nook before he would be visible from the air; but not on this day.

His wait was an exquisite balancing of instincts. Hunger was sufficient reason to start forth, and the pond's flow was a stimulation. The current, passing through the walls of the beaver house, divided around the Trout. All night its touch had slid along his skin, from nose to tail, as though he ceaselessly swam forward. Now he was awake to feel the fine strokes down his sides — the touch of moving water; only the sight of moving prey could be more quickening to a trout. But he submitted to the quieting urge. He stayed in his groove, with ears and lateral lines both listening for the hawk.

The fluffs of moonlight disappeared in a tremulous green shine. No wind rocked the surface now, but the Trout could see the current draining toward the dam. It was a checkered wavering, unhurried and unaltering. Daylight reached the bottom, where the water's ripples had been fixed in sandy silt.

Directly over him the Trout could look into the air. His view was circular, and small; his own length would have spanned it. Beyond that opening the surface was an opaque silver cover, stretching to the shores. Reflected in it were the floor of the pond, the swimming animals, and the underwater plants. The Trout could see the lustrous belly of a leopard frog spring past. He also saw, in the mirror spread above, the frog's bronze, spotted back. The pond was a shallow layer of the world, with a ceiling on which its life was repeated upside down.

Upon the surface crashed a huge light-feathered breast. Claws reached and speared a bullhead. A brown throat, then a beak and eyes came through the top of the pond, and wings and tail. A shower of bubbles scattered downward as the long wings lowered in a sweep. The wings began to lift the Osprey. A final thrashing took him out of the surface, leaving the reverberations of his dive.

The wariness of the Trout released its check. He floated from his groove, still seeming motionless, as if the current had dislodged him. Slowly his fins commenced a ribbonlike stroke. His tail pressed gently on the water, left and right.

Freeing his entire strength in a tail thrust then, he was across the pond. A spinning turn, and, energy closely held, he slanted toward the bottom silt — the touch, and a spasm of upward speed had flung him into the dangerous dazzling air.

A slicing dive back deep in the pond, a glimpse of another trout, and he whipped in its pursuit. But just before his teeth would have nicked its tail, he whirled, and the trout ahead whirled too, in perfect unison.

He cut forward in the channel of the current, throwing his tail from side to side as he tried to find in his own speed some full outlet for his strength. The water of the pond would give him nowhere more than a mild and yielding pressure. He was a native cutthroat of the Snake, a turbulent swift river, but the placid pond and little brook that fed it were the only home that he had known. In early summer of the year the beavers built the pond, his parents had come up the brook to spawn. The new dam trapped them and their offspring. The river poured along the east side of the marsh, so near that the Trout could feel its deep vibration. He had not seen it, but his spirit cried for its stronger flow, its more combative force.

Yet idle swimming could be pleasant. He glided to the backwash past the brook, toward food not scented, seen, or heard, but certain to appear. Sculled by his tail, he wove through bare elastic water lily stalks, beneath a cover of translucent leaves. He was at rest in motion, fins outspread to ride the smooth support, his slippery skin quick-sliding through the wetness. But he stiffened, shot ahead, bent nose to tail, kicked back the tail in a sharp return, perhaps to savor the grace of a body incapable of awkwardness in an element incapable of angles: beautiful play.

He saw a streaming like fine grasses drawn by the current —

dace! With a forward spring he snatched a minnow at the side of the school. Alarm flashed through them all, and the leaders swung to flee into the brook. The milling of the others would have made each one available to the Trout, but he swerved away.

He'd seen a pair of reedy, jointed legs, seeming to be rooted in the silt, but still, not quivering as reeds would in the flow of the pond. The dace swam toward them. The dace had left the safety of the shallows because a harmless moose was splashing there. The Trout had captured one, and now the great blue heron certainly would catch another. But would not catch the Trout! Already he was far beyond the stab of the bird's beak.

Near the shore the waters swished with the feet of ducks. A quick look: no mergansers' feet, with paddle toes for diving, there among the webs of mallards, pintails, and of baldpates. The Trout swam under them. He need not dread an enemy's unexpected dive here while the feet were moving the ducks about in search of food, while they were easy, pushing webfuls of water back and folding in and drawing forward; not while one foot hung, a pivot, and the other swung an oval breast; or both of a duck's webs splashed at the surface, holding him bill down. As long as no fear tensed the feet, the Trout felt safe.

The long stripe on a pintail's neck shone white as it lowered the bird's head, swanlike, to the bottom. But swiftly it was pulled above the surface. Now all the feet were quiet, spread from the feathered bellies, ready for a leap. The Trout, alert, poised in midwater.

He did not know what animal had frightened the ducks. While they continued their wary wait, the white keel of the pelican dipped through the surface, slid ahead, and, checked by its wide webs, glided to a stop. The Trout streamed off, away from the watchful ducks, and gradually forgot their warning.

When he was a young fish, nearly every animal he saw seemed hungry for him. One by one then he outgrew the threat of frogs, kingfishers, snakes, and larger trout. He learned the tricks of human fishermen. Minks and mergansers chased him still but could not capture him. No other creature in the pond was quite so swift. And he almost was too heavy to be carried by an osprey. Soon the Trout might reach security that few wild creatures know, unless the alien of the early morning proved a danger.

Every instinct whispers some command; for him the loudest command was always, *live*. He listened for it, always deferred his other urges to it. Survival was so strong an impulse in him that the most involuntary workings of his body helped him hide. The pale sheen on his belly matched the cover of the pond, to an eye below. One watching from across the surface might confuse the iridescence of his scales with scales of sunlight on the ripples. The black spots spattered on his skin disguised his shape when seen from any angle. To a mate or rival he might show two crimson gashes on his throat, but usually he folded them beneath his jaws.

When his alarm had quieted, he started to the beaver house. First he passed a bank of sedges. In summer when their shade was green, the Trout had turned to emerald here. This autumn day the grass was tawny, and its color, focused in his eyes, had caused the grains of yellow in his skin to scatter out and tint him olive. If the inborn guardian in his tissues could arrange it, he would live. Yet other animals also had ingenious aids, some useful in attack.

He circled the island on the dam, now moving through a tunnel of grasses, bent with the tips of the blades awash. The sun was laying gold bars over him. He moved with a little flourish, for it seemed that he was really safe. Beyond the far side of the island a floating log pressed down the top of the pond. He started under — and was circled with a crash.

Escape! Escape to a nook in the dam! He split the water and was there. Wheeling, he shot in the hole and flung out his fins to check him. The water bulged in after him, as the one who chased him surged to a stop outside.

He had not seen what creature dived from the log. But his dash to the shelter, finished between heartbeats, was long enough to tell him that the other gained. Gained! Did panic echo, now, from days when the rush of most pursuers swept upon him like a wave?

His refuge was a space in the roots of cottonwood, the dead

tree anchoring the dam. Through interwoven fibres he could see his enemy, an animal he did not know, the Otter. The creature darted around the root maze, trying to peer in. His eyes would show in one place, reaching for the Trout. A drive with a quick foot, and the brown-furred face would push into another hole. Eagerly it was weaving forward, cocked ears sharp as claws.

The Otter found a looser tangle, which his paws began to tear. The water was tainted with the scent of his excitement, acrid in the nostrils of the Trout. Close beside the Trout's face now a lean webbed paw had grasped a root. The claws were scratching as the toes kept tightening in convulsive grips. The Otter tried to burrow through, but the tangle held. Should the Trout attempt to reach the sturdier beaver house? No longer was there safety in a flight. He tensed his tail for a great thrust; yet he hesitated.

As suddenly then as if the Otter had seen a more accessible fish, he drew back out of the roots. He swam away with a vertical sculling, so that each roll took him to the top. The pulses in the water matched the surging that had stirred the pond at dawn.

The water beat for some time with his strokes and other creatures' startled movements. When the Trout could feel the light quick overlap of wavelets nearly spent, he knew that the Otter had gone to the far end of the pond. Then he could have fled to the beaver house, but he was waiting for the Osprey's midday dive. His new fear had not blurred his sense of the older menace.

The Osprey's perch was in the tree whose roots now hid him. He could not see the hawk, but when the spread wings glided from the upper boughs, they came into his air-view. He watched, as he never had from the beaver house, the way the Osprey hovered high above his victim, and how he plunged, so slanting his dive that he dropped from behind an unsuspecting fish. The Trout could recognize the jolting of the pond, the splashing as the Osprey struggled from the water, the sudden quiet, and widening of the echoes. The hawk returned in his air-view, carrying a mountain sucker to his branch. After he ate the fish, he flew back down to clean his claws. The Trout could see them cross the pond, thin hooks that cut the surface, trailing silvered sacs of air.

At last the water near the cottonwood roots sucked up, a motion meaning that some heavy animal was climbing out. A gust of drops fell onto the surface, as the creature shuddered the moisture from its fur. Feet ran over the top of the dam. As they passed the base of the tree, a sift of dirt fell through the roots and briefly stuck to the mucous coating on the skin of the Trout.

The pond was all in motion, for the wind had risen. The wind had stirred the marsh for several days, with short lulls. The Trout sensed that it brought a change of season. He could even taste the proof of summer's end, as dust, seeds, crumbling leaves and bark washed through the pond.

Bright-edged shadows of the waves were racing over the bottom silt. They swept across the underwater plants and seemed to shake them. The surface layer of the pond was blowing to the upper end of the backwash. There the water turned below, to sweep back down along the bottom. Against the dam this flowing sheet rolled up. It pressed beneath the Trout's fins as a breeze will lift the wings of a bird.

Whenever the wind would strain the top of the rigid dead tree, he could feel a pulling in the roots. Abruptly they began to writhe, to tear. The Trout was out of the maze and back in the beaver house as if the water had parted for him.

The Osprey's tree, upturned by the wind, fell into the pond. Billows met rebounding billows, whirls and eddies struggled, surges rocked the Trout. Gradually the violence quieted. Through a cloud of mud he dimly saw that the trunk of the tree was under the surface, propped up from the bottom on its boughs.

He settled himself to feel the current's long touch on his sides. But what disturbing change was this: the water's stroking soon was regular, yet took a new course — not from his nose to tail but downward now. The water's pressure was becoming lighter and its color rosier. The top of the pond was falling.

Inherited memories warned him that the change was ominous. But he did not leave his shelter, for it seemed that a greater danger threatened him outside: the otter had returned. Sometimes the trout could hear him in the water, sometimes out along the narrowing shores. The Trout would not be caught through panic. He lay in his nook and watched the surface drop.

Only when it reached the nook itself did he nose outside. Feeling the Otter's surging near, he turned down to a refuge lower in the wall. The top of the pond descended on him there. The water, draining off the bank beside the house, was roily, so that he could not see where he would go. But he entered it and let its motion guide him.

The currents were not flowing in familiar paths. They all converged in a powerful new suction. Since the roots of the cottonwood tree had been interwoven with the dam, its fall had torn apart the beaver's masonry of mud and sticks. The whole marsh seemed to be swirling toward the gap and plunging through it.

The Trout turned back. He would escape to the brook. He sensed that he must leave the doomed pond and would seek the water's source, as many of the other fish had done. He could not reach it. While he, the one most wary, stayed in the house to escape the Otter, the pond had shrunk below the mouth of the brook. The only water now connecting them was a thin sheet crinkling over a pebble bar.

Gone, lost above the surface, were the undercut banks of roots, the grassy tunnels, brush, and other shoreline hideaways. The Trout returned to the lower end of the pond. He glided with his fins streamlined in the depressions in his sides, and with so slight a sculling that he might be trying to make smoothness hide him. As he approached the dam, he saw the Otter. Dodging up the bottom toward the island, he slipped beneath the log, which drifted now with one end resting on the silt.

The Otter was walking on the pond floor, moving with a swing from his shoulders to his high arched rump. He somersaulted to the surface for a breath; then looped and tumbled through the water. He straightened toward the hole in the dam. The fluent column of his body merged with the strands of the current, and he vanished.

The surface soon was shattered by a splash. The Otter was back. He had climbed up over the dam, beside the gap. He dived in, disappeared through the break, and again returned. A plunge, a joining with the water's sweep, and a swift ride: he had found a game.

The Trout was holding down his top fin, tense with fear. He spread it, and it struck the under side of the log. And yet his belly touched the silt. The log was the pond's last refuge, but the water soon would leave it.

Nothing in the Trout's experience could help him. He only could give himself to the urge that so intensely pressed to have him live. He waited until the Otter had dived and once more swung out through the hole. Leaving the log with a jet of speed, the Trout had reached the gap. A gushing force took hold of him. It hurled him through the break. Too quick for thought he dodged the wreckage of the dam. He leapt to pass the brink of the fall and dropped in the foam beneath. The cascade lightened, slowed, and he found himself in a shallow creekbed, moving over cobblestones.

His high emotion quickened his choice of route: to the left, through streamers of emerald algae; right, along a slit between the stones; here a turn to miss a piece of driftwood, there to pass a boulder. The air was seldom far above his topmost fin. Sometimes he drew a breath of it, and it seared his gills with dryness. Avoiding one by one the unfamiliar hazards, he progressed.

His lateral lines were jarred by a new sound, a tremendous, heavy pouring. He swam around a bend in the creek and slid across a bar. And there a torrent plunged upon him, water more swift than any he had known. He was in the river, the violent tumult of the Snake.

It nearly overwhelmed him, but he found a milder flow along the bank. A curve there held a pool as in a shell. The pool was covered by a sweeper, a willow with its caught debris. The Trout discovered the refuge, entered it, and spiraled down into the cool green quiet.

Through the afternoon he stayed there, gaining back his poise and fitting his spirit to the strange new shape of his life. Most of the time he hung in the water, motionless, but now and then a ripple ran through his fins, and he chopped his breaths as with excitement. When the first gray wave of dusk washed over the pool, he rose to the top.

He swam along the bank, where ripples pattered into crevices among the roots. The motion of the water here was light and peaceful, like the pond's. Turning out, he met a crisper current, stimulating as the pond had never been. An even greater challenge growled from the center of the river, from grinding rocks that yielded to the push of water irresistibly strong. The Trout began to slant his strokes into the torrent. With a leap he sprang to the very heart of its taut pressure. Enormous weight bore down upon him, but he gripped it, driving his way against it with exultant power.

To fight! To fight the turbulent flow! To sharpen his nerves on its chill; to cut quick arcs through the weaving water; to throw so much force into his muscles' swing that they could drive him upstream, past the rocks beneath, with the whole flood pounding toward him; to fling himself out into the air and see the river under him, a river wider than the pond, wide for his play — all this, the heritage of a trout, he knew now for the first time.

He faced the flood and, sculling exactly at the current's pace, remained above the same stone. Swirling past were many insects, blown in the river. He stayed to take a cricket only, for exhilaration sang in his nerves. He leapt —

But stopped, caught. Talons had stabbed into his flesh, were now locked through it. They were holding him in the center of a splash. A feathered throat was lowering before his eyes. Wings were sweeping down at the sides, enclosing him. The Osprey, forgotten in his conquest of the river, had made its sunset dive.

His torn nerves stung the Trout to action. The claws were powerful that bound him, but his thrashing bent their grip. They almost rigidly resisted, but they did bend. They were a pressure, like the river's force — to fight!

His instinct focused on one urge, to get himself in deeper

water. Arching his body downward, he furiously tried to scull from side to side. The hawk's wings beat, attempting to lift his own weight and the Trout's. The wings and the driving paddle of the Trout's tail pulled against each other. So far the Trout had not been able to drag the bird down, but he held him under the surface of the water.

The river was aiding the fish. For the Osprey was growing desperate for a breath. At first the spines on the pads of his feet had pierced the skin of the Trout. They pressed their hold no longer. And the Trout could feel the talons in his flesh release their clutch. The hawk was trying to withdraw them, but their curving points were caught securely.

The bird and fish were swirling downstream. They jolted to a stop, snagged by the willow sweeper. The water's force was beating at them. It poured through the Osprey's feathers. The push of the wings was weakening. They suddenly relaxed, awash in the flow. And the claws were limp.

The Trout had fought another pressure, his exhaustion. When the straining of the talons ceased, he too relaxed. For long enough to gather a little strength, he waited. Then he began an intermittent thrashing. With bursts of effort he tried to jerk himself away. One by one the claws worked out, some slipping loose but more of them tearing through his sides. Finally a twist of his body sent him forward, free.

He turned down under the willow, lower and lower in the dark pool. With his flesh so cut, his lateral lines no longer clearly caught the echo of his motions, thus to guide him. He was careful therefore not to swim against the bottom. His chin touched, and he sank upon a stone. The stone was smooth, and soft with slime-coat algae. Soon he had drifted over on his side. His eyes were dull and his fins closed. His consciousness sank lower.

The Trout had been so stimulated by the river that he had ignored his innate caution. But now he was listening again to instinct, not to the water's roar. As he lay and waited for his strength to seep back into him, no creature could have been more passive, none more acquiescent.

The water's cold had numbed the anguish in his severed nerves. It would draw his wounds together. Already it had put in winter sluggishness the parasites that possibly would enter his exposed flesh. And gradually, as he rested, the cold became a tonic to his temper. Cold was as sharpening to him as the warm sun is to insects. By midnight he was swimming experimentally around the bottom. He circled higher. The Osprey was gone from the willow sweeper. The Trout moved out of the pool.

He found a backwash near the bank and held himself on the edge, where a smooth flow passed. Moonlight, falling on the surface, showed that a drift of small debris was swirling by. Drowned insects should be in it. His eye discovered a bright bit up ahead. He swayed forward. His mouth opened, touched it, and it broke with a singing snap. More came floating toward him — little round stars. Some winked out. He let the others pass.

But here was what he liked, a mayfly. Earlier in the day the year's last swarm had left the river for their brief erotic life. Now their delicate spent bodies would be nourishment for the Trout. Many others came his way. After his hunger had been satisfied, he took one more, and shot it out of his mouth for the chance of catching it again, of biting it in two and tossing out and snapping up the pieces.

Now he was not shaped like a smooth wedge, for the cover of one gill was hanging loose, and his sides were ragged. And so his balance in the turns of the water was not perfect. His fins were spread, all needed to aid his sculling tail. Yet the fins were rippling with an easy motion, easy as a creature can be only when it feels that more of living is ahead.

The winter, when a trout is quiet, would be long enough for his wounds to heal, and for his nerves to sharpen. Soon the last migrating Osprey would be gone — but would come back. And otters might be hunting here. The Trout must learn the dangers of this flood, and learn to be wary even while he was exhilarated by it. He would. The wisdom of instinct, as of intelligence, can be disregarded, and it also can be drawn upon.

By the time he would be ready to try his strength once more against the river, the Snake would be a slapping, dodging, driving, wild spring torrent.

Something Was Fishy About Stonehenge

Ed Zern

While in England last May I spent some time in a small village in Hampshire, home county of such sacrosanct trout waters as the Test, the Itchen and the Tichborne. Not long after settling myself at the inn I began to hear stories of the local fishing wizard, a Mr. Smythe-Preston, whose incredible success in extracting limit bags of large trout from hard-fished chalk streams at times when other anglers were going fishless was the talk of the sporting community. Naturally my curiosity was aroused, and I determined to seek Mr. Smythe-Preston out and, if possible, learn his secret.

"It's no use," said the innkeeper, himself a veteran angler and skilled fly tier. "He won't say a word. All we know is that he prefers fishing alone, observes all the local regulations as to hours and tackle and, although generally friendly, is somewhat peculiar in his habits. The fact is, there are those who say he's a practicing Druid, and there is talk of witchcraft and ancient rites. Some even say he has a pact with the devil. But, of course, that's all nonsense, and for myself I think he's a topflight trout man who's also exceptionally lucky."

Later, at a dinner party, I met the local curate, another dedicated trout fisherman, and asked him about the fabulous Mr. Smythe-Preston. "I know him only slightly," said the reverend angler, "and he seems a nice enough chap. As for his remarkable success at fishing, I simply don't know how to account for it. Twice I've met him along the stream and observed him carefully, and although he handles a rod and presents a fly as well as most of us, the truth is, he's not really a brilliant — ah — technician. Some of the villagers claim they've followed him on several mysterious predawn expeditions, and declare that he drives to Stonehenge — it's not far from here, you know, less than an hour — where, they say, he goes through some sort of ritualistic rigmarole just as the sun rises over Salisbury Plain. Frankly, I suspect those self-appointed gumshoes of having had one too many at the Crown and Creel — at any rate, he doesn't seem the sort of chap to belong to a pagan sect, and I can't take it seriously."

Ironically, it was at the Crown and Creel, the village's one and only pub, that I finally met the mystery man in person, and was surprised to find him the most unmysterious-appearing of mortals, about as sinister in aspect as an Iowa Sunday school superintendent. The grayness of his face and mustache was alleviated only by the mild twinkle of his eyes, and not at all by the drab and rumpled tweeds that failed to disguise a middle-aged paunch. When I asked if I might stand him a pint he accepted politely if not cordially, but when I said I had heard of his phenomenal ability to produce limits of large trout each time he went fishing and asked straight out if he would tell me his secret, he modestly laughed and said the talk was exaggerated. "Although I must admit," he added, "that I *am* fairly lucky occasionally. And I try not to fish on an east wind — the usual sort of stuff every fisherman knows. But tell me about American trout fishing — your Large Hole River that I've read so much about, and all that."

I told him about the Big Hole and the Madison, and was

starting on the Letort when I overheard one of a group of villagers at the next table laughingly offer to take a lie-detector test over some boast he had just made. It was then that I recalled the tiny envelope in my wallet, and realized that it might be the answer to my problem.

The packet had been given to me by a young friend who, while interning at a New York hospital, had been involved in some research experiments with sodium pentothal, the so-called "truth serum." In this case, however, it had been produced in the form of pills that could be administered orally and, when dissolved in liquid, affected neither color nor taste. "Frankly," my friend had said, "I don't know how effective this stuff will turn out to be, but I thought you might use it to help in locating some of your friends' woodcock covers. Slip a couple of these into their martinis — it can't do them any harm, and it might start them chattering like magpies!" He had meant it for a joke, but I had put the packet into my wallet and forgotten it, until that instant.

At the same moment, by one of those fortuitous coincidences that occur more often in real life than in fiction, Mr. Smythe-Preston was called to the telephone; on a reckless impulse I took the pills from my wallet and popped two of them into the half pint of beer in his mug; then, seeing that there was only one pill left, I popped that one in, too. On returning, Smythe-Preston drained his tankard and said he'd have to be getting back to his cottage. When I said I needed some exercise and asked if I might walk with him, he agreed without much enthusiasm and we set out.

I had no idea how soon the pills would take effect, or indeed if they would take effect at all. For the first half mile I was sure they wouldn't — it would not have been beyond my medical friend to have given me some kind of sugar-pill placebo together with a cock-and-bull story — and then, as we started across the village common, I thought I detected a change in the tone of Smythe-Preston's voice. He had been mumbling noncommittal answers to my questions about local history, but when I asked about the remnants of what seemed to be a Roman wall he began talking at considerable length, in a slightly higher-pitched voice and quite rapidly. When my next remark brought an even more effusive response and a reference to some personal matter that an Englishman would ordinarily not mention to a stranger, I pretended to stumble and twist my ankle. He could hardly refuse when I asked if he'd mind sitting on the wall with me for a minute, until I could determine if the ankle was sprained.

Naturally, as soon as we were seated I asked him point-blank to tell me the secret of his fishing prowess. Not to my surprise, he commenced talking at once, in the manner of a man who is slightly tipsy and feeling well pleased with the world and himself. "Oh, that?" he babbled happily. "Damnedest thing, old chap. I've always been a bit of an archaeologist, y'know — fascinating hobby, and something to do between fishing seasons. And, of course, with that Stonehenge thing so close at hand I did a lot of rummaging around there, taking measurements and calculating meridians and sidereal angles and generally trying to outguess all the others who were trying to unriddle that ring of great boulders. I say, am I boring you, old boy?"

"Not at all," I assured him.

"Well, then," he said, "it could hardly have been that I was the first really keen fisherman to poke about there, and I may not have been the first to discover it. Possibly others unearthed it too, and kept their faces shut, as I did."

"Discovered what?" I asked eagerly, and Smythe-Preston laughed.

"Discovered what all those monstrous stones were put there for," he said. "It was all so absurdly simple, once I'd broken the code. And to think that it took me nearly five years to see what should have been obvious right from the start."

"For heaven's sake, man," I said, "*what* should have been obvious?"

Smythe-Preston looked at me in disbelief. "Look, old boy, since you seem a bit dense I shall spell it out for you. These chalk streams you've been fishing all week — they were here before man, of course. God knows who kept the weed cut then, but the trout were here, too, and when the ancient Britons came tromping onto the scene they found old *Salmo fario* ahead of them, and well established. And so they did what any self-respecting Briton would have done — they started fishing for trout! Of course, it wasn't easy. The poor brutes weren't much on finesse — just barely down out of the trees, you might say — and the arts of angling weren't highly developed. But, of course, the trout weren't so awfully sophisticated either, and that helped. At any rate, they fished — for food at first, and then, of course, for sport as well, since they were British.

"And being fishermen," Smythe-Preston went on, a mile a minute, "they soon developed most of the appurtenances of anglers everywhere — crude rods and lines, no doubt some type of artificial fly, since the principal food of the fish was, even then, natural insects. Do you follow me?"

"Yes, indeed," I said.

"Good," said Smythe-Preston, "because, frankly, you don't strike me as frightfully bright. Well, then. Along with the rods and such, these primitive trout fishers invented other necessities — the alibi, for example. The trout that keeps growing after being caught, more rapidly than it ever did in the water. The pre-Potter one-upmanship of the fly fisher over the worm-soaker. And — as you've undoubtedly seen by now — the fisherman's calendar."

"Undoubtedly seen what by now?" I asked, bewildered.

"Sir," said Smythe-Preston, "if you will forgive my saying so and, indeed, even if you will not, you are most incredibly obtuse. Frankly, I wonder I waste my time with you. But you have asked me a question, and for some peculiar reason I feel impelled to answer it — truthfully!"

"For God's sake, *do!*" I urged.

"Can't you get it through your thick colonial skull," he said, "that Stonehenge, that so-called riddle of antiquity, is nothing more nor less than a fishing calendar — a monstrous, megalithic solunar table, so to speak, constructed by a prehistoric race of trout fishermen! Once I got to wondering why it had been built in the heart of the chalk-stream country, everything fell into place. And so, you see, I go there every morning I'm able, during the season, and by observing exactly where the sun's rays strike at sunup — which means crawling about on my hands and knees sometimes in the outer ring — I know precisely, virtually to the split second, when the trout will be voraciously, passionately, uncontrollably on the feed, and will take almost any fly that's presented to them. As I've long ago learned where most of the larger fish lie, it's a simple matter to be there at precisely the right time. And while that overpowering compulsion to feed is affecting the trout, sometimes for as long as three or four minutes, I can take every fish within reach of my cast. The problem is that, having hooked a three or four-pounder, I may need the entire feeding period to land him. However, there are usually several such periods during the day, sometimes of as short a duration as 15 seconds, and by the time the sun has been up a few minutes I can have determined exactly when they will occur and arrange my itinerary accordingly."

"Fantastic!" I said, and meant it. "But tell me, how do you determine the exact times of day?"

"Look here, old man," said Smythe-Preston, peering at his watch. "I can't stay here any longer. My wife is frightfully jealous and has the silly notion that I dally sometimes with a widow on the other side of the common, no matter how convincingly I deny it. And, of course, it might be that she has reason — bound to be a bit of fire where there's that much smoke, eh? But since I've told you this much of my secret, I suppose I might as well go the entire pig, as I believe you Americans have it, and fill in the details. If you'll meet me here tomorrow morning at five o'clock, I'll take you over to Stonehenge and show you."

"You will?" I said incredulously, thinking even as I spoke of the story I'd be able to tell my friend at the research center. "You're not just putting me on?"

"On my word of honor," said Smythe-Preston sadly, "although, for the life of me, I can't imagine why. Good night, sir." And he hurried off down the lane.

That night I lay awake calculating the possibilities of a genuinely accurate system of forecasting fishing; it was certain that the secret of Stonehenge, once known, could be adjusted for latitudinal, longitudinal and altitudinal variations to apply to any part of the world on which the sun shines, and that the pattern of recurring feeding periods could be projected far in advance.

When five o'clock came I was at the appointed spot, but waited in vain. At seven, having formed some uncharitable opinions as to the value of an English angler's word of honor, I walked back to the inn, where I was informed by my host that Mrs. Smythe-Preston had just been arrested for the murder of her husband, into whose gizzard, in the course of a family discussion, she had plunged a carving knife.

I suppose I shouldn't have used that third pill.

The Intruder

Robert Traver

It was about noon when I put down my fly rod and sculled the little cedar boat with one hand and ate a sandwich and drank a can of beer with the other, just floating and enjoying the ride down the beautiful broad main Escanaba River. Between times I watched the merest speck of an eagle tacking and endlessly wheeling far up in the cloudless sky. Perhaps he was stalking my sandwich or even, dark thought, stalking me. . . . The fishing so far had been poor; the good trout simply weren't rising. I rounded a slow double bend, with high gravel banks on either side, and there stood a lone fisherman — the first person I had seen in hours. He was standing astride a little feeder creek on a gravel point on the left downstream side, fast to a good fish, his glistening rod hooped and straining, the line taut, the leader vibrating and sawing the water, the fish itself boring far down out of sight.

Since I was curious to watch a good battle and anxious not

to interfere, I eased the claw anchor over the stern — *plop* — and the little boat hung there, gurgling and swaying from side to side in the slow deep current. The young fisherman either did not hear me or, hearing, and being a good one, kept his mind on his work. As I sat watching he shifted the rod to his left hand, shaking out his right wrist as though it were asleep, so I knew then that the fight had been a long one and that this fish was no midget. The young fisherman fumbled in his shirt and produced a cigarette and lighter and lit up, a real cool character. The fish made a sudden long downstream run and the fisherman raced after him, prancing through the water like a yearling buck, gradually coaxing and working him back up to the deeper slow water across from the gravel bar. It was a nice job of handling and I wanted to cheer. Instead I coughed discreetly and he glanced quickly upstream and saw me.

"Hi," he said pleasantly, turning his attention back to his fish.

"Hi," I answered.

"How's luck?" he said, still concentrating.

"Fairish," I said. "But I haven't raised anything quite like you seem to be on to. How you been doin' — otherwise, I mean?"

"Fairish," he said. "This is the third good trout in this same stretch — all about the same size."

"My, my," I murmured, thinking ruefully of the half-dozen-odd barely legal brook trout frying away in my sun-baked creel. "Guess I've just been out floating over the good spots."

"Pleasant day for a ride, though," he said, frowning intently at his fish.

"Delightful," I said wryly, taking a slow swallow of beer.

"Yep," the assured young fisherman went on, expertly feeding out line as his fish made another downstream sashay. "Yep," he repeated, nicely taking up slack on the retrieve, "that's why I gave up floating this lovely river. Nearly ten years ago, just a kid. Decided then 'twas a hell of a lot more fun fishing a hundred yards of her carefully than taking off on these all-day floating picnics."

I was silent for a while. Then: "I think you've got something there," I said, and I meant it. Of course he was right, and I was simply out joy-riding past the good fishing. I should have brought along a girl or a camera. On this beautiful river if there was no rise a float was simply an enforced if lovely scenic tour. If there was a rise, no decent fisherman ever needed to float. Presto, I now had it all figured out. . . .

"Wanna get by?" the poised young fisherman said, flipping his cigarette into the water.

"I'll wait," I said. "I got all day. My pal isn't meeting me till dark — 'way down at the old burned logging bridge."

"Hm . . . trust you brought your passport — you really are out on a voyage," he said. "Perhaps you'd better slip by, fella — by the feel of this customer it'll be at least ten-twenty minutes more. Like a smart woman in the mood for play, these big trout don't like to be rushed. C'mon, just bear in sort of close to me, over here, right under London Bridge. It won't bother us at all."

My easy young philosopher evidently didn't want me to see how really big his fish was. But being a fisherman myself I knew, I knew. "All right," I said, lifting the anchor and sculling down over his way and under his throbbing line. "Thanks and good luck."

"Thanks, chum," he said, grinning at me. "Have a nice ride and good luck to you."

"Looks like I'll need it," I said, looking enviously back over my shoulder at his trembling rod tip. "Hey," I said, belatedly remembering my company manners, "want a nice warm can of beer?"

Smiling: "Despite your glowing testimonial, no thanks."

"You're welcome," I said, realizing we were carrying on like a pair of strange diplomats.

"And one more thing, please," he said, raising his voice a little to be heard over the burbling water, still smiling intently at his straining fish. "If you don't mind, please keep this little stretch under your hat — it's been all mine for nearly ten years. It's really something special. No use kidding you — I see you've spotted my bulging creel and I guess by now you've got a fair idea of what I'm on to. And anyway I've got to take a little trip. But I'll be back — soon I hope. In the meantime try to be good to the place. I know it will be good to you."

"Right!" I shouted, for by then I had floated nearly around the downstream bend. "Mum's the word." He waved his free hand and then was blotted from view by a tall doomed spruce leaning far down out across the river from a crumbling water-blasted bank. The last thing I saw was the gleaming flash of his rod, the long taut line, the strumming leader. It made a picture I've never forgotten.

That was the last time ever that I floated the Big Escanaba River. I had learned my lesson well. Always after that when I visited this fabled new spot I hiked in, packing my gear, threading my way down river through a pungent needled maze of ancient deer trails, like a fleeing felon keeping always slyly away from the broad winding river itself. My strategy was twofold: to prevent other sly fishermen from finding and deflowering the place, and to save myself an extra mile of walking.

Despite the grand fishing I discovered there, I did not go back too often. It was a place to hoard and save, being indeed most good to me, as advertised. And always I fished it alone, for a fisherman's pact had been made, a pact that became increasingly hard to keep as the weeks rolled into months, the seasons into years, during which I never again encountered my poised young fisherman. In the morbid pathology of trout fishermen such a phenomenon is mightily disturbing. What had become of my fisherman? Hadn't he ever got back from his trip? Was he sick or had he moved away? Worse yet, had he died? How could such a consummate young artist have possibly given up fishing such an enchanted spot? Was he one of that entirely mad race of eccentric fishermen who cannot abide the thought of sharing a place, however fabulous, with even *one* other fisherman?

By and by, with the innocent selfishness possessed by all fishermen, I dwelt less and less upon the probable fate of my young fisherman and instead came smugly to think it was I who had craftily discovered the place. Nearly twenty fishing seasons slipped by on golden wings, as fishing seasons do, during which time I, fast getting no sprightlier, at last found it expedient to locate and hack out a series of abandoned old logging roads to let me drive within easier walking distance of my secret spot. The low cunning of middle age was replacing the hot stamina of youth. . . . As a road my new trail was strictly a spring-breaking bronco-buster, but at least I was able to sit and ride, after a fashion, thus saving my aging legs for the real labor of love to follow.

Another fishing season was nearly done when, one afternoon, brooding over that gloomy fact, I suddenly tore off my lawyer-mask and fled my office, heading for the Big Escanaba, bouncing and bucking my way in, finally hitting the Glide — as I had come to call the place — about sundown. For a long time I just stood there on the high bank, drinking in the sights and pungent river smells. No fish were rising, and slowly, lovingly, I went through the familiar ritual of rigging up: scrubbing out a fine new leader, dressing the tapered line, jointing the rod and threading the line, pulling on the tall patched waders, anointing myself with fly dope. No woman dressing for a ball was more fussy. . . . Then I composed myself on my favorite fallen log and waited. I smoked a slow pipe and sipped a can of beer, cold this time, thanks to the marvels of dry ice and my new road. My watching spot overlooked a wide bend and commanded a grand double view: above, the deep slow velvet glide with its little feeder stream where I first met my young fisherman; below a sporty and productive broken run of white water stretching nearly a half mile. The old leaning spruce that used to be there below me had long since bowed in surrender and been swept away by some forgotten spring torrent. As I sat waiting the wind had died, the shadowing waters had taken on the brooding blue hush of evening, the dying embers of sundown suddenly lit a great blazing forest fire in the tops of the tall spruces across river from me, and an unknown bird that I have always called simply the "lonely" bird sang timidly its ancient haunting plaintive song. I arose and took a deep breath like a soldier advancing upon the enemy.

The fisherman's mystic hour was at hand.

First I heard and then saw a young buck in late velvet slowly, tentatively splashing his way across to my side, above me and beyond the feeder creek, ears twitching and tall tail nervously wigwagging. Then he winded me, freezing in midstream, giving me a still and liquid stare for a poised instant; then came charging on across in great pawing incredibly graceful leaps, lacquered flanks quivering, white flag up and waving, bounding up the bank and into the anonymous woods, the sounds of his excited blowing fading and growing fainter and then dying away.

In the meantime four fair trout had begun rising in the smooth tail of the glide just below me. I selected and tied on a favorite small dry fly and got down below the lowest riser and managed to take him on the first cast, a short dainty float. Without moving I stood and lengthened line and took all four risers, all nice firm brook trout upwards of a foot, all the time purring and smirking with increasing complacency. The omens were good. As I relit my pipe and waited for new worlds to conquer I heard a mighty splash above me and wheeled gaping at the spreading magic ring of a really good trout, carefully marking the spot. Oddly enough he had risen just above where the young buck had just crossed, a little above the feeder creek. Perhaps, I thought extravagantly, perhaps he was after the deer. . . . I waited, tense and watchful, but he did not rise again.

I left the river and scrambled up the steep gravelly bank and made my way through the tall dense spruces up to the little feeder creek. I slipped down the bank like a footpad, stealthily inching my way out to the river in the silted creek itself, so as not to scare the big one, *my* big one. I could feel the familiar shock of icy cold water suddenly clutching at my ankles as I stood waiting at the spot where I had first run across my lost fisherman. I quickly changed to a fresh fly in the same pattern, carefully snubbing the knot. Then the fish obediently rose again, a savage easy engulfing roll, again the undulant outgoing ring, just where I had marked him, not more than thirty feet from me and a little beyond the middle and obliquely upstream. Here was, I saw, a cagey selective riser, lord of his pool, and one who would not suffer fools gladly. So I commanded myself to rest him before casting. "Twenty-one, twenty-two, twenty-three . . ." I counted.

The cast itself was indecently easy and, finally releasing it, the little Adams sped out on its quest, hung poised in mid-air for an instant, and then settled sleepily upon the water like a thistle, uncurling before the leader like the languid outward folding of a ballerina's arm. The fly circled a moment, uncertainly, then was caught by the current. Down, down it rode, closer, closer, then — *clap!* — the fish rose and kissed it, I flicked my wrist and he was on, and then away he went roaring off downstream, past feeder creek and happy fisherman, the latter hot after him.

During the next mad half hour I fought this explosive creature up and down the broad stream, up and down, ranging at least a hundred feet each way, or so it seemed, without ever once seeing him. This meant, I figured, that he was either a big brown or a brook. A rainbow would surely have leapt a dozen times by now. Finally I worked him into the deep safe water off the feeder creek where he sulked nicely while I panted and rested my benumbed rod arm. As twilight receded into dusk with no sign of his tiring I began vaguely to wonder just who had latched on to whom. For the fifth or sixth time I rested my aching arm by transferring the rod to my left hand, professionally shaking out my tired wrist just as I had once seen a young fisherman do.

Nonchalantly I reached in my jacket and got out and tried to light one of my rigidly abominable Italian cigars. My fish, unimpressed by my show of aplomb, shot suddenly away on a powerful zigzag exploratory tour upstream, the fisherman nearly swallowing his unlit cigar as he scrambled up after him. It was then that I saw a lone man sitting quietly in a canoe, anchored in midstream above me. The tip of his fly rod showed over the stern. My heart sank: after all these years my hallowed spot was at last discovered.

"Hi," I said, trying to convert a grimace of pain into an amiable grin, all the while keeping my eye on my sulking fish. The show must go on.

"Hi," he said.

"How you doin'?" I said, trying to make a brave show of casual fish talk.

"Fairish," he said, "but nothing like you seem to be on to."

"Oh, he isn't so much," I said, lying automatically if not too well. "I'm working a fine leader and don't dare to bull him." At least that was the truth.

The stranger laughed briefly and glanced at his wrist watch. "You've been on to him that I know of for over forty minutes — and I didn't see you make the strike. Let's not try to kid the marines. I just moved down a bit closer to be in on the finish. I'll shove away if you think I'm too close."

"Nope," I answered generously, delicately snubbing my fish away from a partly submerged windfall. "But about floating this lovely river," I pontificated, "there's nothing in it, my friend. Absolutely nothing. Gave it up myself eighteen-twenty years ago. Figured out it was better working one stretch carefully than shoving off on these floating picnics. Recommend it to you, comrade."

The man in the canoe was silent. I could see the little red moon of his cigarette glowing and fading in the gathering gloom. Perhaps my gratuitous pedagogical ruminations had offended him; after all, trout fishermen are a queer proud race. Perhaps I should try diversionary tactics. "Wanna get by?" I inquired silkily. Maybe I could get him to go away before I tried landing this unwilling porpoise. He still remained silent. "Wanna get by?" I repeated. "It's perfectly O.K. by me. As you see — it's a big roomy river."

"No," he said dryly. "No thanks." There was another long pause. Then: "If you wouldn't mind too much I think I'll put in here for the night. It's getting pretty late — and somehow I've come to like the looks of this spot."

"Oh," I said in a small voice — just "Oh" — as I disconsolately watched him lift his anchor and expertly push his canoe in to the near gravelly shore, above me, where it grated halfway in and scraped to rest. He sat there quietly, his little neon cigarette moon glowing, and I felt I just had to say something more. After all I didn't *own* the river. "Why sure, of course, it's a beautiful place to camp, plenty of pine knots for fuel, a spring-fed creek for drinking water and cooling your beer," I ran on gaily, rattling away like an hysterical realtor trying to sell the place. Then I began wondering how I would ever spirit my noisy fish car out of the woods without the whole greedy world of fishermen learning about my new secret road to this old secret spot. Maybe I'd even have to abandon it for the night and hike out. . . . Then I remembered there was an uncooperative fish to be landed, so I turned my full attention to the unfinished and uncertain business at hand. "Make yourself at home," I lied softly.

"Thanks," the voice again answered dryly, and again I heard the soft chuckle in the semidarkness.

My fish had stopped his mad rushes now and was busily boring the bottom, the long leader vibrating like the plucked string of a harp. For the first time I found I was able gently to pump him up for a cautious look. And again I almost swallowed my still unlit stump of cigar as I beheld his dorsal fin cleaving the water nearly a foot back from the fly. He wallowed and shook like a dog and then rolled on his side, then recovered and fought his way back down and away on another run, but shorter this time. With a little pang I knew then that my fish was a done, but the pang quickly passed — it always did — and again I gently, relentlessly pumped him up, shortening line, drawing him in to the familiar daisy hoop of landing range, kneeling and stretching and straining out my opposing aching arms like those of an extravagant archer. The net slipped fairly under him on the first try and, clenching my cigar, I made my pass and lo! lifted him free and dripping from the water. "Ah-h-h . . ." He was a glowing superb spaniel-sized brown. I staggered drunkenly away from the water and sank anywhere to the ground, panting like a winded miler.

"Beautiful, *beautiful,*" I heard my forgotten and unwelcome visitor saying like a prayer. "I've dreamed all this — over a thousand times I've dreamed it."

I tore my feasting eyes away from my fish and glowered up at the intruder. He was half standing in the beached canoe now, one hand on the side, trying vainly to wrest the cap from a bottle, of all things, seeming in the dusk to smile uncertainly. I felt a sudden chill sense of concern, of vague nameless alarm.

"Look, chum," I said, speaking lightly, very casually, "is everything all O.K.?"

"Yes, yes, of course," he said shortly, still plucking away at his bottle. "There . . . I — I'm coming now."

Bottle in hand he stood up and took a resolute broad step out of the canoe, then suddenly, clumsily he lurched and pitched forward, falling heavily, cruelly, half in the beached canoe and half out upon the rocky wet shore. For a moment I sat staring ruefully, then I scrambled up and started running toward him, still holding my rod and the netted fish, thinking this fisherman was indubitably potted. "No, no, no!" he shouted at me, struggling and scrambling to his feet in a kind of wild urgent frenzy. I halted, frozen, holding my sagging dead fish as the intruder limped toward me, in a curious sort of creaking stiffly mechanical limp, the uncorked but still intact bottle held triumphantly aloft in one muddy wet hand, the other hand reaching gladly toward me.

"Guess I'll never get properly used to this particular battle stripe," he said, slapping his thudding and unyielding right leg. "But how are you, stranger?" he went on, his wet eyes glistening, his bruised face smiling. "How about our having a drink to your glorious trout — and still another to reunion at our old secret fishing spot?"

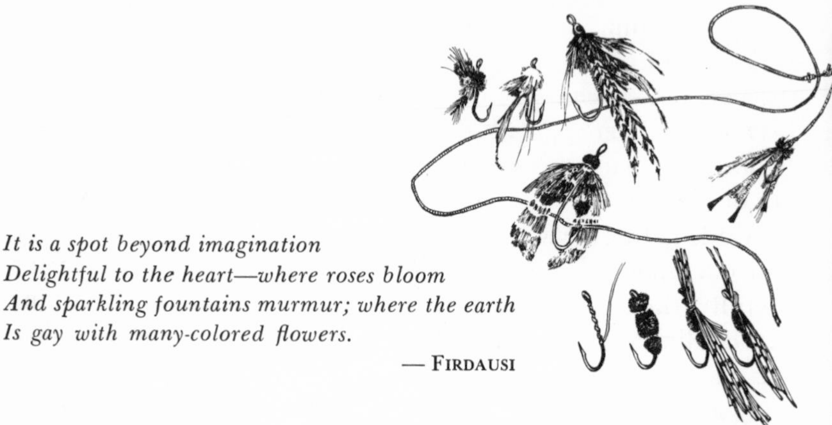

It is a spot beyond imagination
Delightful to the heart—where roses bloom
And sparkling fountains murmur; where the earth
Is gay with many-colored flowers.

— FIRDAUSI

Along a Trout Stream

L. F. Brown

An ill man is walking down Broadway to his office. Overworked for months, he shrinks from the hard, practical duties of rushing modern business. The half-grown foliage of late May is on the trees in Bowling Green and Battery Park. Robins are calling to each other there. He joys in the fresh wind, and the gulls soaring above North River!

How green the grass is! And there, peeping through, he sees several wild violets, blue as the sky at which they gaze. Presto! the jaded and listless look is gone from the man's face; his heart leaps and hope comes strong and welcome; for before him, summoned by memory, are the violets and the vistas, the thorn-blossoms, robins, pheasants, arbutus, and lilies along the chattering flow of his favorite trout stream!

Trinity bells are pealing "Rock of Ages"; but the echoes of those peals sing another song to him in his need of rest. It is: "Only two weeks more! Then you shall be fishing for trout on the little Slagle River!"

How slowly the fortnight drags by! But a morning comes when, before three o'clock, he is actually wading that stream. At last! Since midnight all the jewels of the skies of June have been shining keenly. It is wild, remote, with even the camp a mile away. He is at the entrance to the Lower Glen. Over the high banks are thickets of thorn bushes, their wealth of snow-white blossoms filled with dewdrops which have caught and hold the starlight!

Through that sweetest of all earthly things, wildflower air, comes the far hooting of owls in lonely nocturne. There are whiffs of mint scents, faint smells of fragrant birch and pine-balsam. The slight stir of a sleepy breeze wakes a low whisper in some of the treetops, while the stream sings to the sleeping forest, with

> . . . . . *the still sound*
> *Of falling waters — lulling as the song*
> *Of Indian bees at sunset, when they throng*
> *Around the fragrant Nilica, and deep*
> *In its blue blossoms, hum themselves to sleep.*

"In the night the great old troutes bite very boldly," said Izaak Walton: so the angler is wading the stream at what the roused camp cook has called an "unearthly" hour. Far better, he is here to drink in the beauty of the sylvan environment as the mystic hour runs from gold of stars to gold of sunshine.

The stream is wide enough for casting flies without trouble from the white thorn bushes. Fifty feet below him is a deep pool, just beyond the wraith of foam at the foot of short rapids. Gloom and mystery lie over and in it; he can see the white of foam slowly eddying over its black water under two leaning pines. He moves slowly, then pauses with rubber-clad feet on the white and golden gravel, covered with two feet of rushing water.

Poising the pliable lancewood rod, while the left hand pulls the line from the reel in unison at each pass of the rod back and forth above him, he extends the line with its leader and flies until forty feet of line are in motion. Then, true as bow from arrow, light as down, fluttering as if alive, the White Miller lures go straight to the center of the pool, and kiss the water.

A flash, gleam, flying spray as a large trout darts from his home under the bank! It is an experience that has often thrilled the real angler. The fish has jumped at and missed the leading fly!

But the next cast is successful. An even fiercer rush, and the angler, with the well-known turn of the wrist on the rod, has the fish hooked! Straight downstream flies the quarry, the reel screaming and the heart of the angler beating hard and fast! A long struggle follows. Almost in the landing net twice, and yet the trout makes savage rushes for liberty! Soon the prize is secured; joy of possession as a wild, twelve-inch king of the jeweled coat lies on the bed of fern leaves in the bottom of the trout creel! For this, and for the gladness of returning health among some of earth's fairest scenes, the angler has journeyed almost one thousand miles. Already he is mastered by the spell of the remote, wild life, with its mystery and music.

Three beautiful trout are taken from the pool while the starlight dies and the sky grows lighter. Then, startling the ear of earliest dawn, a solitary bird fills the forest with its first note, clear, pure, and thrilling, as if Heaven itself had sent its own winged messenger to herald the coming day! Then another bird takes up the song; then another and another, until all the woods are vocal with melody — now near and joyous, now far and sweet, like "the horns of elf land faintly blowing."

"Skir-reee!" cries a scared chipmunk as he darts away. A gray squirrel, with tail well cocked, barks and scolds at a safe distance. From far down the stream comes the low drumming of a partridge. Across the bend is a sudden splash, followed by the rattling cry of a kingfisher, who has had his first dive of the day for nothing. A screaming hawk sails away from the dry tree that tops the high bank. *"Up all night?"* inquires a quail.

The hypnotism and delight of it to the man escaped from a busy city office are beyond all expression in words! Blessed hours of recreation!

In the air is the faint odor of smoke, and of boiling coffee. The cook has gone farther down the stream with a heavy lunch basket, has put six big potatoes before a kindled campfire on the brookside, and then has caught five larger trout from a deeper pool; breakfast there is nearly ready. The roasted potatoes are done to a turn — how well the cook can prepare them! And out from the little frying pan come the five trout, swimming a half hour ago, and now garnished with tender watercress from that bank of it close at hand. Abundant coffee, cream, toast, butter! The breakfast is served on two snowy napkins spread over a mossy knoll: the dishes are pieces of freshly cut birch bark, the seat is a birch log. Peerless dining room — a June sky curved in azure benediction above a wild pine forest filled with sough of the wind through its aisles — with bird notes, with the voice (so glad!) of the soul of the wilderness — the talking stream whose rapids reflect the early sunlight down one of the long aisles, and cause it to dance on the foliage. Not all the chefs and banquets in the cities of the round world could produce such a meal as this, with such a breakfast chamber!

For the wealth of beauty is everywhere. Laurel and rhododendron blossoms are around him — wild lilies, trailing arbutus, and white strawberry blossoms! Finally, the forest rises above a blue carpet of violets. How the angler loves them! He stops the cook from plucking them for a boutonniere. He almost wishes, as he lies beside a thick cluster of their blooms, that he might strike hands and feet in the kind earth, take root himself beside his favorite flowers, and nevermore abandon the happy companionship. The little, nodding, blue comrades! He feels that they are sentient — know and are grateful for his love and insight. He is charmed by their wild, shy life. As he lies prone and drinks from the spring below the bank, one of them takes advantage of a sudden gust of wind to actually nod *at him* several times!

It is just a little violet on the bank above the spring;
Just a little point of blue that nods before the saucy air:
And as he notes the beauty of the wee and winsome thing,
He feels that it is glad to see him back and drinking there.

And now comes proof that the angler sees and knows the beauty of his environment. For he is not fishing. He could talk for hours of rods, lines, leaders, and reels — of camping, guides, tents, pack horses, canoes; of the various flies to be used according to season, location, lights, hours of day or night, on a dozen widely separated streams. He has fished on the Peribonca in Quebec, the best salmon streams in Newfoundland, the far-famed Nepigon, and the fierce waters of a dozen rivers in British Columbia that are guarded by black mountains whose bases were green with foliage; while their peaks, sometimes two miles high, carried snow-banners in every high wind. He knows Pennsylvania's best trout streams; and the waters of the Muskoka region; besides the Au Sable, Shuswap, Two Medicine and St. Mary's Lakes in Montana, and Square and the Sourdnahonk Lakes in Maine. Trout from the Margaree in Cape Breton, from the Tabusintac and Bartibog rivers in New Brunswick, and the Morell Stream on Prince Edward Island, have been brought to his creel by hundreds. The best cruising for edible saltwater fishes — that around Albemarle and Pamlico Sounds — is familiar to him. But *nowhere else* exist such wildness, remoteness, wealth of sylvan enchantment, such flavor to trout, such health and life in air and water, such music in a stream, as along the peerless little Slagle River!

He is realizing this, and is happy to the point of fear. He could easily fill his creel with trout; yet he does not cast the flies. For he is in a hypnotized state. He will not even light his morning cigar; its smoke would pollute the air of a place which has "become religion." And he would sooner take a drink of whiskey before St. Peter, the ancient fisherman who now guards the gates of Paradise, than here, right in a Paradise upon earth.

The rod is laid on the half-submerged log where he sits, with his rubber-clad feet in the water. He really hears and sees!

What a contrast to the scenes he beheld last summer along Granite Creek, which flows into the head of St. George's Pond in Newfoundland! There, the hillsides were yellow with ripe bake-apple berries; barrens were gray with Arctic moss; caribou grazed in plain sight on many hills. Moosebirds, tame by reason of their ignorance of human presence, roosted on the ends of the little logs on the campfire before the tripod tent. Marsh hens called and fluttered; and at night, from far above, could be heard the quacking of ducks and the thrilling *honk! honk! honk!* of the stout-hearted old wild ganders, each winging his way toward Labrador at the head of invisible wedges of night-flying geese. Great trout were in the pools of that stream; and the steel-gray color of its gravelly bed was very beautiful. And yet, even among such scenes, the angler had longed for the music, the flower and bird life, foliage and mystery of the Slagle! Its waters flow around his legs now! And they seem to talk to him as they rush:

Where have you been, my devotee?
Why have you roamed so far from me?
Thrice welcome back to my fair shore!
Now learn to love me more and more.

He sees the flash of the body of a brook trout as he leaps from the brook, in pursuit of a butterfly, wandering too near the water's surface for safety. The line and flies have drifted from the log. Flash! a trout strikes one of the lures, pulls the rod into the stream, and the owner scrambles after it. Now he is casting again, and filling the creel. Nearly every effort brings some response. In pools, behind rocks, on the ripples, here by the bank, there beneath those logs, yonder in the foam of the rapids, and in places where least suspected, glittering in beauty, crimson-spotted, always ready for a bait, lurk and play the wild brook trout. The wild trout is the ideal fish, the fish of the poets and the sportsman, who often feels that the breeding pond is the halfway house to a fish stall in a market.

And so he wanders down the brook, happy, filling his hours with best recreation. Steeper, higher, wilder, in lordly, many-colored scenes, grow the banks of the Glen. Great trout lie in the waters which eddy, rush, and glance in silvery wilfulness over an intaglio of white and golden gravel that beautifies the swift current.

Thus, all too quickly, passes the angler's day. The late afternoon light is over all as he again stops, and looks, and listens.

To his right is a high knoll, mottled with moss growths, its base sandaled with the white star-points of wild strawberry blooms, and the tiny pale-blue flowers of forget-me-nots. Beyond is the brown, far-spreading carpet of the forest, splashed by blue of violets, white of lilies, yellow of daffodils! The whole left bank is a mass of dark wintergreen growth, edged at the water with mint and cress. Yonder is a little slope exquisite with the pale pink flowers of the anemone. Buds of wild honeysuckle are opening down there on the little island. Blossoms of laurel, rhododendron, trailing arbutus! Forest odors, bird notes, whispering stream, murmuring foliage! Mottled patches of sunlight and shadow dance under the great trees where, last night, the strident calls of the whippoorwills were ringing. A mother partridge is trying to coax her brood of chicks across that log over the stream! Beautiful! No wonder the gray-haired angler loves it all.

> The infinite Night with her solemn aspects, Day, and the sweet approach of Even and Morn, are full of meaning for him. He loves the green Earth with her streams and forests, her flowery leas and eternal skies — loves her with a sort of passion in all her vicissitudes of light and shade: his spirit revels in her grandeur and charms — expands like the breeze over wood and lawn, over glade and dingle, stealing and giving odors. Nature is to him no longer an insensate assemblage of colors and perfumes, but a mysterious Presence with which he communes in unutterable sympathies.

So this angler looks, listens, and feels more and more.

Every water-curve is full of grace, fantasy, and ease of motion, like a wind-swayed flag. And he studies the currents, full of color, clearness, mantlings of shadows, prismatic lights running over the white gravel of the bed, or darting through the foam-fire. And at still pauses is as much in the water as above it — boughs, foliage, blue sky, drifting clouds, all softened and etherealized by reflection.

Sweet views which in our world above
Can never well be seen,
Are imaged by the water's love
Of this fair forest green.

And all is interfused beneath
With an Elysian glow;
An atmosphere without a breath,—
A softer day below.

This effect is heightened by the music of the waterflow. Old anglers have ears trained to nicest sense of sound in the music of running water, and will know the physical conditions, even when unseen, which cause many of the notes of sound in a trout brook. The impact of the hurrying water on the air causes vibrations that determine the notes of the liquid oboe.

When deflected from a bank in mass, the water has the swishing sound of swift volume — crisp and full of life. Confined and made rapid in a little canyon or cut, its tone is deepened and becomes sonorous.

Or it falls over a half-buried timber and deepens to a low roar, which is slashed with purling dots of sound as drops fall singly into the current. From underneath this shell of swift water come echoes of partly drowned notes from the back-current below, and purls from roots and boughs around which the turned stream hurries. Gurgles ensue — the compressed air below varying in density with the varying volume of the water-leaps, the tones of the back-flow struggling through, with the whisper of air intermingled as it comes from the breaking bubbles with which the boiling pool is brightly opaque.

Or a fallen tree with its hundreds of boughs and twigs forms obstructive points of sounding current — tiny, but the whole furnishing a low, droning complaint. All these notes are varied by the width of stream, volume, depth, speed, angles of obstruction, character of the bed, kind, amount, and density of foliage, incline and height of banks, changes in echoes and resonance being endless, and even being affected by the dryness or humidity of the air, and the mingling of foliage sounds as winds are light or strong.

Up the stream is a broad shallow where the brook flows over partly submerged rocks, spread evenly, with a slumberous sound, like a steady wind moving through thick woods. Falling over the even edge of a wide dam the water has much the same sound. Unobstructed on inclines, rapidly flowing water in small volume has the inimitable purl, so exquisite that even in music the sweetest sounds are called liquid, like a tinkling rill. And the notes that blend from different water tones are always in concord, never in dissonance. Flowing under many conditions, meeting multiform obstacles over even a single rod of its course, these notes combine and make a certain "tone" or pitch of musical sound. Put a log across the brook, choke it with rocks, or remove those already there, and all the minor sounds are changed — also the general tone and pitch of the water music. Or the stream will part with some portion of its water volume, which will run into still nooks and limpidly go to sleep.

Thus the tone, volume, and blended orchestral effects of the water along a rushing trout stream are endless in variety and beauty — but all perfect. And the feeling of the hearing, sensitive student will be played upon until some echo of that music will be roused in his own spirit as he studies it all in its light and gloom, sunshine and shadow, storm and peace. So in all ages the best poets have studied and sung of the sound of flowing water, and have peopled their musical brooks with singing nymphs and wraiths of water sprites.

Wild life, hypnotism, the home of health! The true angler sees much, but will realize that as compared with what is about him, he sees very little.

Pluck a single leaf and look at it carefully. Even a skilled artist must keep it before him as a model, to mimic the delicate veinings and exact shape. Break a bough from a maple tree, and try to see it. Some of the leaves are mere lines to the sight — edgewise; others are foreshortened; many are shaded by companions. Through them reigns an intensity of reflection and brilliant semi-transparence acting upon and through surfaces extremely complex in shape, curve, and relative position. The light is in among the leaves and alters the appearance of the bough from within as well as without. Turn it, hold it in any position, and it is perfect; yet not another bough in all these miles of forest is just like it! Multiply the woods until they are a wilderness swayed by wind or quiet in unity of rest — flecked by driving cloud-shadows or flooded with moonlight or sunshine. Manifestly, we cannot see them. Only a few of even the subtle and weird patterns woven by ferns and mosses, and flowering grasses and plants, on the floor of the forest can be noted or understood.

Above all, mystery reigns. The stream drowses under long, partly seen roofs of foliage, or under loving, interlacing boughs of a water tunnel whose portals and winding sides are a tapestry of leaf and twig, misty with rain, unearthly as they shine in the wan smile of dying sunlight; even more real and divine in ghostly semidarkness at night! Opaline lights play through still lagoons in deep glades where the twin sisters of silence and twilight keep noonday watch, and "all the cheated hours sing vespers." Foliage melting away in distance to mystery of banks and masses, softest shadows deepening into black gloom, lonely stretches of the stream covered with nature-glory in their remote windings! Yet over each small section of such a scene is the mystery of color, form, interlaced shade. Here is what a man of sharpest sight has said of it:

> The stones and gravel of the banks catch green reflections from the boughs above. The bushes receive grays and yellows from the ground. Every hair-breadth of polished surface gives back a little bit of blue of the sky or gold of sun. This local color is again disguised and modified by the hue of the light, or quenched in the gray of the shadows.

But over and in all reigns the deeper mystery of life. Visible forms and their beauty are not the strongest attractions of the trout stream. Grant that mystery of soft depth of gloom, grace of motion in water, and of greatest delicacy of color are before the angler. What enchantment is there in even all this lovely environment to create such fierce longing for it, such content when possessed? Blue sky-fire may burn like a steadfast sapphire through emerald foliage; the pride of fern plumes may wave and rustle in their green refreshment — gold and pearl may throb in clouds whose shadows wing their way over mountain, glen, and forest — all through a sun-shafted fantasia of gold-dusted wine-air which is perfumed by arbutus, lily, violet, and forget-me-not, — the blossoming life all in a tangle of fragrant daydreams. Fairy tints may dance and quiver through that baby of prismatic mist, the tiny rainbow as it spans the cascade. All the glamour and riot of wild freshness may dwell in the mysterious woods, waters, sky, as a June breeze makes the whole a harp of whispering leaves, purling crystal, and curving blue. Place the angler in closest touch with it all, as he wades the stream with ears, heart, and spirit receptive and alert — foliage near, rushing water about him, changing, intermingling light and shadow over him as it falls in dancing fretwork. Yet even all this does not explain his great love. What causes it?

It is because in this nature about him is a mystery of life. An evasive, sleeplessly unwearied living principle dwells in the leaf he may pluck and crush, and is forming its colors, shaping its forms. Fern and flower, traced with life-streaming veins, specially textured, with hues that blend and part again, substantially present, possessed, yet hold a secret of living being and growing life that forever eludes his search, and always will. Life even more mystic than the spirit that he feels in himself is present before him, inscrutable, regnant, locked and barred away from his knowledge. Thus for him nature wears a double aspect — that of substantial presence and infinite remoteness. She dominates him with love of possession and of unattainable desire. He looks with mortal eyes upon her material features; yet he may gaze forever upon the veil that hides her invisible secret of life, and she is yet Isis — a magnet of mystery. Therefore he kneels, a rapt, glad, and humble devotee, before the closed gates, the thin wall beyond which are the secrets of her vivifying existence. Besides, she stands, like himself, between an eternity of the past and one of the future, seeming to call and beckon from a fathomless abyss whose depths his eyes will never pierce. She is fairest of the fair in visible forms; yet in her mystery of life she is unseen and unapproachable even in closest communion. So he loves her with unutterable love.

But he knows all is benign, and the vital import of the power that has created. But how, and by what facts and mysteries of life? No answer comes. He will not fathom the secrets; but he will realize more and more the divine wisdom in making so much unknown as all is borne forward. He will be sure that it is inconceivable that all is not of holy import and being—sure that all the mystery is blessed. Half-read messages and tones of sphere music will come to him as he wonders at the earth, and at himself, standing there with her, both between two eternities. And thus his faith is satisfied, and his love is crowned!

The result is inevitable. With bowed and reverent head the angler hopes that when he has crossed the delectable mountains, and, one poor thread in the web of universal history, has waved back his mute farewells to his favorite trout stream before he enters the unknown and is swallowed by oblivion, a merciful and loving heaven may furnish to him the counterpart of this brook. Will he not find a heavenly stream on that other side? Will not its waters sing as with a new song, its forests whisper, its flowers enchant? Yes, for there stands the message of Holy Writ, the last words of John, seer and prophet—words of inspiration and promise: "And he shewed me a pure river of water of life."

The Old Crawdad

Philip Wylie

Mr. McLaen hated Miami. It made him unpopular there. "Crawling with insects," he said, when an unusual west wind blew in a few black flies from the Everglades. His married daughter anxiously explained that the trade winds generally kept back the vermin. But Mr. McLaen merely peered down from his daughter's *cabaña* and called the celebrated beach below a "swarming purlieu" — which was going pretty far even for a man whose taste in phrases was on the gaudy side.

His daughter was depressed by that. Her name was Evelyn and she had two charming children as well as a young husband whom she considered more than charming.

"I'd hoped Dad would like it here," she said sadly. "Because if he doesn't . . ."

Her husband looked at his father-in-law's haughty back. He spoke without reserve: "Your old man is a human meat grinder. He doesn't like me. He doesn't like Florida. He has the temper of a water buffalo."

"He's a lamb," Evelyn replied. But her gray eyes were rueful. "Up at home — in Michigan —"

"There!" said her husband. "Michigan! He thinks there is only one state — Michigan! Night and day for two weeks!" He made a sound like the collapse of a stovepipe. "If I wanted him to invest in timberland in Michigan he'd go for a county. But since it's sugar cane . . ."

Evelyn tried to soothe him. "Some people don't like the tropics. Dad's one. We'll just have to give up the sugar cane idea and go back to St. Louis again."

She rose hastily then, because Ellis, who was four, had waded experimentally into the sea where the water was deeper than Ellis.

Mr. McLaen was having trouble with children too. He had walked to the diving board at the end of the pool, a fine figure of a man of fifty-nine, with a deep chest and beetling, red eyebrows, and he had dived as expertly as any youngster. Unfortunately, his plunge was intercepted by a child's balsa-wood surfboard.

He came up treading water and bellowing. "Lifeguard," he roared, taking no heed of the many onlookers, "this thing!" He hurled the board ashore. It hit a cement cornice and cracked. "Have you no rules in this pool?"

A lifeguard hurried forward.

"I'm sorry, Mr. McLaen!"

"You're sorry! In the Great Lakes area, you'd be sacked for such negligence! A noisome pesthole!" By that time, the child had retrieved his split board and was bawling. There was a rush of mothers, waiters, infants and others to the vicinity. Mr. McLaen sputtered to himself, "Miami! A nitwit's Mardi Gras!"

All in all, it made a bad day for Evelyn and Ralph and the two little Owenses. The last straw, which was laid on before supper, came in the form of a palm beetle in grandfather's chair. He sat on it. His daughter began to worry about her father's heart, and to regret fiercely the hour in which her now frayed young husband had decided there was a future in Florida sugar cane.

"Dad's not used to being a house guest," she explained in a

tone that was placating, but fairly hopeless. "He's accustomed to running things. Up home —"

"I know." Ralph couldn't put heat even in sarcasm. "He's a sort of chronic president. An order giver. A policy shaper. Temperamental, if you consider it temperamental to throw an ashtray because you've sat on a beetle; but a heart of gold. Gold brick!"

Thus the Owenses progressed into domestic squabble.

The subject of their discussion was not present. He was striding through the twilight of Miami, pounding with his cane, looking neither to the right nor to the left, and not giving any heed to the orange clouds or the glimpses of blue water in the bay. Not, that is, until the Gulf Stream Fishing Dock hove in sight dead ahead. Then he gave heed indeed, for he realized that his formidable stroll was less to calm his wrath than to find a fresh object for it. The pier was such an object: crowded with people, hemmed by the bright cockpits of fishing boats, and heaped with trophies from the day's catch. Mr. McLaen went out on the planking like a tank.

It was natural that he chose Desperate for his victim. Desperate was a quiet-looking young man. He had a vague way of staring at people which was disconcerting to some and vexing to others. He never stood, but leaned or sprawled, letting his support, be it chair or railing, absorb his weight. Sometimes, when Desperate was thinking, his mouth opened. Frequently, he chewed gum. All that appealed, negatively, to Mr. McLaen. He would not have tackled Desperate's partner and skipper — Crunch Adams. Anybody could see that Crunch, master of the *Poseidon,* was not a person to trifle with. And the disgruntled magnate from Michigan intended, consciously or not, to trifle a little.

He frowned so that his eye thatch met in the middle and he walked with a leering simulation of curiosity toward the place where Desperate leaned. He said, "Good evening, young man."

Desperate, scenting a customer, came to near-attention. He smiled amiably and said it was a wonderful evening. Like most, he added.

Mr. McLaen cleared his throat.

"Looks as if the fishing had been good today."

"Pretty fair."

It had been excellent. But Desperate was no man to tempt providence by boasting. Besides, he was modest.

"My name's McLaen," said the other man. He pronounced it to rhyme with "fine."

Desperate said, "How do you do?" and continued, "Interested in a trip out?"

Mr. McLaen hesitated. With his cane, he pointed at some fish which were being dressed by the captain of the adjacent *Firefly*. "What do you call those?"

"Those are kings. Kingfish. Some people call them king mackerel."

"Hmmm. And those?" The cane swung in a short arc.

"Bonitos. They're members of the mackerel family too."

"Edible?"

"The kings are. The bonitos aren't. We're having a run of kings now. They're also caught commercially here."

Mr. McLaen winced. Desperate noticed it, and wondered why. He was beginning to detect a difference in the approach of this gentleman, but he could not guess its significance.

"I fish a good deal," said the tall man.

Desperate smiled pleasantly. Any man who fished a good deal was almost certain to be a right guy. He waited. Fishermen are likely to advance confidences piecemeal. Mr. McLaen had the shoulders for anything. Tuna, if he felt like it. Maybe he was thinking of a Bimini trip.

"But not," said Mr. McLaen in a voice suddenly loud and irate, "for squid!"

"Squid?" Desperate repeated perplexedly.

"Squid!" the other man thundered. "Squid and cod. Lings, halibut, haddock, flounders — whatever you drag out of the ocean on this insane tackle!"

The *Poseidon*'s mate flushed lightly. Mr. McLaen had named no Gulf Stream gamesters, and Mr. McLaen was pointing to a proud acquisition — a brand-new heavy rod, reel and line on display in the cruiser's cockpit. "We only use that on big stuff," Desperate said. He felt apologetic, and he didn't like the feeling.

"It would make a fine winch, that reel!" Mr. McLaen's voice had started a drift of people in the direction of the *Poseidon*. He seemed to have a peculiar knack for drawing crowds. "And the line!" he went on. "What do you use that for? Lariats? Be first-rate for calf roping."

"Some of the fish," Des answered moodily, "are bigger than calves."

Mr. McLaen was worked up by that time. Also, he had an audience. "My dear young man," he said scathingly, "it is quite conceivable that a person could catch a whale — if the whale would take a bait — and the line were a hawser — and the angler could run the animal down with one of these motor boats. It is conceivable, but it is not sport. It is not fishing. It is a form of assassination." He raised his cane again and pointed down the pier. "Look. Scores of fish. Saltwater fish. Turgid monsters, ugly and badly made. Hulks. You take people into the sea with this — this — salvage apparatus, and you haul fish out of the water and you say you are fishing! You call yourselves sportsmen! Why, the very temperature of the water hereabouts precludes any gaminess in the fish! It's a kind of wrecking operation that you practice! A rodeo! A roping contest!"

Desperate was blushing deeply by that time and looking down at the planks. To his simple way of thinking, an assault of this sort could be remedied by one method alone: A straight sock on the chin. But Mr. McLaen's age, and Desperate's sense of his dignity as a mate, prevented that. There was nothing to do but stand by and let people laugh.

They did. The ignorant laughed because they thought that the distinguished-looking man was probably right. The sophisticated laughed at the mate's discomfiture. And Mr. McLaen had no way of realizing that the apparently ashamed youth in front of him was on the very equator of homicide. He took a quick bow from his audience and barged recklessly ahead: "You're not anglers, really. You're trawlers! You chaps are a libel on the commercial fishermen who earn a decent living catching these — things."

"I thought," Desperate finally replied in a cool tone, "you said you were a fisherman?"

"I am. Yes, I'm a fisherman. I've won several cups and medals for what little skill I have. At the moment, indeed, I hold a championship or two. Not, however, for hauling these torpid monsters from the sea by main force. I was taught by my father that fishing is a gentleman's sport and that it demands skill. Skill with rod, reel and line. Skill in casting. The stamina to wade cold streams for hours in a northern woods. The ability to select the right lure, to cast it accurately, to strip line, to maintain a difficult stance! A hundred skills! I was given the impression that angling is more than just sunning yourself in a chair while engines fish for you."

"Oh," said Desperate. "Trout."

Mr. McLaen glared. "Trout! A profanation on the lips of a saltwater fisherman! Trout, young man! Rainbows! Browns! Steelheads! And salmon — if I may mention it here!"

"I've heard of them," said Desperate.

"Heard of them!" Mr. McLaen's voice shook. "I daresay! You may even have seen a nine-foot rod — or a fly reel! You may have read of men who could cast so accurately that they could fetch back dollar bills at thirty paces!"

Desperate sighed and nodded. It wasn't a threatening response. But he was on familiar ground. His anger did not abate, although the attack had been wanton and ignorant; however, it congealed with purpose. He met Mr. McLaen eye to eye. His voice was quiet. "I've seen some of you fellows fish. And a few Florida men have taken sailfish on salmon rods from rowboats. But most of you bait fishermen aren't good enough to — "

"Bait fishermen!" Mr. McLaen's voice squeaked.

"M-m. What you hang in your club walls we use for bait down here."

The chuckle in the crowd was for Desperate.

Mr. McLaen bristled. "In Michigan," he said, "we take a trout, young man. We don't lead it out of the water on a leash."

Desperate turned suddenly and jumped down into the cockpit of the *Poseidon*. From there, he hurried to the cabin. He was so perturbed that his hands were shaking. Presently, he came back with what he had sought. It was a rod, shorter than a fly-casting rod, but as light as any. Attached to its butt was a large reel. The reel was loaded with six-thread line — line the thickness of ordinary grocery string. He handed it silently to Mr. McLaen.

The magnate from Michigan swished it in the air. "Miserable balance," he said.

"A fellow," Des replied, "took a sixty-one-pound white marlin with that rig last week."

"Towed it in," the other man retorted. "Or else you ran the boat up to it. And in this warm water they can't fight."

"I doubt," Desperate continued gently, "if you could boat a ten-pound dolphin on it."

Mr. McLaen had been fiddling with the handle of the reel. Its purring sound seemed to fascinate him. But when Des spoke, he snorted. "Why, I wouldn't be seen fishing on the ocean! My salmon club would probably throw me out. Michigan would be convulsed! Dolphin, eh? I'd prefer to play a harnessed house cat with my four-ounce fly rod!"

"Sure. You might catch the cat."

Mr. McLaen's steely eyes brightened to the challenge. "See here. How much do you charge for a fish-towing expedition in one of these power launches?"

"Thirty-five a day." Bitterness welled in Des. Nobody could call the *Poseidon* a power launch. "If you have it," he added. "In your case, though, I'll make it ten if you're not satisfied and pay the difference myself."

Desperate said that and shivered. The difference would be half a month's pay. Crunch would be furious. But the insult was worth the risk.

The old gentleman looked as if he might froth at the mouth in a minute. He was fumbling in his pocket. "Busy tomorrow?"

"No."

He pulled out an amalgamated chunk of money. There were hundred-dollar bills in the lump. He sorted out three tens and a five. He handed them to Desperate. "I'll be here at four," he said. "Four-thirty, if you prefer!"

Desperate gulped. "We usually go out around eight or nine."

The older man blew his cheeks. "Eight or nine! There you

are! What fish worth taking would rise at noon? That isn't fishing, young man! It's herding sheep! Good evening to you!"

He plowed his way through the crowd. The people dispersed slowly, arguing the pros and cons of Mr. McLaen's subject. Captain Emery, who had finished dressing the kings, winked "Nice going, Des."

But Desperate was not amused. His mouth was a firm line. His face was spotted with red. He kicked back his yachting cap with the heel of his hand. "If I don't teach that old nail chewer a lesson tomorrow, I'll smother myself in my bunk!"

About an hour later, when Desperate had relaxed somewhat, Crunch and Sari and young Bill appeared on the dock. Crunch hurried up to his mate. "Woman named Mrs. Owens phoned me at the apartment," he said. "What's this about you making her old man so mad he came home and busted open a front screen because it was locked? He's a big shot in Michigan, this Mrs. Owens says, and she says will we please take good care of him and get him some fish tomorrow because he's got to like Miami — "

"That guy," Desperate interrupted with hideous solemnity, "is never going to forget Miami, if I have anything to do with it. He's going to loathe the word Miami. It'll haunt him!"

"But why?"

"He said," Desperate answered, "we weren't sporting. He said we were trawlers. He said we caught practically dead fish. He called the *Poseidon* a launch."

Crunch was startled. "Yeah?"

"He's a trout fisherman." Desperate expectorated the words.

Crunch's wife Sari was worried. "But if he's so important, boys . . ."

It had no weight with her husband. He was smiling at his mate and colleague.

"Is that so?" he said amiably. "A trout fisherman, eh? Well, well, well. Think of that!"

There was justice. Desperate said that, the minute Crunch showed up the next morning. During the night the wind had hauled around from the northwest to the northeast and risen steadily. Not to a gale by any means, but to a fresh, incessant breeze in the teeth of which the Gulf Stream was pouring a river of water. They knew what that meant: big, steep seas, bright blue skies, gulls slanting on the air, white crests, good fishing, but bad sailing for a landlubber.

Cheerily they prepared to go out, purchasing fresh balao for bait and filling the two iceboxes. On the possibility that Mr. McLaen would dislike the Stream that day, Crunch also bought four pounds of shrimp. Then they sat in the two side chairs astern, waiting. Crunch thought of something. "What's this oaf's name?"

"McLaen," Desperate replied. "Rhymes with swine."

"That him?"

Desperate looked. Mr. McLaen was stalking down the pier. He wore a rawhide shirt, breeches, woolen puttees, heavy high brown shoes, a bandanna tied around his neck, and an old, floppy-brimmed slouch hat which would neither shade his eyes from the sun nor stay on his head in the wind.

Crunch covered his grin with his hand. "Think we'll find any rainbow trout out there?" he asked.

"Come on," Des replied. "We'll cut this guy down to our size."

The man from Michigan lowered himself aboard. His shoes, ideal for fording a stony stream, slipped on the linoleum deck. Crunch caught him. "Maybe you'd better take those shoes off," he said. His customer grunted and sat down. "And the shirt too," Crunch continued.

"It's blowing, man! This shirt is a fine windbreaker!"

"Sure. But the cockpit's not very breezy on most tacks, and the sun's going to be hot."

The *Poseidon* headed into the cut. Mr. McLaen took off his shoes. Then his woolen puttees and socks. His shirt came last. Crunch saw his relatively untanned torso and gave him a shirt of Desperate's. At the mouth of the cut the water was boiling. Heavy seas roared in against the ebbing tide. The *Poseidon* heeled, rose, banged down, took spray clean over the cabin, shuddered, and came up skidding on the next wave.

Mr. McLaen looked at Desperate with alarm. Desperate

wasn't even holding on to anything. He seemed engrossed with the business of trimming a bait.

The man from Michigan decided that the thing to do was to grin. He grinned. Then he thought about fishing — from a chair that was shooting around like a roller-coaster car. "Must be kind of difficult, at that," he said loudly, "to handle a fish in such weather."

Desperate shrugged. "Nothing, when you compare it to slippery rocks. Of course if you weren't set right and you got a big strike you might get pulled overboard." Desperate didn't add that no customer, to his knowledge, had ever fallen overboard. He did not say that both he and Crunch would consider themselves eternally disgraced if Mr. McLaen so much as fell down while he was a paying guest on their boat. He just allowed his passenger to ruminate over the idea.

The *Poseidon* was clear of the boil and tumult between the stone jetties. Clear, and at sea. She rode the combers sturdily. But Mr. McLaen, viewing first irregular walls of blue water and then the sharp profile of the ever retreating Miami skyline, felt insecure. Not only insecure, but queasy. "I suppose people do occasionally get sick on these craft?" he ventured.

"Oh, a few." Desperate cut bait. Mr. McLaen, for the first time in his life, felt an antagonism to the odor of fish, however fresh.

"What do you do in such an event?"

Desperate looked up. "Depends. If they're game, we keep on for a couple of hours and sometimes they get well. If they fade out completely we take 'em in."

Mr. McLaen gritted his teeth. All he could see was wheeling sky and vast pyramids of water which took form and vanished before he could be certain of what the form had been. The motors were humming headily. A large dark bird with a forked tail floated into his vision and circled sickeningly. He realized that he was lying down, more or less, on one of the day beds. He realized, also, that he was perspiring. Clammily. He did not know that his initiation was too abrupt for a beginner. He did not know that fewer people suffer from *mal de mer* on clean, open boats than on ocean liners, after the first few trips have relieved them of their initial anxieties. He knew only that his will was at war with his inclinations.

"Comfortable?" Desperate asked presently.

"This is great!" Mr. McLaen replied.

The mate found himself reluctantly admiring his passenger. Obviously, to Desperate's experienced eye, it was anything but great for the trout fisherman. He had turned the unromantic color of bituminous ash. His head was beginning to loll.

"We have a few hazards and troubles in connection with deep-sea fishing," Desperate said conversationally, after another interval. "Adds to the sportsmanship of it, don't you think? For example, if you hang one on light tackle and have to fight him standing up, with the boat slewing around in these seas, it gets tricky. Of course it may not be as hard as trout fishing."

"Sounds exciting," Mr. McLaen said.

But that was about all he said. He had never before been at sea in a small boat. He had scorned small boats on the Great Lakes: no fish worth going after there. Not in his opinion, anyway. He lay quietly. He realized that death was near at hand. It was going to be a slow and ugly death, with a white-and-indigo universe revolving around and over him, surging, eddying, diving, dropping, lifting him up agonizingly against the whole weight of his body and sinking out from under him just as he had begun to hope for stability. Stability, in fact, became an illusion that had belonged to another, better world.

He saw Desperate looking at him. He attempted to smile. A sea frosted with golden weed swelled up and tilted the *Poseidon*. It polished off Mr. McLaen. He hastened to the rail of the boat.

A few minutes later, he lay on the bed again with his eyes closed. Dimly, hopelessly, he toyed with the idea that the mate might soon summon him to fish. That was out of the question. He thought that perhaps he would be unconscious before it came time to admit he couldn't sit there and troll. He hoped so. The *Poseidon* began a new and unfathomable series of slides and convolutions. He groaned a little. And suddenly, all was tranquil. The heaving had stopped. The boat was running smoothly through quiet water. His head began to clear. He drew a breath and the air was fresh and good. He opened his eyes.

Desperate was sitting on the fish box in the stern, his solemn Scandinavian profile expressionless. Beyond Desperate, Mr. McLaen saw a large sign that said, DOG TRACK.

The mate turned. "We ran in," he said. "No sense in staying out if you feel that bad."

A rush of human warmth came over Mr. McLaen. These Florida boatmen were not, after all, the callous and sadistic salts of legend. When a fellow was about to die, they brought him in to water that was calm and turquoise and mighty good to look at. Not like the sailors he had read about in sea books who let you lie unconscious for hours if you happened to get seasick, who laughed at you, kidded you. Mr. McLaen presently tried his feet. They were pretty firm. His stomach had found its accustomed niche in his abdomen. He looked at his watch. Ten. Thirty-five dollars for an hour and a half. A bargain. He would have given a thousand to have been able to get ashore without losing face. And they were making it pretty easy.

"Feel better?" Crunch asked from the deck above.

Mr. McLaen peered. "Have you been standing up there through all that surf?"

Crunch smiled. "That was nothing. I mean for us. Do it often. All day. But when you're not used to it it sometimes gets you."

The man from the inland waters stretched himself. "I feel pretty fine — now. I guess I'm too old for that sort of stuff. And I'm perfectly willing to hand it to anybody who can take it. They're born lucky."

Desperate disliked that. His customer was hedging again. "You probably wouldn't care to do any bay fishing," he said provocatively. "In calm water — in the dinghy?"

"Bay fishing? For what? Catfish?"

"Bonefish."

"Never heard of 'em."

Desperate nodded.

"Most people haven't. You catch 'em on the shoals. They're supposed to be pretty gamy."

"How big?"

"Oh, a big one would run nine or ten pounds. I've even heard people say it reminded them of trout."

Mr. McLaen, who had thought within the past hour that he would never smoke again, found himself biting off the end of a cigar. "Trout?" he said. "Nonsense!"

"People on the dock would think we were pretty smart if we managed to bring in a bonefish or two," Desperate continued. "But I suppose you're all tuckered out."

"Tuckered out?" Mr. McLaen was altogether himself. "See here, young man. I tramp all day with the best of 'em. Up mountains or down ravines. I've crossed glaciers on foot to fish, and packed canoes up the edges of hundreds of miles of white water. Take me to these — these carp."

Desperate looked up at Crunch. Crunch looked down at Desperate. The *Poseidon* turned south in Biscayne Bay and proceeded at an increased speed. Mr. McLaen watched a pelican. "Bonefish," he said. "Any relation to a shark?"

Desperate merely shook his head.

The bonefish is not so much a fish as it is a cult. An eight-pounder is a big one. A ten-pounder is enormous. It is an all-silver fish which reflects so much sunlight that snapshots of proud catches often show only a blurred glitter. It feeds on the flats as the tide comes in, nosing along the bottom in search of small crustacea. It is taken on shrimp, live or dead, or small crabs. It will, on occasion, seize other baits. Muddy clouds in the water mark its searching progress and quite often it swims in such shallows that its dorsal may be seen. The bonefish angler baits up, casts, and sits in a small boat waiting. If he feels a nibble — or sees one, because the tropic ocean is gin-limpid — he allows the fish to swallow the bait and then strikes.

What happens after that can be fully understood only through experience. The antics of the trout are usually confined to small areas. The bonefish has the whole sea to move through. Trout leap. Bonefish merely run. But they are regarded as the fastest thing with fins. They smash reels. They break rods. They circumnavigate boats so swiftly that lines are wound around unwilling necks. Strong men go mad because of such fireworks. They rave and curse and weep — and come back to the old

Spanish Main every year for the rest of their lives to get another shot. Inland anglers are unfamiliar with this fish — as they are in general with the power and stamina of all marine species.

A dyed-in-the-wool trout fisherman — a McLaen — who ties his own flies from hand-picked bird breasts — will smile superciliously at a black bass fisherman. A brawny catcher of marlin will turn away from a man who describes the zest and glamor of fresh water. But a bonefish addict never discusses any sort of fishing save with another bonefisherman. Then the colloquy is obsessive, even paranoid. Bonefish break up homes, unless the wives go along. Then they cement marriages with a tie that is like fused quartz.

In the full knowledge of those facts, Desperate rowed Mr. McLaen away from the *Poseidon,* which lay at anchor in the middle of a tidal wash or "creek." He smiled beatifically at Crunch as he rowed, and the *Poseidon's* skipper smiled back; then he lay down on the starboard day bed and opened a magazine. He had fallen asleep before Des stopped rowing an eighth of a mile away.

Mr. McLaen looked over the side. "Must be a good foot deep here," he said with marked scorn. "Maybe we'll hook a crawdad."

Desperate took an oar from its lock and planted it deep in the softly matted sea bottom. "Crawdad?"

"We used to call 'em that when we were kids. Crayfish. You find them in brooks. Some of them grow as long as six inches."

"If you see any crawdads here," Des replied, "and you might, they may measure three feet from whisker to tail. Here's your rod." He unwrapped the shrimp and put one on a hook. "Just cast over toward that little white patch of coral, and then take it easy."

Mr. McLaen examined the rod. "Nice," he said.

"I made it," Desperate answered.

"The devil you did! Why, Parsons himself — "

"Parsons makes good tackle, too."

Mr. McLaen stood up. Desperate, from habit, ducked. But the Michigan trout fisherman knew one thing. He knew how to cast. He felt out the reel by allowing the bait to fall free.

Then he wound up again and slung, putting his wrist in it. The bait sailed like a well-driven golf ball across the coral patch and it fell lightly a good fifty feet beyond it. Mr. McLaen grunted. "I sure do hate to cast bait! Now, if I had a good fly rod I could at least amuse myself."

The mate made no answer. He settled himself in the middle of the dinghy. His customer also settled down. Presently he squirmed. Without saying anything, Desperate produced two cushions. Mr. McLaen's grunt was more or less appreciative.

Time began to pass. The sun warmed them. Far to southward the Keys stretched in a dull green arc. Around them the bay sparkled. Along the northern horizon, in the mist, Miami hung half miraged, like a ghost city or a city that floated above the ground through an enchantment. Nearer by, on an island, palms leaned over the water and an old lighthouse stood red and rigid against the bluer water of the sea outside. Birds passed. Boats moved along by power and by sail, well beyond hailing distance, but near enough to be visible in detail. A plane took off from Dinner Key and floated south toward Havana like a dragonfly pinned on a blue blotter.

"Pleasant," said Mr. McLaen.

"If you feel a nibble let him take it," said Desperate.

More time passed.

"The sun gets into your bones. Makes you feel kind of good."

Des nodded.

The guy had called the *Poseidon* a power launch. Said they were trawlers. But he'd been plenty seasick. That was a good first lesson. Now, with a little luck —

"I feel a nibble," said Mr. McLaen.

Des looked. The line was running slowly off the reel, in little jerks. "All right. Now push on the thumb-stall and hit him."

Mr. McLaen did so.

Something tore the reel limb from limb. Crunch heard the sound across the water, woke instantly, and looked with fascination. Trying to control the takeoff of a hooked bonefish is like toying with a handful of lightning. The fish unwound a hundred yards of line in zero seconds. Mr. McLaen stood up. His eyes bulged out from beneath his beetling brows. He touched the reel, and regretted it with passionate profanity. The fish stopped and charged back. In his astonishment, Mr. McLaen tried to strip his line, peeling it from the rod and dropping it on the bottom of the boat. By that method he achieved nothing. The bonefish was within fifteen feet of the boat in an instant. It made a fast circle.

Mr. McLaen saw it: a silvery thing that went past like light from a mirror flicked a mile away. An unearthly thing. A glittering fragment of the sea itself, alive and incandescent. He saw it brake to an impossible stop, hold still for a fragment of time, and then disappear. His line snapped across his chest.

"Little fellow," Des said, though it was actually medium-sized. "Can't strip off your line on these fish. They aren't trout. Gotta wind."

Desperate's voice had been calm. But Mr. McLaen gave tongue. He called the fish a multitude of names, and, toward the end, he even included himself. At last he just stared raggedly at the mate. "It isn't possible," he said, panting. "It can't be! Why, he covered a hundred yards in — I — I don't know what to say. I was helpless. Clumsy!"

"Aw," said Des, "you were all right. I saw a guy fall overboard once and sit smack on a sea urchin. We took eleven spines out of him."

"But — the fish! Why, man, if they saw that in Michigan . . ."

Desperate shrugged. He repaired the damage and baited. "Try again," he said.

An hour went by. Mr. McLaen had waited at the beginning with inattention; now he kept his eyes glued on the water. The sun was overhead and hot then.

"A bottle of cold beer would go good," Des ventured.

Mr. McLaen glowered at him. "Don't torment yourself — or me!"

The mate lifted one of the dinghy seats. Underneath was a nest of cracked ice. In the ice were four bottles of beer. Mr. McLaen gasped. Not loudly, but earnestly. Desperate opened a bottle on the seat edge and passed it up. The eyes of the man from Michigan were expressive.

He had finished his beer when Des saw him quiver. "Look! Astern!"

Des raised himself and yawned. "Leopard ray."

"But, man, it's beautiful! A magnificent thing! And it's got grace! Look at it! By George! Amazing!"

Desperate had admired leopard rays many times. But he allowed himself only another yawn. "Plentiful," he said.

A while later Mr. McLaen had another start. "There! Something shot through the water like a torpedo! Greenish — and a yard long."

"Barracuda."

"Good Lord! Like a big pike, eh? Only quicker. And — what's that?"

"Another bonefish," Desperate answered placidly. "Sit tight. Maybe he'll mosey up to your shrimp."

Mr. McLaen sat tight. His knuckles blanched around the butt of his rod. He was breathing hard when the bonefish picked up his bait. He struck. And it happened all over; though, on the second occasion, Mr. McLaen endeavored to reel. The bonefish made a half dozen mile-a-minute runs at various angles. Mr. McLaen managed them skillfully. Then the fish went under the boat. He followed that too. But the last sweeping arc confounded him. He yanked too hard, and Desperate's rod snapped.

Mr. McLaen sat down, a saddened man. "I guess you've got something here," he said slowly, as he wound in the segment of the tip.

"I think we have. You're pretty good."

"Do you believe I could learn to nail one of those cannonballs?"

"Yep. Ought to get the next, if the tide's not too high."

But the next wasn't a bonefish. Mr. McLaen just thought it was: a strong fish that swam less swiftly than the two others, but fought like a bulldog. He was soaked with sweat when Des gaffed it. And he stared bug-eyed again. A diamond-shaped fish, bluish and silver, with fins that turned into long spines. A fish the like of which he had never dreamed of catching.

"Permit," said Desperate laconically. "Fair scrapper. Fair." That, too, was classic understatement.

"How many more kinds of fish do you have around here?" Mr. McLaen inquired, after a pause.

The mate's next words seemed like a poor effect at humor until he looked at the mate's face. Des said, "Six hundred."

"Six hundred, man!"

"Yeah. You can catch — I mean 'take' — thirty or forty kinds at different times right over on that dark patch near where the *Poseidon*'s anchored." Des pulled up the oar to which the dinghy was moored. "Of course, the real fishing, in my mind, is outside."

Mr. McLaen allowed himself to be rowed back to the cruiser. When Crunch helped him aboard he said in a businesslike manner, "I'd like to charter you boys for a week of bonefishing. Just to get the hang."

Crunch shook his head. "Why? You can hire a kicker for a couple of bucks and fish all you want. You don't need us."

"You mean I can just come out myself and fish?"

"And fish," Crunch said. "No sense paying out thirty-five a day for that. Too bad you lost those bonefish. Perhaps sometime you'd like to try it outside. On a calm day."

"Maybe I would," said Mr. McLaen. "Yes, I think I would."

They ate lunch. Then they tried for snappers. Mr. McLaen caught one. Desperate caught eleven. There is a knack in snapper fishing, too, as any Florida cracker will readily testify.

The Owenses, *père, mère, fils et fille,* were waiting apprehensively at the dock when the *Poseidon* came in. Mr. McLaen bounded ashore. He had the permit in his hand. "Look, Evelyn," he bellowed. "I got this thing! I forget what you call it."

Evelyn nudged her husband. "Dad is in better spirits," she said.

Mr. McLaen was waving the permit at the crowd that had quickly gathered — not for him this time, but from custom — to inspect the catch of a returning fishing boat. "This is the doggonedest fishing hole on earth," he said loudly. "I took this fellow on six-thread line, they tell me. A beauty, eh?"

Evelyn's husband helped his father-in-law ashore. "Glad you had a good day, Dad. If we were staying down here any longer you could get in a lot of them. But Ev and I . . ."

Mr. McLaen put down the permit. His grandchildren began dancing around it and chanting, "Grandpa caught a whale!" He smiled at them with tacit agreement.

"What is this nonsense?" he asked gruffly. "About not staying?"

"If I can't start that sugar cane enterprise — "

"Who said you couldn't! Tomorrow we'll hire a smaller boat and go out on the flats and talk the whole thing over. It's my hunch cane is a comer down here. Now, about getting fish mounted as trophies . . ."

A couple of days later, Desperate was tenderly examining two of the finest casting rods he had ever seen. He then scrutinized the aluminum butts which went with them and the two reels. Presently he took the end of the six-thread line from a spool and knotted it onto a spindle. He was winding carefully when Crunch came aboard the *Poseidon*.

"Old man McLaen," Crunch said, "wants to take a shot at it outside this afternoon. It's a flat calm day." Idly he reread the card that had come with the rods. "From an old Crawdad," it said, "to a pair of anglers."

Desperate chewed gum slowly and nodded. "Yeah. Emery had seven sails up this morning. I think if we get Mac a sailfish, he'll plant sugar cane clear to Jacksonville. You know, it's funny. At first, I didn't like that guy."

The Big Brown Trout

Robert Travers

Clay Miller leaned against the slope of his spring-green pasture and watched the co-op milk truck spiraling down the road toward the city. The city was a long way from the Schoharie hills; it was at the far-away end of the truck route. And that's the way Clay Miller wanted it. At this end of the route — Clay's end — was the farm. The farm was the way he wanted it, too.

Turning toward the higher acres, he saw his spread of Ayr-shires drifting away from the patches of early morning sun. By noon they would be under the maples, hunched together in the shade. The late afternoon would nudge them easterly again toward the high red barn and the milking stalls. The Ayrshires moved with the sun and the seasons, and Clay Miller moved with them.

Near the barn was the hundred-year-old house he had restored with his own hands and his own tools. It also operated on the time of sun and season. Right now, Clay knew, his wife would be in the kitchen, pushing the buttons on the electric stove. The boys, both of them towheads, would be coming down for breakfast; they'd eat and run for the school bus. Then the chores, the orderly pattern of the day's labor, until the sun moved all the way across the sky.

To Clay Miller, there was nothing more important than the routine of house and farm. He didn't have time left over for the city, or for the world either. In politics he supported the objectives and the involvements of the free world without paying too much attention to what was going on in Vietnam or in Cuba. He was a dairy farmer. His world was enclosed by the rim of the Schoharie hills. As he headed for the house, he was thinking about the things that were closest to him, things such as bacon and eggs and, after a couple of cups of coffee, the repairs to be made on one of the milking machines.

His wife, Helen — she was as towheaded and blue-eyed as the two boys — met him at the kitchen door. "They phoned a telegram from town," she said.

"Those tractor parts finally arrived?" he asked.

"No. It's signed 'Sergeant Sales.'" Then she read the words she had scribbled on the telephone pad: "In New York for a sales conference. Any chance for a weekend reunion with Corporal Hayfoot? How is the fishing up there?"

"That's Harry Larkin!" Clay said. And just saying the name took him back a long, long time. Clay and Harry had been in the same infantry company, in the same squad and often in the same foxhole throughout the Korean War. They were young then, perhaps too young to understand what it was all about. They concentrated, instead, on survival. Clayton Miller, from upstate New York, and Chicago-born Harry Larkin were tossed together in a bleak village in southern Korea, and they learned how to stay alive as they moved north over the alien plains and rocky steeps.

After the truce, Clay returned to Albany and tried to readjust to civilian life. It wasn't easy; he had no goal or direction. What he did have, though, was a small legacy left by his father and a driving need to make his own, and separate, peace. He finally found the place he was looking for — an old farmhouse surrounded by eighty grassy acres in the Schoharie hills. His inheritance covered the down payment, with a little left over for enough Ayrshires to build a herd. Then, starting along the way he wanted to go, he married the girl he'd known before Korea. They settled on the land, and Clay learned dairy farming the hard way.

Harry Larkin went back to Chicago, joined a high-powered manufacturing firm and lit into his new job as if he were still fighting a war. After five years, he was sales manager and, after three more, vice-president in charge of sales. He was smart and ambitious. He got around. His Christmas cards, expensively engraved, and the occasional letters were postmarked from every industrial city west of the Mississippi. Now, for the first time in almost twelve years, he had come this close to the army buddy he used to call Corporal Hayfoot.

"I've told you about him," Clay said to his wife. "We were in Korea."

While she put his breakfast on the table, he phoned a telegram to Harry Larkin's hotel: TAKE ROUTE 145 TO SCHOHARIE. GET DIRECTIONS TO OUR PLACE AT FEED STORE THERE. HAVE SET OUT THE JUG, AND THE FISH ARE BITING IN THE CREEK.

Harry Larkin arrived at the farm the following Friday evening in a Cadillac, bringing with him a cowhide traveling bag and a handful of beat-up fly rods. He was older, of course; the gray was starting to show around his temples. But he still looked strong and very sure of himself.

Harry took one look at Helen Miller, grinned, and said something about old Corporal Hayfoot being a lucky guy. Helen liked him; when she went out to the kitchen, Clay could tell she was going to dig the best steaks out of the freezer. The boys liked him, too.

Later, when Clay and Harry were alone with a bottle between them and the quiet house like some kind of a cover around them, they talked about the army. It was nostalgic talk. They didn't recall any of the tough times; they remembered only the sunny days. Soon, since there hadn't been many sunny days in Korea, they were talking about their peacetime careers.

"Old Corporal Hayfoot," Harry said, grinning. "I was afraid you'd end up pushing a plow. What happened to you?"

"Happened?" Clay asked. "What do you mean? Man, I've got it made!"

Harry wasn't so sure about that. "I thought you were going into electronics. You had the head for it."

"I changed my head."

Harry laughed. "I guess a real campaigner can get used to anything."

"Depends on what you want to get used to," Clay said.

"Well . . ." Harry glanced around the living room. There was a stack of magazines, farming and animal husbandry journals, on the table. Also, a few books and a country newspaper, creased and unread.

"It's kind of quiet," he remarked. He let it go at that and shifted to a discussion of what was going on in the world. But, on that subject, Clay didn't have much to say.

"I'm not getting to you," Harry said.

"I'm not a debater," Clay replied. "I'm a farmer."

"And that's enough for you?"

"Sure is. Tomorrow, I'll show you around the place. You'll see what I mean."

"Okay," Harry said. "After I get back from the creek."

Harry left right after breakfast the next morning, wearing grimy flannels, a felt hat decorated with hand-tied flies and a nicely blackened briar pipe. The older Miller boy, ten-year-old Tommy, went with him.

Clay called after them: "Good luck!"

Harry signaled the all okay sign. As he swung the Cadillac around, he shouted: "Tell Helen we'll bring fish for supper."

They did get back in time for supper, but Harry didn't have any fish.

"I thought Schoharie Creek was a real trout stream," he said. "There's nothing in it bigger than your hand!" He glanced at

Tommy. "Even an experienced guide, the best one I ever had, couldn't get me a good strike."

Tommy grinned. He'd had a fine day; he learned something about fly-casting and heard a lot of good stories. But Clay could see that Harry was disappointed. To Harry, taking a fish would be like landing a new account. He'd hate to lose.

"You can try it again tomorrow," Clay told him. "Your luck will change."

Harry shook his head. "It's not luck. The water's too high; the big ones just aren't hitting."

Later on, as the sun was starting to touch the top of the hills, Clay took Harry out to the barn and showed him the gleaming equipment racked up under massive oak beams. They inspected the milking stalls, the feed bins, the cooling room. Finally, they went up the back path and looked at the Ayrshires standing philosophically in the dusk. There was a breeze with the new-grass smell in it, and the birds were as busy and noisy as they always were just before sundown.

"It's peaceful," Harry admitted. "But what the hell, Clay. You're cut out for more action."

"What kind of action?" Clay asked.

"There's a job opening with my outfit. On the management side. You'd be good at it. You'd save more in a year than you'll make here in ten. And you'd be *doing* something."

"I *am* doing something," Clay pointed out. He couldn't quite find the words for the way he felt about his eighty acres. He kicked out a bit of pasture dirt. "This is my land," he said. "I'm working it."

Harry wasn't convinced, "I'm not just talking about a job," he said. "Or about money. Things are going on, Clay. Over in the Pacific. In the Caribbean. Even in Europe. The people in Washington, the ones who know the score, are saying we're in a fight for our lives. You know — our national lives. We're fighting for everything we are, everything we stand for. It's a lot bigger than Korea ever was. A lot bigger. And everything we have depends on how it turns out."

"I know it," Clay said.

"Sure you know it." Harry was talking fast, like a salesman selling something he really believed in. "But you're not in it. You're way back in the hills. You're ducking away from the front lines — something you never did before."

"That's kind of rough talk," Clay said.

"It's straight talk," Harry said.

Clay looked at him. They were friends, good friends; they had covered a lot of ground together. In Korea, they had talked bluntly about what they thought and believed. They were still talking that way — as though the time between this hour and the hours in Korea hadn't changed anything at all.

"See if you can get this through your head," Clay said. "Right here is the front lines for me."

"No," Harry said. "You're on the sidelines; you're sitting it out."

"What does your company make?" Clay asked. "Machine parts?"

"Right."

"And that's more important than running a dairy farm?"

"It might be," Harry said. "We're ready to convert to essentials, to weapons, in twelve hours. But that's not what I mean. I mean the thinking part of it. You're . . . well, you're isolated. You're not part of what's going on."

"You think what I'm doing doesn't count?" Clay asked.

"It's not just doing something, Clay. Plenty of people aren't doing anything. I mean, they're not up in the front lines. But they're *still* involved. Even in just thinking. They're part of what's going on."

Clay used one of the phrases they had tossed around in Korea. "You figure I've been brainwashed?"

"Something like that," Harry said.

"Let me tell *you* something," Clay said. "All this is part of what's going on, too." He motioned toward the darkening stretch of his acres. "The land is what the shooting is all about in the first place. It gives men something to fight for. Don't you see that?" There was passion in his voice. "This farm went through the Revolution. And the Civil War. And all the rest of them. And the people on the land went through those wars. They were in them just staying here, just *being* here. That meant as much, in the long run, as joining up with a regiment." He paused. "The land is in the war. In any war, a cold war or a hot one. Remember how we held those hills in Korea? Now I'm holding these hills. The way the families living here before us held them. The way the same kind of people in Vietnam are holding *their* hills. You understand what I mean?"

"Let me think about it," Harry said. He was starting to turn away. "Anyway, we better knock it off for a while — before we start slugging."

They didn't talk any more as they crossed the meadow. The evening was quiet, too. They could hear the water tinkling in the pool long before they elbowed through the fringe of laurel.

When Clay Miller bought his eighty acres, the pool wasn't much more than a trickle of water coursing along an old stream bed. But after the house and barn were in shape, he found time to build a timber dam along the downgrade end of a little valley. Thereafter, the mud of several Aprils and the leaves of October chinked the dam. It became as solid as stone; the water, flowing steadily from a hillside spring, collected and spread out against it and deepened into a broad pool. There was a screen of laurel around it, and the birches had grown and leaned their branches toward the water.

Harry had forgotten his salesman's pitch about the cold war. He was looking at the pool with a fisherman's eye. "Nice," he said. "Ever think of stocking it?"

"There's some bluegills in it," Clay said. "And a few perch."

"I mean *fish,*" Harry said.

As he spoke, the big brown trout — which Clay Miller knew was also in the pool — started to feed. There was a dimpling of the darker water near the dam as he rolled over lazily and scooped up a hatch of insects. Then he broke water, leaping, throwing a lot of spray.

"That's a trout!" Harry shouted.

Clay didn't say anything.

"How'd a buster like that get in there?" Harry asked. He was excited.

"I don't know," Clay said.

That was a fact. Clay didn't know where the big brown trout came from. Perhaps when he was a fingerling, he was washed down in the flood waters following a late winter thaw. Perhaps some bird picked him up out of the creek and, on the way to his nest, dropped him into the widening pool. There were a lot of possibilities. But who could tell now where the trout came from? And what difference did it make? He was there.

Clay Miller first saw the trout two years after the dam was built. During the following years, he watched him grow, and he developed a real feeling, a kinship, for him. Sometimes, in the summery dusk, he stood by the pool and heard the trout finning near a submerged root. It occurred to Clay that the fish lived in water which was as calm, on its surface anyway, as the farm. You wouldn't expect to find so big a fish in such a placid pool. And you wouldn't believe he'd be content to stay there — he had a heritage linked to the freedom of a running stream. But there he was; he had adapted to the backwaters. Even so, he was still close to his origins. The water the trout lived in came down from the hills. Before that, it came from a river. And, before that, from the sky.

Harry was saying: "Nothing to match him in the Schoharie."

"I suppose not," Clay said.

"You ever cast for him?"

Clay shook his head.

The trout jumped again. After a moment, Harry said, "I'd sure like to try a couple a' lures on him."

Clay hesitated. Then, as heartily as he could, he said, "It's okay with me. I'll give you an early call."

Sunday was Harry's last day. He was up, dressed and at the pool by sunrise. Clay took a lot of time over a cup of coffee and then joined him there.

Harry cast and retrieved skillfully, until the sun was an hour high. Handling the four-ounce rod as though he'd been born with it, he worked the sides and then the center of the pool. He showed more patience than one might suspect he had. He was surely a match for the big brown trout. They both were wise and wary. And they both could play the old waiting game.

Clay watched and said nothing. He knew the trout did most of his feeding in late afternoon. Harry must have realized it, too. "I'll try again," he said. "Later."

It was a pleasant day, but neither Clay nor Harry was with it. They were thinking, in different ways, about the pool. And at five o'clock they were back there.

"This is it," Harry said. "Last round."

After he cast a fly into the center of the pool, Clay sat down, put his shoulders against one of the birches and took it easy. He wasn't worrying much. He knew Harry would never catch the trout that way.

Harry switched to a silver-colored streamer, a Gray Drake, and then to one of the flies he had tied himself. But nothing happened.

"Other side may be better," he decided.

Sitting silently, facing into the last slants of the sun, Clay watched Harry cross the log dam. Standing well back from the opposite shore, he cast again into the center of the pool.

Clay got out a cigarette and struck a match. There was less than half an hour's fishing time, and he was beginning to think the big brown trout was safe because he never fed in the center of the pool. He stayed close to a deep hole at the base of the dam, and even the most expert angler couldn't coax him away from it. That was one thing Harry didn't know. And Clay didn't tell him. He was neutral. He was giving both Harry and the trout an even break. He leaned against the birch, waiting to see what would happen.

As he watched the smooth cast and retrieve, cast and retrieve, Clay's thoughts wandered back to a particular night in Korea. In a darkness torn with flares and shell bursts, they were starting the long journey to the crest of some nameless ridge. It was a position they had taken and lost, and taken and lost again. This time, they had to go up and stay there. And they went up, and they did stay there. But not all of them made it all the way.

Clay Miller was one of them. A few crouching steps from the top, he stumbled into a blinding flash that was half hit and half concussion. Panic and fear flooded into every part of his mind. He retreated away from it into something darker than the night. Then Harry Larkin was bending over him, pulling him back to consciousness. As he got his eyes open, he heard Harry talking, telling him to hang on until the medics come.

During the next half hour, Harry kept talking, talking and holding on to him. And when he couldn't think of anything else to say, he talked about a trout stream he had fished years before he ever heard of Korea. He told Clay how it felt to wade in the stream and cast and get a strike. He described the water, the cool feel of it, the warmth of the sun, the sound of a breeze in the weeds along the shore.

That's how Clay Miller first learned Harry was a fisherman. He was a good deal more than that, of course. He had ideas about how to get through a war and what to do afterward. Maybe he had different notions about things. Maybe there were some things, such as a feeling for eighty acres and a remote farmhouse, which he didn't understand. But he *was* a fisherman. More than that, he was a friend.

Clay rubbed his cigarette out and stood up. He looked at Harry, still on the far side of the pool. There wasn't much light left. "Come on back over here," he called.

Harry made a fast retrieve and crossed the dam.

"You see that snag over there?" Clay said, when Harry was standing beside him. He was pointing to the spot above the deep hole, where he knew the big brown lived.

Harry nodded.

"That's the best place," Clay said. "There's some old roots down there. If you drop a fly easy, you might raise him."

Harry was glancing at Clay and smiling a little — a good smile, a warm one. "I noticed that spot myself," he said. He hesitated a moment. "But I figured I better stay away from it. Just casting is sport, too." He hesitated again. "I'll tell you the truth. I get the idea you don't want anyone to take that trout."

"You're crazy!" Clay said gruffly. "Work around that snag. Go ahead."

Harry cast deftly, in exactly the right place. On the third delicate, tantalizing retrieve, the fly disappeared in a sudden scoop of water. Harry flipped up the rod, bending it almost double, and set the hook. The brown trout reacted like lightning. He came out of the water in an explosive leap.

The reel zipped. Harry let it go, just for a few seconds, and then put on the pressure. If the trout got enough line, he'd wrap it around half a dozen roots and rocks and snap it like cotton thread. He was feeling the drag now, and he fought it, breaking out again, curving and twisting, and then running back toward the base of the dam. But Harry judged the run nicely and checked it, gaining a few feet of line. The trout's next leap wasn't as high. He arched slowly, showing his full length, the streamline form, the spotted sides, the wild head shaking in a frantic effort to throw the barb.

"A four-pounder!" Harry shouted. "A real fighter! Look at him!"

Clay looked. He was a fighter, all right. Harry was a fighter too. It took him ten pulse-pounding minutes to work the trout close to the bank. He worked carefully, gaining slowly and steadily, wearing the trout down until he couldn't surge any more, until he was quiet and beat at the end of the line.

Harry held up the rod tip. He was stepping into the shallows. The trout made a final, stout-hearted run, and Harry yielded some line. "Still game," he said admiringly. He won the line back and led the trout closer, bringing him in under the shadow of the trees.

There was a landing net swinging on Harry's belt. He groped for it with his right hand and started to unhook it. His fingers stopped moving, though, before the net was clear. He was remembering the trout's final run, and then he was glancing back over his shoulder at Clay. Since Harry was a fisherman, he understood — and respected — the trout. And he could understand, now, some of the same things about Clay. He could express it best in angler's language: the fish, in a way, was part of the fisherman, but this trout had a stronger bond to the pool. It was the same kind of deep-going, fiercely loyal bond that held Clay to his land.

Clay watched, surprised, as Harry turned back toward the pool. He hadn't unhooked the net. Instead, he clamped the handle of the rod under his arm and leaned over to wet his hands in the pool. "This way it won't harm the scales," he said.

"Use your net!" Clay told him. "That's what it's for!"

Harry reached toward the water. Swiftly, with a sure touch, he held the trout for a flailing instant and backed the hook out of his lip.

There was a moment when nothing happened, a complete stop, with Harry still bending over, hands outstretched, and the trout motionless beyond his fingers. Then, action again; a new start. Harry straightened up. The big brown trout moved too. He rolled, steadied and finned away, heading back toward the deep hole by the dam. His shadow, blurred by the water, went deeper. Then he was gone.

"Why didn't you take him?" Clay said. "He was yours! You had him!" His voice was strained. He hadn't said anything while Harry played the trout, but his throat felt as though he had been shouting.

Harry was staring after the fish. "Be a long time before he strikes another hook," he said.

"Why didn't you take him!"

"Remember what you were telling me last night?" Harry said. "About the land?" He was smiling. "That trout belongs here. The same as you."

Clay swung away. He didn't want Harry to see his eyes. "We better go up to the house and get some coffee," he said. "You got some miles ahead of you."

"We both have," Harry said, coming along after him, unjointing his fly rod. "You stay here and hold onto these hills." He added: "As long as you don't let anyone talk you out of it, I guess maybe everything will turn out all right."

Crocker's Hole

R. D. Blackmore

I

The Culm, which rises in Somersetshire, and hastening into a fairer land (as the border waters wisely do) falls into the Exe near Killerton, formerly was a lovely trout stream, such as perverts the Devonshire angler from due respect toward Father Thames and the other canals round London. In the Devonshire valleys it is sweet to see how soon a spring becomes a rill, and a rill runs on into a rivulet, and a rivulet swells into a brook; and before one has time to say, "What are you at?" — before the first tree it ever spoke to is a dummy, or the first hill it ever ran down has turned blue, here we have all the airs and graces, demands and assertions of a full-grown river.

But what is the test of a river? Who shall say? "The power to drown a man," replies the river darkly. But rudeness is not argument. Rather shall we say that the power to work a good undershot wheel, without being dammed up all night in a pond, and leaving a tidy backstream to spare at the bottom of the orchard, is a fair certificate of riverhood. If so, many Devonshire streams attain that rank within five miles of their spring; aye, and rapidly add to it. At every turn they gather aid, from ash-clad dingle and aldered meadow, mossy rock and ferny wall, hedge-trough roofed with bramble netting, where the baby water lurks, and lanes that coming down to ford bring suicidal tribute. Arrogant, all-engrossing river, now it has claimed a great valley of its own; and whatever falls within the hill scoop, sooner or later belongs to itself. Even the crystal "shutt" that crosses the farmyard by the woodrick, and glides down an aqueduct of last year's bark for Mary to fill the kettle from; and even the tricklets that have no organs for telling or knowing their business, but only get into unwary oozings in and among the water grass, and there make moss and forget themselves among it — one and all, they come to the same thing at last, and that is the river.

The Culm used to be a good river at Culmstock, tormented already by a factory, but not strangled as yet by a railroad. How it is now the present writer does not know, and is afraid to ask, having heard of a vile Culm Valley Line. But Culmstock bridge was a very pretty place to stand and contemplate the ways of trout; which is easier work than to catch them. When I was just big enough to peep above the rim, or to lie upon it with one leg inside for fear of tumbling over, what a mighty river it used to seem, for it takes a treat there and spreads itself. Above the bridge the factory stream falls in again, having done its business, and washing its hands in the innocent half that has strayed down the meadows. Then under the arches they both rejoice and come to a slide of about two feet, and make a short, wide pool below, and indulge themselves in perhaps two islands, through which a little river always magnifies itself, and maintains a mysterious middle. But after that, all of it used to come together, and make off in one body for the meadows, intent upon nurturing trout with rapid stickles, and buttercuppy corners where fat flies may tumble in. And here you may find in the very first meadow, or at any rate you might have found, forty years ago, the celebrated Crocker's Hole.

The story of Crocker is unknown to me, and interesting as it doubtless was, I do not deal with him, but with his hole. Tradition said that he was a baker's boy who, during his basket rounds, fell in love with a maiden who received the cottage loaf, or perhaps good "households," for her master's use. No doubt she was charming, as a girl should be, but whether she encouraged the youthful baker and then betrayed him with false *rôle,* or whether she "consisted" throughout — as our cousins across the water express it — is known to their *manes* only. Enough that she would not have the floury lad; and that he, after giving in his books and money, sought an untimely grave among the trout. And this was the first pool below the breadwalk deep enough to drown a five-foot baker boy. Sad it was; but such things must be, and bread must still be delivered daily.

A truce to such reflections — as our foremost writers always say, when they do not see how to go on with them — but it is a serious thing to know what Crocker's Hole was like; because at a time when (if he had only persevered, and married the maid, and succeeded to the oven, and reared a large family of short-weight bakers) he might have been leaning on his crutch beside the pool, and teaching his grandson to swim by precept (that beautiful proxy for practice) — at such a time, I say, there lived a remarkably fine trout in that hole. Anglers are notoriously truthful, especially as to what they catch, or even more frequently have not caught. Though I may have written fiction, among many other sins — as a nice old lady told me once — now I have to deal with facts; and foul scorn would I count it ever to make believe that I caught that fish. My length at that time was not more than the butt of a four-jointed rod, and all I could catch was a minnow with a pin, which our cook Lydia would not cook, but used to say, "Oh, what a shame, Master Richard! They would have been trout in the summer, please God! if you would only a' let 'em grow on." She is living now, and will bear me out in this.

But upon every great occasion there arises a great man; or to put it more accurately, in the present instance, a mighty and distinguished boy. My father, being the parson of the parish, and getting, need it be said, small pay, took sundry pupils, very pleasant fellows, about to adorn the universities. Among them was the original Bude Light, as he was satirically called at Cambridge, for he came from Bude, and there was no light in him. Among them also was John Pike, a born Zebedee, if ever there was one.

John Pike was a thick-set younker, with a large and bushy head, keen blue eyes that could see through water, and the proper slouch of shoulder into which great anglers ripen; but greater still are born with it; and of these was Master John. It mattered little what the weather was, and scarcely more as to the time of year, John Pike must have his fishing every day, and on Sundays he read about it, and made flies. All the rest of the time he was thinking about it.

My father was coaching him in the fourth book of the Aeneid and all those wonderful speeches of Dido, where passion disdains construction; but the only line Pike cared for was of horsehair. "I fear, Mr. Pike, that you are not giving me your entire attention," my father used to say in his mild dry way; and once when Pike was more than usually abroad, his tutor begged to share his meditations. "Well, sir," said Pike, who was very truthful, "I can see a green drake by the strawberry tree, the first of the season, and your derivation of 'barbarous' put me in mind of my barberry dye." In those days it was a very nice point to get the right tint for the mallard's feather.

No sooner was lesson done than Pike, whose rod was ready upon the lawn, dashed away always for the river, rushing headlong down the hill, and away to the left through a private yard, where "NO THOROUGHFARE" was put up, and a big dog stationed to enforce it. But Cerberus himself could not have stopped John Pike; his conscience backed him up in trespass the most sinful when his heart was inditing of a trout upon the rise.

All this, however, is preliminary, as the boy said when he put his father's coat upon his grandfather's tenterhooks, with felonious intent upon his grandmother's apples; the main point to be understood is this, that nothing — neither brazen tower, hundred-eyed Argus, nor Cretan Minotaur — could stop John Pike from getting at a good stickle. But, even as the world knows nothing of its greatest men, its greatest men know nothing of the world beneath their very nose, till fortune sneezes dexter. For two years

John Pike must have been whipping the water as hard as Xerxes, without having ever once dreamed of the glorious trout that lived in Crocker's Hole. But why, when he ought to have been at least on bowing terms with every fish as long as his middle finger, why had he failed to know this champion? The answer is simple — because of his short cuts. Flying as he did like an arrow from a bow, Pike used to hit his beloved river at an elbow, some furlong below Crocker's Hole, where a sweet little stickle sailed away downstream, whereas for the length of a meadow upward the water lay smooth, clear, and shallow; therefore the youth, with so little time to spare, rushed into the downward joy.

And here it may be noted that the leading maxim of the present period, that man can discharge his duty only by going counter to the stream, was scarcely mooted in those days. My grandfather (who was a wonderful man, if he was accustomed to fill a cart in two days of fly fishing on the Barle) regularly fished downstream; and what more than a cartload need anyone put into his basket?

And surely it is more genial and pleasant to behold our friend the river growing and thriving as we go on, strengthening its voice and enlarging its bosom, and sparkling through each successive meadow with richer plenitude of silver, than to trace it against its own grain and goodwill toward weakness, and littleness, and immature conceptions.

However, you will say that if John Pike had fished upstream, he would have found this trout much sooner. And that is true; but still, as it was, the trout had more time to grow into such a prize. And the way in which John found him out was this. For some days he had been tormented with a very painful tooth, which even poisoned all the joys of fishing. Therefore he resolved to have it out, and sturdily entered the shop of John Sweetland, the village blacksmith, and there paid his sixpence. Sweetland extracted the teeth of the village, whenever they required it, in the simplest and most effectual way. A piece of fine wire was fastened round the tooth, and the other end round the anvil's nose, then the sturdy blacksmith shut the lower half of his shop door, which was about breast-high, with the patient outside and the anvil within; a strong push of the foot upset the anvil, and the tooth flew out like a well-thrown fly.

When John Pike had suffered this very bravely, "Ah, Master Pike," said the blacksmith, with a grin, "I reckon you won't pull out thic there big vish," — the smithy commanded a view of the river — "clever as you be, quite so peart as thiccy."

"What big fish?" asked the boy, with deepest interest, though his mouth was bleeding fearfully.

"Why that girt mortial of a vish as hath his hover in Crocker's Hole. Zum on 'em saith as a' must be a zammon."

Off went Pike with his handkerchief to his mouth, and after him ran Alec Bolt, one of his fellow pupils, who had come to the shop to enjoy the extraction.

"Oh, my!" was all that Pike could utter, when by craftily posting himself he had obtained a good view of this grand fish.

"I'll lay you a crown you don't catch him!" cried Bolt, an impatient youth, who scorned angling.

"How long will you give me?" asked the wary Pike, who never made rash wagers.

"Oh! Till the holidays if you like; or, if that won't do, till Michaelmas."

Now the midsummer holidays were six weeks off — boys used not to talk of "vacations" then, still less of "recesses."

"I think I'll bet you," said Pike, in his slow way, bending forward carefully, with his keen eyes on this monster; "but it would not be fair to take till Michaelmas. I'll bet you a crown that I catch him before the holidays — at least, unless some other fellow does."

II

The day of that most momentous interview must have been the fourteenth of May. Of the year I will not be so sure; for children take more note of days than of years, for which the latter have their full revenge thereafter. It must have been the fourteenth, because the morrow was our holiday, given upon the fifteenth of May, in honor of a birthday.

Now, John Pike was beyond his years wary as well as enterprising, calm as well as ardent, quite as rich in patience as in promptitude and vigor. But Alec Bolt was a headlong youth, volatile, hot, and hasty, fit only to fish the Maëlstrom, or a torrent of new lava. And the moment he had laid that wager he expected his crown piece; though time, as the lawyers phrase it, was "expressly of the essence of the contract." And now he demanded that Pike should spend the holiday in trying to catch that trout.

"I shall not go near him," that lad replied, "until I have got a new collar." No piece of personal adornment was it, without which he would not act, but rather that which now is called the fly cast, or the gut cast, or the trace, or what it may be. "And another thing," continued Pike; "the bet is off if you go near him, either now or at any other time, without asking my leave first, and only going as I tell you."

"What do I want with the great slimy beggar?" the arrogant Bolt made answer. "A good rat is worth fifty of him. No fear of my going near him, Pike. You shan't get out of it that way."

Pike showed his remarkable qualities that day, by fishing exactly as he would have fished without having heard of the great Crockerite. He was up and away upon the mill stream before breakfast; and the forenoon he devoted to his favorite course — first down the Craddock stream, a very pretty confluent of the Culm, and from its junction, down the pleasant hams, where the river winds toward Uffculme. It was my privilege to accompany this hero, as his humble Sancho; while Bolt and the faster race went up the river ratting. We were back in time to have Pike's trout (which ranged between two ounces and one-half pound) fried for the early dinner; and here it may be lawful to remark that the trout of the Culm are of the very purest excellence, by reason of the flinty bottom, at any rate in these the upper regions. For the valley is the western outlet of the Black-down range, with the Beacon hill upon the north, and Hackpen long ridge to the south; and beyond that again the Whetstone hill, upon whose western end dark portholes scarped with white grit mark the pits. But flint is the staple of the broad Culm Valley, under good, well-pastured loam; and here are chalcedonies and agate stones.

At dinner everybody had a brace of trout — large for the larger folk, little for the little ones, with coughing and some patting on the back for bones. What of equal purport could the fierce rat hunter show? Pike explained many points in the history of each fish, seeming to know them none the worse, and love them all the better, for being fried. We banqueted, neither a whit did soul get stinted of banquet impartial. Then the wielder of the magic rod very modestly sought leave of absence at the tea time.

"Fishing again, Mr. Pike, I suppose," my father answered pleasantly; "I used to be fond of it at your age; but never so entirely wrapped up in it as you are."

"No, sir; I am not going fishing again. I want to walk to Wellington, to get some things at Cherry's."

"Books, Mr. Pike? Ah! I am very glad of that. But I fear it can only be fly books."

"I want a little Horace for eighteenpence — the Cambridge one just published, to carry in my pocket — and a new hank of gut."

"Which of the two is more impotant? Put that into Latin, and answer it."

"Utrum pluris facio? Flaccum flocci. Viscera magni." With this vast effort Pike turned as red as any trout spot.

"After that who could refuse you?" said my father. "You always tell the truth, my boy, in Latin or in English."

Although it was a long walk, some fourteen miles to Wellington and back, I got permission to go with Pike; and as we crossed the bridge and saw the tree that overhung Crocker's Hole, I begged him to show me that mighty fish.

"Not a bit of it," he replied. "It would bring the blackguards. If the blackguards once find him out, it is all over with him."

"The blackguards are all in factory now, and I am sure they cannot see us from the windows. They won't be out till five o'clock."

With the true liberality of young England, which abides even now as large and glorious as ever, we always called the free and enlightened operatives of the period by the courteous name above set down, and it must be acknowledged that some of them deserved it, although perhaps they poached with less of science than their sons. But the cowardly murder of fish by liming the water was already prevalent.

Yielding to my request and perhaps his own desire — manfully kept in check that morning — Pike very carefully approached that pool, commanding me to sit down while he reconnoitered from the meadow upon the right bank of the stream. And the place which had so sadly quenched the fire of the poor baker's love filled my childish heart with dread and deep wonder at the cruelty of women. But as for John Pike, all he thought of was the fish and the best way to get at him.

Very likely that hole is "holed out" now, as the Yankees well express it, or at any rate changed out of knowledge. Even in my time a very heavy flood entirely altered its character; but to the eager eye of Pike it seemed pretty much as follows, and possibly it may have come to such a form again:

The river, after passing though a hurdle fence at the head of the meadow, takes a little turn or two of bright and shallow indifference, then gathers itself into a good strong slide, as if going down a slope instead of steps. The right bank is high and beetles over with yellow loam and grassy fringe; but the other side is a flinty shingle, low and bare and washed by floods. At the end of this rapid, the stream turns sharply under an ancient alder tree into a large, deep, calm repose, cool, unruffled, and sheltered from the sun by branch and leaf — and that is the hole of poor Crocker.

At the head of the pool (where the hasty current rushes in so eagerly, with noisy excitement and much ado) the quieter waters from below, having rested and enlarged themselves, come lapping up round either curve, with some recollection of their past career, the hoary experience of foam. And sidling toward the new arrival of the impulsive column, where they meet it, things go on, which no man can describe without his mouth being full of water. A V is formed, a fancy letter V, beyond any designer's tracery, and even beyond his imagination, a perpetually fluctuating limpid wedge, perpetually crenelled and rippled into by little ups and downs that try to make an impress, but can only glide away upon either side or sink in dimples under it. And here a gray bough of the ancient alder stretches across, like a thirsty giant's arm, and makes it a very ticklish place to throw a fly. Yet this was the very spot our John Pike must put his fly into, or lose his crown.

Because the great tenant of Crocker's Hole, who allowed no

other fish to wag a fin there, and from strict monopoly had grown so fat, kept his victualing yard — if so low an expression can be used concerning him — within about a square yard of this spot. He had a sweet hover, both for rest and recreation, under the bank, in a placid antre, where the water made no noise, but tickled his belly in digestive ease. The loftier the character is of any being, the slower and more dignified his movements are. No true psychologist could have believed — as Sweetland the blacksmith did, and Mr. Pook the tinman — that this trout could ever be the embodiment of Crocker. For this was the last trout in the universal world to drown himself for love; if truly any trout has done so.

"You may come now, and try to look along my back," John Pike, with a reverential whisper, said to me. "Now don't be in a hurry, young stupid; kneel down. He is not to be disturbed at his dinner, mind. You keep behind me, and look along my back; I never clapped eyes on such a whopper."

I had to kneel down in a tender reminiscence of pastureland, and gaze carefully; and not having eyes like those of our Zebedee (who offered his spine for a camera, as he crawled on all fours in front of me), it took me a long time to descry an object most distinct to all who have that special gift of piercing with their eyes the water. See what is said upon this subject in that delicious book, *The Gamekeeper at Home.*

"You are no better than a muff," said Pike, and it was not in my power to deny it.

"If the sun would only leave off," I said. But the sun, who was having a very pleasant play with the sparkle of the water and the twinkle of the leaves, had no inclination to leave off yet, but kept the rippling crystal in a dance of flashing facets, and the quivering verdure in a steady flush of gold.

But suddenly a mayfly, a luscious gray-drake, richer and more delicate than canvasback or woodcock, with a dart and a leap and a merry zigzag, began to enjoy a little game above the stream. Rising and falling like a gnat, thrilling her gauzy wings, and arching her elegant pellucid frame, every now and then she almost dipped her three long tapering whisks into the dimples of the water.

"He sees her! He'll have her as sure as a gun!" cried Pike, with a gulp, as if he himself were "rising." "Now, can you see him, stupid?"

"Crikey, crokums!" I exclaimed, with classic elegance; "I have seen that long thing for five minutes; but I took it for a tree."

"You little" — animal quite early in the alphabet — "now don't you stir a peg, or I'll dig my elbow into you."

The great trout was stationary almost as a stone, in the middle of the V above described. He was gently fanning with his large clear fins, but holding his own against the current mainly by the wagging of his broad-fluked tail. As soon as my slow eyes had once defined him, he grew upon them mightily, molding himself in the matrix of the water, as a thing put into jelly does. And I doubt whether even John Pike saw him more accurately than I did. His size was such, or seemed to be such, that I fear to say a word about it; not because language does not contain the word, but from dread of exaggeration. But his shape and color may be reasonably told without wounding the feeling of an age whose incredulity springs from self-knowledge.

His head was truly small, his shoulders vast; the spring of his back was like a rainbow when the sun is southing; the generous sweep of his deep elastic belly, nobly pulped out with rich nurture, showed what the power of his brain must be, and seemed to undulate, time for time, with the vibrant vigilance of his large wise eyes. His latter end was consistent also. An elegant taper run of counter, coming almost to a cylinder, as a mackerel does, boldly developed with a hugeous spread to a glorious amplitude of swallowtail. His color was all that can well be desired, but ill-described by any poor word palette. Enough that he seemed to tone away from olive and umber, with carmine stars, to glowing gold and soft pure silver, mantled with a subtle flush of rose and fawn and opal.

Swoop came a swallow, as we gazed, and was gone with a flick, having missed the mayfly. But the wind of his passage, or the skir of wing, struck the merry dancer down, so that he fluttered for one instant on the wave, and that instant was enough. Swift as the swallow, and more true of aim, the great trout made one dart, and a sound, deeper than a tinkle, but as silvery as a bell, rang the poor ephemerid's knell. The rapid water scarcely showed a break; but a bubble sailed down the pool, and the dark hollow echoed with the music of a rise.

"He knows how to take a fly," said Pike; "he has had too many to be tricked with mine. Have him I must; but how ever shall I do it?"

All the way to Wellington he uttered not a word, but shambled along with a mind full of care. When I ventured to look up now and then, to surmise what was going on beneath his hat, deeply set eyes and a wrinkled forehead, relieved at long intervals by a solid shake, proved that there are meditations deeper than those of philosopher or statesman.

III

Surely no trout could have been misled by the artificial mayfly of that time, unless he were either a very young fish, quite new to entomology, or else one afflicted with a combination of myopy and bulimy. Even now there is room for plenty of improvement in our counterfeit presentment; but in those days the body was made with yellow mohair, ribbed with red silk and gold twist, and as thick as a fertile bumblebee. John Pike perceived that to offer such a thing to Crocker's trout would probably consign him — even if his great stamina should overget the horror — to an uneatable death, through just and natural indignation. On the other hand, while the mayfly lasted, a trout so cultured, so highly refined, so full of light and sweetness, would never demean himself to low bait, or any coarse son of a maggot.

Meanwhile Alec Bolt allowed poor Pike no peaceful thought, no calm absorption of high mind into the world of flies, no placid period of cobblers' wax, floss silk, turned hackles, and dubbing. For in making of flies John Pike had his special moments of inspiration, times of clearer insight into the everlasting verities, times of brighter conception and more subtle execution, tails of more elastic grace and heads of a neater and nattier expression. As a poet labors at one immortal line, compressing worlds of wisdom into the music of ten syllables, so toiled the patient Pike about the fabric of a fly comprising all the excellence that ever sprang from maggot. Yet Bolt rejoiced to jerk his elbow at the moment of sublimest art. And a swarm of flies was blighted thus.

Peaceful, therefore, and long-suffering, and full of resignation as he was, John Pike came slowly to the sad perception that arts avail not without arms. The elbow, so often jerked, at last took a voluntary jerk from the shoulder and Alec Bolt lay prostrate, with his right eye full of cobbler's wax. This put a desirable check upon his energies for a week or more, and by that time Pike had flown his fly.

When the honeymoon of spring and summer (which they are now too fashionable to celebrate in this country), the heyday of the whole year marked by the budding of the wild rose, the start of the wheatear from its sheath, the feathering of the lesser plantain, and flowering of the meadowsweet, and, foremost for the angler's joy, the caracole of mayflies — when these things are to be seen and felt (which has not happened at all this year), then rivers should be mild and bright, skies blue and white with fleecy cloud, the west wind blowing softly, and the trout in charming appetite.

On such a day came Pike to the bank of Culm, with a loudly beating heart. A fly there is, not ignominious, or of cowdab origin, neither gross and heavy-bodied, from cradlehood of slimy stones, nor yet of menacing aspect and suggesting deeds of poison, but elegant, bland, and of sunny nature, and obviously good to eat. Him or her — why quest we which? — the shepherd of the dale, contemptuous of gender, except in his own species, has called, and as long as they two coexist will call, the Yellow Sally. A fly that does not waste the day in giddy dances and the fervid waltz, but undergoes family incidents with decorum and discretion. He or she, as the case may be — for the natural history of the riverbank is a book to come hereafter, and of fifty men who make flies not one knows the name of the fly he is making — in the early morning of June, or else in the second quarter of the afternoon, this Yellow Sally fares abroad, with a nice well-ordered flutter.

Despairing of the mayfly, as it still may be despaired of, Pike came down to the river with his masterpiece of portraiture. The artificial Yellow Sally is generally always — as they say in Cheshire — a mile or more too yellow. On the other hand, the Yellow Dun conveys no idea of any Sally. But Pike had made a very decent Sally, not perfect (for he was young as well as wise), but far above any counterfeit to be had in fishing tackle shops. How he made it, he told nobody. But if he lives now, as I hope he does, any of my readers may ask him through the G. P. O., and hope to get an answer.

It fluttered beautifully on the breeze, and in such living form, that a brother or sister Sally came up to see it, and went away sadder and wiser. Then Pike said: "Get away, you young wretch," to your humble servant who tells this tale; yet being better than his words, allowed that pious follower to lie down upon his digestive organs and with deep attention watch. There must have been great things to see, but to see them so was difficult. And if I huddle up what happened, excitement also shares the blame.

Pike had fashioned well the time and manner of this overture. He knew that the giant Crockerite was satiate now with mayflies, or began to find their flavor failing, as happens to us with asparagus, marrow fat peas, or strawberries, when we have had a month of them. And he thought that the first Yellow Sally of the season, inferior though it were, might have the special charm of novelty. With the skill of a Zulu, he stole up through the branches over the lower pool till he came to a spot where a yard-wide opening gave just space for spring of rod. Then he saw his desirable friend at dinner, wagging his tail, as a hungry gentleman dining with the Lord Mayor agitates his coat. With one dexterous whirl, untaught by any of the many books upon the subject, John Pike laid his Yellow Sally (for he cast with one fly only) as lightly as gossamer upon the rapid, about a yard in front of the big trout's head. A moment's pause, and then, too quick for words, were the things that happened.

A heavy plunge was followed by a fearful rush. Forgetful of current the river was ridged, as if with a plow driven under it; the strong line, though given out as fast as might be, twanged like a harp string as it cut the wave, and then Pike stood up, like a ship dismasted, with the butt of his rod snapped below the ferrule. He had one of those foolish things, just invented, a hollow butt of hickory; and the finial ring of his spare top looked out, to ask what had happened to the rest of it. "Bad luck!" cried the fisherman. "But never mind, I shall have him next time, to a certainty."

When this great issue came to be considered, the cause of it was sadly obvious. The fish, being hooked, had made off with the rush of a shark for the bottom of the pool. A thicket of saplings below the alder tree had stopped the judicious hooker from all possibility of following; and when he strove to turn him by elastic pliance, his rod broke at the breach of pliability. "I have learned a sad lesson," said John Pike, looking sadly.

How many fellows would have given up this matter, and glorified themselves for having hooked so grand a fish, while explaining that they must have caught him, if they could have done it! But Pike only told me not to say a word about it, and began to make ready for another tug of war. He made himself a splice rod, short and handy, of well-seasoned ash, with a stout top of bamboo, tapered so discreetly, and so balanced in its spring, that verily it formed an arc, with any pressure on it, as perfect as a leafy poplar in a stormy summer. "Now break it if you can," he said, "by any amount of rushes; I'll hook you by your jacket collar; you cut away now, and I'll land you."

This was highly skillful, and he did it many times; and whenever I was landed well, I got a lollypop, so that I was careful not to break his tackle. Moreover he made him a landing net, with a kidney bean stick, a ring of wire, and his own best nightcap of strong cotton net. Then he got the farmer's leave, and lopped obnoxious bushes; and now the chiefest question was: what bait, and when to offer it? In spite of his sad rebuff, the spirit of John Pike had been equable. The genuine angling mind is steadfast, large, and self-supported, and to the vapid, ignominious chaff, tossed by swine upon the idle wind, it pays as much heed as a big trout does to a dance of midges. People put their fingers to their noses and said: "Master Pike, have you caught him yet?" and Pike only answered: "Wait a bit." If ever this fortitude and perseverance is to be recovered as the English Brand (the one thing that has made us what we are, and may yet redeem us from niddering shame), a degenerate age should encourage the habit of fishing and never despairing. And the brightest sign yet for our future is the increasing demand for hooks and gut.

Pike fished in a manlier age, when nobody would dream of cowering from a savage because he was clever at skulking; and when, if a big fish broke the rod, a stronger rod was made for him, according to the usage of Great Britain. And though the young angler had been defeated, he did not sit down and have a good cry over it.

About the second week in June, when the mayfly had danced its day, and died — for the season was an early one — and Crocker's trout had recovered from the wound to his feelings and philanthropy, there came a night of gentle rain, of pleasant tinkling upon window ledges, and a soothing patter among young leaves, and the Culm was yellow in the morning. "I mean to do it this afternoon," Pike whispered to me, as he came back panting. "When the water clears there will be a splendid time."

The lover of the rose knows well a gay voluptuous beetle, whose pleasure is to lie embedded in a fount of beauty. Deep among the incurving petals of the blushing fragrance, he loses himself in his joys sometimes, till a breezy waft reveals him. And when the sunlight breaks upon his luscious dissipation, few would have the heart to oust him, such a gem from such a setting. All his back is emerald sparkles; all his front red Indian gold, and here and there he grows white spots to save the eye from aching. Pike put his finger in and fetched him out, and offered him a little change of joys, by putting a Limerick hook through his thorax, and bringing it out between his elytra. *Cetonia aurata* liked it not, but pawed the air very naturally, and fluttered with his wings attractively.

"I meant to have tried with a fern web," said the angler; "until I saw one of these beggars this morning. If he works like that upon the water, he will do. It was hopeless to try artificials again. What a lovely color the water is! Only three days now to the holidays. I have run it very close. You be ready, younker."

With these words he stepped upon a branch of the alder, for the tone of the waters allowed approach, being soft and sub-lustrous, without any mud. Also Master Pike's own tone was such as becomes the fisherman, calm, deliberate, free from nerve, but full of eye and muscle. He stepped upon the alder bough to get as near as might be to the fish, for he could not cast this beetle like a fly; it must be dropped gently and allowed to play. "You may come and look," he said to me; "when the water is so, they have no eyes in their tails."

The rose beetle trod upon the water prettily, under a lively vibration, and he looked quite as happy, and considerably more active, than when he had been cradled in the anthers of the rose. To the eye of a fish he was a strong individual, fighting courageously with the current, but sure to be beaten through lack of fins; and mercy suggested, as well as appetite, that the proper solution was to gulp him.

"Hooked him in the gullet. He can't get off!" cried John Pike, laboring to keep his nerves under; "every inch of tackle is as strong as a bell pull. Now, if I don't land him, I will never fish again!"

Providence, which had constructed Pike, foremost of all things, for lofty angling — disdainful of worm and even minnow — Providence, I say, at this adjuration, pronounced that Pike must catch that trout. Not many anglers are heaven-born; and for one to drop off the hook halfway through his teens would be infinitely worse than to slay the champion trout. Pike felt the force of this, and rushing through the rushes, shouted: "I am sure to have him, Dick! Be ready with my nightcap."

Rod in a bow, like a springle riser; line on the hum, like the string of Paganini; winch on the gallop, like a harpoon wheel, Pike, the head center of everything, dashing through thick and thin, and once taken overhead — for he jumped into the hole, when he must have lost him else, but the fish too impetuously towed him out, and made off in passion for another pool, when, if he had only retired to his hover, the angler might have shared the baker's fate — all these things (I tell you, for they all come up again, as if the day were yesterday) so scared me of my never very steadfast wits, that I could only holloa! But one thing I did, I kept the nightcap ready.

"He is pretty nearly spent, I do believe," said Pike; and his voice was like balm of Gilead, as we came to Farmer Anning's meadow, a quarter of a mile below Crocker's Hole. "Take it coolly, my dear boy, and we shall be safe to have him."

Never have I felt, through forty years, such tremendous responsibility. I had not the faintest notion how to use a landing net; but a mighty general directed me. "Don't let him see it; don't let him see it! Don't clap it over him; go under him, you stupid! If he makes another rush, he will get off, after all. Bring it up his tail. Well done! You have him!"

The mighty trout lay in the nightcap of Pike, which was half a fathom long, with a tassel at the end, for his mother had made it in the winter evenings. "Come and hold the rod, if you can't lift him," my master shouted, and so I did. Then, with both arms straining, and his mouth wide open, John Pike made a mighty sweep, and we both fell upon the grass and rolled, with the giant of the deep flapping heavily between us, and no power left to us, except to cry, "Hurrah!"

Don't Fish While I'm Talking

Robert Manning

Trout fishing does not come easily to an Eastern city boy, even a small-city boy. By the time I was six, barely old enough to snap off the fly on every other cast, the bulldozers and civil engineers were tearing up, and forever ruining, the one good trout stream within thirty miles of my home in upstate New York. Twenty-five years passed before I was to find the luxury of time, the circumstance of geography, and the loan of a rod, line, and wet black gnat #12 that enabled me to hook my first trout.

The creature was a Brown of no more than eight inches, so unfortunate as to be hooked in spite of all that I was doing. A paltry specimen perhaps. But at that age my threshold was so low and my system so unresistant (remember: within the comparable span of years wherein Alexander had achieved his greatness and died, I had caught my first trout) that I succumbed immediately to that fever of excess that seems to afflict late-in-the-game discoverers, as in the case of Henry VIII when he discovered divorce, or Casey Stengel when he discovered words.

By then I was a not very provident big-city dweller, and I found myself limited to one or two trouting expeditions a year, usually of no more than three days each on the Esopus and its tributaries in the Catskills. With so little real fishing to enjoy, the natural way to prolong the savor, to re-enjoy it, was to talk about it. For this kind of angling there is open season. It is a myth that fishermen like to drink for the drink itself. They frequent bars in order to find other nonfishing fishermen and engage in talk-fishing, or fish-talking.

I have performed some of my wisest, most delicate angling in saloons, and have been privileged to hear-see feats of fishing that would have caused Izaak Walton, were he present, to abandon the sport in despair and take up spelling (as well he could have). On a late and mellow January afternoon, for example, I watched with fascination as one of the more eloquent brethren, an old-fashioned silk-line and true-gut fellow from the Battenkill in Vermont, played a three-pound Brownie for fifteen breathtaking minutes with a three-ounce Orvis rod and two-pound test leader. The monster rose to a #10 ginger quill about fifteen feet from the bar, where the fast water swirls past the pay telephone. It leaped a good two feet into the air (you could see-hear the splash as far away as the checkroom), balanced for a gorgeous instant on its tail, and then raced seven tables downstream before the startled angler could disentangle from the bar rail and get both rubber boots firmly planted on the rocky bottom. Half a dozen drinkers and a scattering of early diners looked on in silence until the Irish bartender, an accomplished talk-poacher from the Connemara country, could stand it no longer and burst into supplication:

"Keep the p'int up. The p'int! The p'int!" The angler shot him an uncomprehending glance. "The p'int of the rod, you walleyed ass," cried Pat.

Too late. The big Brown had finned upstream, not far from the angler and close by table two, where with quick circles it entwined the line around the nylons of a charming blond, who was supping on linguini with white clam sauce. One last flick of its spine and the trout was off the hook, the rod forlornly loose in the fisherman's hand.

"I'm glad it got away," said the blond.

She returned to her linguini and the drinkers to their glasses, in quiet homage to another one that got away. Pat mopped watery rings from the mahogany. "It's poor luck you had indeed," he said. "Now, did I iver tell you about the big trout that Meehawl Sullivan caught in the postman's hat?"

In such fashion, if nostalgia is strong and tolerance high, can a trout fisherman fill the long, fancy-weaving gaps that stretch between seasons and between each season's real fishing expeditions. Bar-room fish-talking, or talk-fishing (there is a dispute among devotees as to the proper verb, and Fowler's *English Usage* offers no arbitration), is rewarding not only for the pleasure it gives. While of questionable help to the human liver, it beats fly-tying both for human companionship and for its considerably lesser strain on the eyesight and the posture.

So if Pat here will kindly serve us another round, I'll tell you about the time . . .

Pool Number 37

Donal C. O'Brien, Jr.

From the center of the lake the break in the shoreline looked like any other bay or cove. Indeed the pull of current, more persuasive than wind-made drift, was far more telling than what the eye could see. The break seemed to be caused by two points of pressure — on one side a rise of land heavy with pines and on the other a flat, boulder-strewn beach. Together they seemed to squeeze the lake, causing it to bulge and buckle into a heavy run of water which spilled downward, turned white and became a river, furious even now in September.

In the spring of the year when the ice went out, the boulder-strewn beach was itself awash with water and the pull of current was readily visible. Now, however, as the morning sun glanced down through the pines and splayed its rays on rocks and driftwood, it was difficult to believe that the beach was ever covered with water. It looked more arid than a desert, its sun and ice-scorched rocks made even drier by the nearness of green pine, blue lake and white rapids.

An otter came out of the woods and onto the beach. At this particular moment it was the only sign of life. Not a raven soared, not even an insect moved. Yet the otter stopped when it reached the beach. It was only when its eyes were satisfied that it moved gracefully across the rocks to where the first run of white water spread itself out into a spiraling pool. This pool was a mere thirty yards from the run of rapids. It was a big pool — deep, long, extremely wide. It was as if the lake was making one last effort to save itself by gathering up what it had lost in that first furious spilloff. The otter slipped into the pool, was carried by the current, and dove. It hunted easily, well aware that it was only a matter of time before it would find a lesser creature to kill. The current carried it down the center of the pool and over a boulder which caused two spreading furrows in the surface above. Behind the boulder, inches from the bottom, lay a large brook trout. The otter saw him but paid him no heed. The current carried the otter on into the tail of the pool where seconds later it would surprise a smaller brook trout, chase and kill it.

The big trout had seen the otter pass over him and did not move. The past spring he had killed a young otter, hunting too far from its mother, where a freshet boiled into the river not more than a mile from where he now lay. In a pool of this size not even a full grown otter would dare attack him. His gills rose and fell at infrequent intervals. His pectoral fins flickered with only the slightest motion. Nothing but current moved his tail. From the surface only the ivory white of his fins and the sides of his lower jaw showed his presence. His great marbled back blended with river bottom and the long blazes of crimson which slashed each side were mere shadows without sunlight. He was completely at rest. His hooked under jaw was approximately a foot from the boulder's base. Almost three feet of river bottom were covered by his body. A year ago in his prime he weighed almost seventeen pounds. Now his exact weight was fifteen pounds, twelve ounces. He was a full pound over the world's record, perhaps the largest living brook trout in the world.

The Cessna 180 droned small in the cloudless sky, the brilliant sun flashing silver off its wings. It seemed in place in the north woods wilderness, one of a new breed of soaring hawks which carried men into the lake country in search of minerals, timber and sport. Inside the plane the pilot glanced sideways out of the window and watched the river trace its way downward through the pines and shoreline. He was a white man about forty years old. He looked at the river through Polaroid glasses, was unmoved by its beauty, and turned his head to the creased and battered map which lay folded in his lap. The map showed a wilderness area heavily watered with lakes and rivers. At each point where a river flowed out of a lake was a number and at each point where a river flowed into a lake was another number. Most of these numbers were crossed out in pencil. A very few were heavily circled. The pilot's eyes focused on the number 37. It was one of the few numbers which had neither a cross through it nor a circle around it. He studied the number 37 and again glanced through the window, squinting through his Polaroids into the sun. He checked the map. There, a half a dozen miles ahead of the plane was pool number 37, the place between the wooded rise of land and the boulder-strewn beach which seemingly caused the run of rapids pouring into the pool where the large old squaretail lay.

The pilot turned to his right to speak to the Indian sitting beside him. He did not do so. The Indian's head was turned just far enough so that his eyes could glance out of the window and see into the river below. A white man would have cast his head over his shoulder to view the river, might have shifted in his seat as the pilot often did, even while flying, to get a better look. But the position was natural to the Indian and seemed so to the pilot who had know him now for over three weeks.

"The son of a bitch doesn't waste a motion," the pilot thought to himself. "Not even his eyes turn more than they have to."

The Indian shifted his head forward. He made the movement slowly. His eyes now stared straight ahead of him into the whir of the propeller. He was a Cree, twenty, thirty, forty years old, probably closer to forty. His eyes saw nothing now but the blur of air spinning soft and fast from the Cessna's prop. His mind was as empty as his eyes and he sat as if in a trance unlike the pilot who was continually contemplating past, present and future action and whose senses vibrated with energy. Again the pilot started to speak and again turned away. He peered out the window and concentrated on pool number 37.

The Cessna continued its way up the river, which, like all of the major north woods rivers, was periodically broken by lakes. Two such lakes were at either end of the six-mile stretch over which the Cessna was flying. The large brook trout had spent his summer in the lower of the two lakes and had been traveling the six-mile stretch on his way to the spawning grounds. On the pilot's map, where the river flowed into the lower lake, was the number 36 with a cross penciled through it. The big trout had passed through pool number 36 six days ago. He had traveled steadily and was tired. He was not used to moving great distances. Now he moved out from behind the larger boulder and forced his way into the main stream of the current. He swam close to the bottom where the pressure was broken by rocks and pockets. He was moving toward the rapids, the thirty yards of white water which would take him into pool number 37, his homing pool, where he would remain until it was time to spawn. He normally traveled in the evening or at night, but he was close now and anxious to arrive at the pool he knew so well, had known in fact for seven seasons.

The trout reached the place where the otter had entered the river. Ahead was the furious white froth of the initial spilloff. He started his final push still close to the river bottom. He was working hard now. His body surged into the current, was held motionless, then inched forward. The water shallowed and he broke up from the bottom, back, dorsal and tail clear of the surface. Here the pressure was less than where the river pitched downward. He churned forward, the sun catching the dark spots on the rays of his dorsal fin. He was over the worst of it and returned to the bottom. He paused for a moment, hooked jaw pressed to a small rock. Then he moved on. When he reached the crest of the spilloff, he porpoised. His head came clear of water then his shoulders, back and finally his tail. Again he porpoised and took his place behind a flat, wide rock where pool number 37 wedged into the rapids. He was scarcely aware that he routed two lesser trout from their positions behind the rock. He was home.

The Cessna 180 was circling the lake. There was plenty of time. It was not yet noon. The pilot pulled a Camel cigarette from his breast pocket, took out a box of Eddy Sesqui matches and lit it. He had not offered a cigarette to the Indian sitting beside him in over a week and did not do so now. The pilot smoked deeply. He tipped his Polaroids back onto steel gray hair and squinted at the lake shore. It looked like the hundreds of other lakes he had seen during this summer and summers past. But one never knew until a line was cast. This one, this pool number 37, might be a pool which held trophy trout.

The pilot was a fisherman, a professional. Ten years before he was probably the most famous fly fisherman in the country. Even now, in an age when sport fishing was big business, he was still among the top. Each year the major sporting magazines carried his articles. Four books were published under his name. His smiling, leanly rugged face had advertised fly rods, reels, lines and countless flies and accessories. Even so his name had been recently muddled among lesser fishermen who had been made prominent with lucky records or financial backing — both of which had eluded him. This trip, however, gave him a chance to break from the pack. One really good fish should do it. The pilot, the professional fisherman, had been hired by a fishing club to locate a series of pools in western Labrador and northern Quebec which contained trophy trout and on which camps could be built to house the growing number of sportsmen willing to pay fifty dollars a day for a crack at a trophy brook trout. The pilot had been allotted a month for this trip and had selected the last week in August and the first three weeks in September. This would enable him to fish when the trout were moving onto their spawning beds but before the weather broke. It was a good time in the best territory, but the trip had been going badly.

It was difficult for the fisherman to believe that the fishing, now in its fourth week, had been so unsuccessful. He had not taken a brook trout over seven pounds and had caught very few over five. Worst of all, he had not been able to locate a single pool in which he was able consistently to take trophy trout. There were, of course, a few which showed promise, but the best of these were often heavily populated with walleyes, northern pike and occasionally lake trout. The fisherman acknowledged that in these pools the Indian had been at least of some use. Those vacant eyes of his could pierce the surface of the water and distinguish the various species of fish. The fisherman had strong ideas on disrupting a pool. Although forceful with the fish he hooked, he treated the water gently. If he believed that a pool contained trophy brook trout, he would break off big walleyes and northerns, even lakers, rather than risk putting down an old squaretail. Furthermore, the fisherman had long since grown impatient with the prospect of chasing a large pike down a shoreline bordering white rapids. He would, therefore, ask the Cree to identify the fish as soon as possible. With heavy fish the words "pike" and "dore" meant a snapped tippet and lost fly. The word "trout" meant the utilization of the fisherman's great skills and a possible dash down the shoreline. It was a good system.

Otherwise, the fisherman mused, the Indian was useless. Sure, he had tried to get along. He wanted to share his enthusiasm with the Indian, had hoped to instill in the Cree a competitive spirit and a feeling of the importance of the trip. But this was impossible. The Indian could barely speak English, was dirty, could not even cook very well. He did nothing right — had even spent precious hours smoking fish for his winter supply. This had so annoyed the fisherman, even when done at night, that he finally forbade it. Furthermore, the Cree could not learn to keep his paddle from clinking against the sides of the aluminum canoe. He could not understand that you had to be gentle with the water. Whenever possible the fisherman waded the pools and stationed the Cree on shore at the tail of the water where he could at least identify the fish. The pilot checked his memory and brought the plane around into the wind. Skimming over the pines, it started to drop. Then the Cessna tapped down, jiggled the water, and taxied its silver way to the cove behind the rise of land, heavy with pines, which formed one side of the pool that he had marked as number 37.

The fisherman stood on one of the pontoons, checked the depth of the water and decided that he could wade the pool and did not need the canoe. Pulling on waders, he hauled the Cessna to shore and made it fast. The Indian followed carrying a blackened pot. On shore the two men performed the ritual they had performed almost twice daily for over three weeks. The pilot assembled a fly rod. On this day he chose a two-piece, nine-foot, six-and-three-quarter-ounce rod of Tonkin bamboo. He fitted a light salmon reel into the butt section and stripped out an ivory white GAF floating fly line with a thick leader section spliced to the end. Onto the leader he tied a tippet testing six pounds. Being forceful with trout, he always started with heavy tippets. The fly he selected was a variation of a muddler minnow he had tied himself. Its wings were of blue dun marabou. The hook size was a number six, extra long shank. The Indian's performance took about the same length of time. He crunched dried pine ends into jagged balls and dropped them into a pocket of rocks at his feet. He lit the pine ends, added heavier tinder and waited for the fire to catch. Then he wedged a heavier stick between a rock and the ground, filled the blackened pot, hung it on the stick over the fire and waited for the water to boil for tea. He was sitting on the heels of his feet rolling a cigarette when the fisherman walked over.

The fisherman stood over the Indian and lay his rod against a pine bough. He tapped the Indian's leg with his boot and motioned for him to follow. Together they walked down the shoreline to where the flat water began its run into the rapids. They walked gently and were careful not to displace any rocks. Then, well back from the shore, they squinted into the water.

At this point the pool was about two and a half feet deep. Here it began to shelve up to meet the rapids and here behind the flat, wide rock lay the large squaretail. He had arrived at his homing pool only twenty minutes before, and his gills pumped heavily as an aftermath of his run up the white water. He had also toured the pool routing lesser fish from their lies and driving them into the lake or the edges of the pool. He did this out of habit to establish himself. There was neither malice nor pleasure in his attack. Even now the fish were beginning to drift back into their places. He would not disturb them again.

The fisherman had good eyes for a white man, and he made out the shapes of some of the fish in the pool. He saw the telltale white of brook trout fins in two places — pretty good fish of maybe three pounds. These were the trout the old squaretail had routed from behind the flat rock. They were close to the shoreline now — nervous and hesitant. The fisherman's eyes reached the flat rock and noted the huge log-shaped stone which stemmed down behind it. "Did it move? Was it a pike? No," he thought, "just a rock."

The Indian saw more. His eyes found several good brook trout, one a five-pound fish in the center of the pool. He saw some northerns and even, in the deepest portion of the pool, the flicker of small walleyes. He also saw the log-shaped rock which the white man, for a brief moment, had thought was a pike and which the Indian knew was the largest brook trout he had ever seen. His vacant eyes now glistened. He stepped to the shore and turned with a jerk to the fisherman, at the same time throwing his arm in the direction of the pool to draw the other man's attention to the huge fish. The two three-pound trout next to the shore spooked into deeper water as the shadow from the Indian's arm flickered over the surface.

The white man caught the Indian with the back of his hand, hard across the side of his face. The blow sent the Cree reeling onto the rocks, but he twisted as he fell and caught himself on his hands before he landed. He was not hurt and brushed his sleeve against the trickle of blood running down his jaw. A pink blush appeared on the bronze skin of his cheek. He tucked his legs beneath him and sat on his heels.

"You bastard." The white man's voice quavered to keep from shouting, but the word came quietly enough. "You bastard. You scare trout. Understand? You scare trout." His voice began to rise. "I say be quiet, be gentle. Understand? Understand?" he spoke loudly now. "Understand, you Cree bastard." The white man turned and walked back to his fly rod. He was shaking with anger and frustration. He was also embarrassed.

"This god-damn trip," he murmured, "this god-damn trip." He pulled out a cigarette and lit it. He would wait a while before going into the pool. But the presence of the Indian, still crouched where he had fallen, made it impossible for the fisherman to relax. He would get on with it. He rose and took his fly rod and walked to the water's edge. Catching the Cree's eyes, he motioned him into position. Then the fisherman stepped into the water, well above the pool, careful even in his anger not to turn rocks and muddy the bottom. When he was in position, to the left of the pool and still well above it, he stripped out line and began to cast.

The fisherman had exceptional skills. The photographs of his casting which adorned his books did not do justice to his ability. He drove the line with deceiving ease and dropped it gently on the water. He fished out each cast. A single back cast and the line was again on the water a foot further down. The fisherman was fishing a salmon cast, a slack line diagonally across the pool. The muddler minnow barely broke the surface film. When the line started to straighten out, the fisherman would raise his fly rod causing the fly's deer hair head to blurp the surface — very slightly. He would switch to a sinking line if he had no rises.

The fisherman covered the head of the pool without turning a fish. He had lengthened his casts to over fifty feet and was now using a slight double haul on the line. On the first cast over the center of the pool a big brook trout took the fly. The fisherman set the hook. He knew it was a trout, had seen its head and dorsal break the surface before it struck. The fish steadied for a moment and then moved upstream. It was the five-pound trout the Indian had seen from the rocks. The fisherman believed it was over six pounds and started to edge toward the shore. Suddenly the trout turned and headed downstream. The current planed along its sides and it gathered momentum. It passed swiftly over the large brook trout behind the flat rock. The fisherman applied pressure to check the trout before it reached the rapids. The reel screamed. Then stopped. The fish was gone.

The fisherman walked back to his position and then dropped down a yard or so. It was a pretty good trout and he would have liked to have taken it. But he had lost fish before and he was not overly concerned. In fact, he was now completely engrossed in his fishing and had forgotten about the incident with the Indian. He again began to cast.

Although the large brook trout would not again leave his lie to tour the pool, he would protect his position against other fish. Therefore, when he had seen the hooked trout pass over him, he had turned to chase it. But it was too swiftly gone. The large trout was irritable and shifted in his lie. The Cree saw him and turned to watch the fisherman whose eyes were on his fly. When the Cree looked again at the large trout, it had risen in its lie and was restless. The trout watched the dead drifting, then spluttering, fish flies pass in front of him. First one, then another, then another. They were getting closer. When the next one came by it was pulled beneath the surface directly in front of the trout and he sucked it in. The Cree jumped to his feet.

The fisherman did not see the fish which took his fly. He had been double hauling about seventy feet of fly line and the fly had been pulled beneath the surface when he blurped it at the end of the float. But the fish had taken like a trout and it was heavy, very heavy. He felt the run of his heart against his shirt and headed for the shore, walking backwards, rod very high, taking in line as the huge fish swam slowly up into the center of the pool. He thought "This is a big fish, a really big fish."

The large trout had been stung by the hook and had followed the pull of the line hypnotically as it eased him out from behind his rock. He was neither hurt nor worried, but he was confused. He swam steadily on and moved into the head of the pool. The fisherman stopped. He had to pick up slack and did so. The fish was in good position. He was sure now that he had a brook trout. It came up in the current like one. They had not run into lakers in the other pools they had fished in this river. Besides, the water was too low. It must be a squaretail. Remembering the fish he had just lost and aware that his leader tested a heavy six pounds, he raised the rod and struck the fish again. He was about five yards from shore when he did this.

The large trout felt the drive of the hook and a stab of pain ran into his cheek. He turned against the pull of line and slashed across the pool. The fisherman raised the rod higher and the white line blurred through its guides. His heart now pounded. The trout ran across the pool almost to the boulder beach. In another few feet he would be visible to the fisherman. Suddenly the trout turned and made its run diagonally across and down into the tail of the pool, planing against the building current as it neared the rapids. The trout did not want to go down the white water but would do so.

The fisherman cursed himself for striking the fish again before reaching shore. It was the type of stunt a novice would pull. The fish would soon be in the rapids and he had those precious few yards to travel before he could reach shore to follow it. He checked the white water. It was only thirty yards long, not a big run, and the pool beneath was of ample size to hold any fish. He checked his spool. The fly line which he had gathered during the fish's slow swim into the head of the pool was now lost. In an instant he would be down to the backing. Should he stand where he was and let the fish stop in the pool below or should he try to follow it from the shore?

"What in blazes was that Indian yelling?" His mind and eyes snapped from the fish to the Cree.

The Indian was standing at the head of the spilloff only a few feet from the fish which seemed to be driving right at him. Over and over again he was shouting the words, "Pike, pike, pike . . ."

The fisherman heard him. "No," he thought, "it must be a trout." And then he remembered — the long, log-shaped stone behind the flat rock which had seemed to move. The exact spot where his fly had been when the fish had struck. The Indian was almost on top of the fish and his eyes . . . it was a pike. He raised his rod and grabbed the white line as it disappeared from the reel. The rod bowed, very deep. The leader snapped . . .

The Cessna 180 lifted off the lake and tipped up to clear the pine trees. The afternoon sun still glistened silver on its wings. Its hawk's shadow floated smoothly over the lake and then jaggedly onto the trees. Inside, the pilot reached for a creased map and took a pencil stub from his breast pocket. He looked at the map and carefully drew a cross through the number 37 — as he had done through all the numbers which marked unproductive pools. Beside him a Cree Indian stared into the blur of propeller wash and scraped a flake of dried blood from his cheek.

The setting sun flamed red and golden against the black silhouette of pine trees when an otter came out of the woods and stopped before moving down a boulder-strewn beach. It stopped again where a run of rapids spilled into a broad pool, then slipped into the water and was carried away by the current.

In the pool at the other end of the run of rapids behind a flat rock was a very large brook trout. The trout was rolling in the water, nose to the bottom. As he turned from side to side a golden gleam would shine up through the blackening water. The trout continued to roll at a slow and regular pace. Then stopped. A fluff of feathers on a thin shaft of metal dropped from between the trout's jaws and drifted in slow bounces along the bottom of the pool, then gathered speed, rose in the current and vanished in a rush of white water.

Turn Left at the Porcupine

Jack Olsen

The village of Lake City, Colorado, is forty-nine miles over Slumgullion Pass from Wagon Wheel Gap or, if you're coming from the north, it's twenty-five miles from Powderhorn on Highway 149. But don't bother yourself if you forget these jiffy instructions. Just drive to Saw Pit or Bedrock or Cimarron or Telluride or any other southwestern Colorado town and ask somebody how to get to Perk Vickers's place. Better ask a Republican, though. Perk has been Republican chairman of Hinsdale County for twenty-two years, and the handful of Democrats around Lake City resent the fact that out of the county's 208 permanent population — second lowest in the U.S. — Perk somehow gets 250 or 300 of them to vote in every election, and most of them Republican. "We got a lot of absentee ballots," Perk explains, while the outnumbered Democrats peer from their hiding places and exchange knowing glances. Politically Lake City and Hinsdale County have changed little since an itinerant guide named Alferd Packer killed and ate five of his companions and elicited one of history's most pungent accusations: "They was siven Dimmycrats in Hinsdale County, but you, yah voracious man-eatin' son of a bitch, yah et five of them!"

Out at Perk's ranch, just south of town, the boys like to come in from the day's labors and discuss the irremediable blow dealt to Lake City's Democratic machinery by the political actionist Alferd Packer. "What could you expect of a man couldn't even spell his own first name?" Perk says, while his wife Emma Jean warns him not to gloat. The other subject that is always good for a long discussion is trout: care and feeding, habits and environments, future and prospects and general history. Perk's brothers, Joe the cattle rancher and Bob the gold miner, convene in the little office cluttered with ore specimens, fly boxes, daguerreotypes of Vickerses dead and gone, aromatic old saddles and an ancient safe that looks as though it just fell off the Wells Fargo stage from Durango. In the rare and narrow interstices of their conversations one can hear the murmur of the storied Gunnison River's lake fork, which starts as a single, silvery drop way up above Sloane's Lake at thirteen thousand feet, drops quickly to timberline and thence through old mining camps, beaver-dam country, sheer-walled canyons, a deep lake called San Cristobal, over the foam of Argenta Falls, past Perk's place and into more canyons and meadows until it finally joins up with the main branch of the Gunnison fifty miles away. Every inch of the lake fork is loaded with trout. Well, not every inch. Well, not really "loaded" anymore. That's one of the things the boys argue about, the Gunnison River then and now. "Used to be the trout would swim over to the bank and wriggle into your creel." "No, it didn't used to be that way at all. Used to be the mines contaminated the water and there wasn't a trout between here and the lake." "Well, gimme the good old days." "Listen, you stubborn old jackass, *these* is the good old days!"

The visitor to the Vickers establishment might well agree that these is the good old days. Not that you can go down to the river and drag out three-pound rainbow trout with ease or catch a limit with a few hours' casting. Even the famous Gunnison has its off days, and during the early-summer runoff from the snowy San Juan Mountains surrounding the ranch the river becomes cloudy with glacial grindings, and the trout sulk in deep holes and refuse to come out and play. At such times the knowledgeable fisherman may still score, but only if he knows the secret of the Vickers Ranch and only if he meets the mystical and unfathomable requirements of the keeper of the secret, fifty-five-year-old Purvis (Perk) Vickers. Do not hurry unto this task, for Perk cannot be hurried. Do not bluster and make demands, either, for Perk will merely announce in his good-natured way that your reservation has expired. There is only one way to learn the secret of the Vickers Ranch, and that is the hard way — the way of waiting and hoping and keeping on the right side of Perk and not being a pushy Easterner, or a pushy Westerner, either. Then and only then will you be admitted to the secret, and then and only then will you be able to catch three- and four-pound brook trout to your heart's content and dine on orange-red fillets from the sweetest trout that swim.

My wife Su and I knew none of this, of course, when we first wandered into the place that the Vickers brothers insist on calling by the ridiculous name Vickers Dude Ranch, an appellation guaranteed to turn off both true sportsman and travel snob. Who wants to send postcards home from a dude ranch? When I got to know Perk a little better I asked him why he didn't call the place simply the Vickers Ranch or the Vickers Trout Ranch. "We're full up all the time now," he said, drawing on depths of commercial acumen garnered at business school in Tyler, Texas, where he became the only Vickers to learn to type and therefore the one assigned to running the ranch office. "If we changed it to Vickers Trout Ranch we'd have to beat 'em off with shovels."

"All right, Perk," I said, "I came here to catch fish. Now what the hell'll I do?"

"Try way upstream," the bandy-legged little man told me. I didn't know it at the time, but I was about to begin the long procedure that led, step by tortuous step, to the secret. I drove five miles up dirt roads to the narrow reaches of the upper river and cast my arm off catching brook trout that seldom reached six inches. Then Perk suggested a pack trip to a high alpine lake, but after we had booked five horses and lurched our way up steep mountain trails toward a lake supposedly loaded with brook and rainbow trout of monstrous dimensions, we found our way blocked by six-foot drifts of snow that had blown off nearby Uncompahgre Peak, 14,306 feet high and one of the most fascinating sights in Colorado when it's not ruining your fishing trip.

"Perk," I said loudly, "we came here to catch fish and we're not catching anything. What do you suggest?"

"The Deer Lakes," Perk said. "You can't miss at the Deer Lakes." In that rapid-fire manner of his, like a Walter Brennan record played at double speed, he proceeded to tell us the facts about the Deer Lakes. They lie, about eight of them, just up Slumgullion Pass, on public land. What was Slumgullion Pass? Well, about six hundred years ago several million tons of mountain broke off and began a slow crawl down the valley, like those mud slides that bedevil the residents of Los Angeles County. The earth flow kept going until it dammed the lake fork of the Gunnison and created Lake San Cristobal, ninety-two feet deep. Spruce trees grew atop the flow, and they leaned at crazy angles as they inched along — the only ambulatory spruce trees in Colorado. The flow was made of a yellowish clay, and to oldtimers it resembled the slumgullion stew that sustained them — hence the formal name Slumgullion Earthflow. Perk told us that it was one of the great natural wonders of the world, or at least of Hinsdale County.

"The fishing, Perk, the fishing."

"Oh, yes," he said, "you wanted to know about the Deer Lakes." It seemed that fifteen or sixteen years ago Perk had begun to fear that the Gunnison's lake fork would not be able to handle the heavy fishing pressure on it, and he cast about for ways to improve the fishing in the area. He suggested to the local chamber of commerce that the citizens of Lake City buy live trout by the ton and keep replenishing the lake fork all summer long, but to the hidebound conservatives of Lake City such a proposal was considered as wildly Communistic as Social Security or municipal bus lines. "So I noticed that there were a lot of good locations for lakes up above Slumgullion Pass," Perk said, "and we got permission from the government to put in some dams."

To raise money for the project Perk and his associates gave honorary Lake City citizenship papers to contributors of twenty-five dollars and promised to name a lake after anyone who contributed one hundred or more. Thus were created the Deer Lakes — Lake Pat Maloney, Lake Slug Stewart, Lake Emory Carper, Lake Frank Walker and several others. When the project was completed Perk and his helpers proudly erected handsomely carved nameplates by each dam, whereupon the U.S. Forest Service let out a howl of bureaucratic anguish. Such lakes, rangers announced, could not be named after living humans. "This gave us a hell of a problem," Perk recalled. "We could either rename the lakes or kill off the contributors. We decided to rename the lakes."

And there they sit today: the Deer Lakes, cool and emerald behind the earthen dams constructed by Perk and his bulldozing friends. The lakes bear such rustic names as Lake No. 1, Lake No. 2 and Lake No. 3. In a wild burst of creativity one of them was even named Lake No. 4. Some of the natives still refer to one of the larger lakes as Lake Pat Maloney, but not while any of the stern government men are around.

"But how is the fishing there?" I asked.

"First-rate," Perk said. "You can't miss at the Deer Lakes."

We drove up over the Slumgullion Earthflow to the Deer Lakes and fished all day and missed. Oh, not entirely. But one does not push deep into the wildest reaches of the Rocky Mountains for the purpose of catching a couple of skinny rainbow trout and brook trout that have barely left their mothers' breasts. "This doesn't make it, Perk," I said when we returned all covered with dust and frustration at the end of the day.

"Well, what about our ponds?" Perk said. He waved grandly toward some man-made ponds that he had dug in the meadow next to the river and kept stocked with hatchery trout that were fed from sacks of Purina Trout Chow.

"Who the hell wants to catch hatchery trout?" I said.

"I'll tell you who the hell," Perk said. "Just about every

dude that comes here, that's who the hell. Ever since I built those ponds I've had to spend half my time keeping an eye on them." One of the ponds was marked WOMEN AND CHILDREN ONLY, LIMIT FIVE FISH, and because trout are wily and because women and children are not the most skilled anglers some of the rainbows in the pond had survived several seasons and grown to weights of six and seven pounds. Perk said he would show me. He went to a barn, picked up a handful of trout chow and tossed it in. At first there were a few dainty peckings at the floating pellets, but then the water began to boil with lunging and gyrating trout, among which were plainly some fish that were well above the five-pound mark.

"My God!" I said.

"Exactly," Perk said, "and that's what a lot of other people say, too. They lose their perspective. One morning I came down at dawn, and here's this guy with a seven-pound rainbow. 'Look,' he says. 'Look what I caught in the river.' I saw that the fish was from our pond — you could tell by the coloring. The next year when that guy called for a reservation we were full up."

Hardly a day goes by when Perk is not approached by a male guest who explains that he is going to help his wife and children fish the women's and children's pond, "but don't worry, Perk, I won't be fishing myself, I'll just be helping *them,*" and five minutes later Perk will look out his little office window and see that the man is helping them by baiting the hook, making the cast and pulling in the fish. One day he strolled down to the pond and said to a particularly persistent offender: "Mr. Peterson, my main concern is: Where's your dress?" Peterson left in embarrassment. But Perk flatly denies the often-repeated report that he once threw out a man in full female attire. He does not want to be known as a person who discriminates against anyone, including female impersonators. "You have to be diplomatic," Perk says, "but at the same time you can't relax the rules. This greed that's in all of us — the greed for money, the greed to have more than the next fellow — it shows up in fishing, too. Out of every fifty people that come here there's maybe one that'll say, 'I caught my limit of fish and

I threw 'em back.' The other forty-nine'll say, 'I caught my limit of fish, and here they are. *Look at 'em!'* Why, if I let some of them fish in the ladies' pond, they'd use dynamite caps!"

"Perk," I said, "I'd gladly throw back every trout I caught, but I didn't come here to fish for hatchery trout. Now what do you suggest?"

Perk's eyes rolled wildly. Later I was to realize that he was resisting the temptation to let me in on the secret, but at this point I didn't even know that there was a secret to be let in on. He was still sizing me up, and there were still tests for me to pass, frustrations for me to endure. Now he named another one. "Waterdog Lake!" he said. "You'll clean up on 'em at Waterdog Lake." I asked directions and wrote feverishly on the back of a postcard as Perk rattled out the route. "It's mostly straight up," he said. "The lake's around eleven thousand feet, and we're around nine thousand now. You go through the lower gate — make sure you're in low gear — and head up the side of that hill. Don't worry about the road — I made it myself." His instructions included an admonition not to drive across the upper meadows — they were sodden with runoff, and tire tracks would develop overnight into rivulets and brooks — and a warning about bears. "They won't bother you, but there's a lot of 'em up there, and if they have cubs with 'em they can be grouchy." I laughed inwardly — good old Perk was really laying it on thick. He told us to remember to take a left turn or we'd wind up mired in the mud. "Joe killed a porcupine up there the other day and it's still there," he said. "Just turn left at the porcupine."

Su packed a lunch, and we began the grinding journey up from the Gunnison Valley. What Perk had lightly referred to as a road turned out to be a corrugated nightmare of gullies and rocks and fallen trees and holes, and we rattled around inside the Jeep like the occupants of a Waring Blendor. "Enjoying the r-r-r-ride?" I called to Su.

"N-n-n-n-n-n-n-n," Su explained, "-o."

We emerged briefly into a rolling meadow dotted with a hundred or so Hereford cattle but were soon through it and back into the deep woods. We ran along a stream bottom, then came to a few steep pitches that required compound low and a running start and strong faith in the sturdy Jeep. It was like driving up a forehead on Mount Rushmore. Every now and then I had to stop and get out and remove a tree trunk or boulder from our route — proof that we were the first drivers to make the trip up to Waterdog that season.

At last it came into sight — a big lake, almost a mile long, clear and blue and so cold that a hand immersed in it tingled for minutes. At 11,200 feet the lake was just below timberline, and around its shores the final spruces and aspens and pines of the highest altitudes fought for a footing, some of them dying out and others living a compromise life of miniaturization. There were mosses and lichens and some slender, wiry grasses, and here and there a patch of wild iris of electric blue. The aspens were gnawed at elk-height — monuments to severe winters — and a few tender shoots of pine had been completely denuded of bark by porcupines. If there had been good fishing in the lake, the scene would have been idyllic. If. We flang everything into the cool blue depths, but we couldn't raise a strike. We tried flies, wet and dry; nymphs, weighted and unweighted; spinners, Colorado and Indiana; flatfish and spoons and streamers and even a little lure shaped like a kitchen sink and called "the Kitchen Sink" so that anglers could go back home and brag that they had thrown everything at the fish including the kitchen sink. But trout that would not hit classic lures would not hit gimmick lures either. Looking to left and right and finding ourselves alone, we dug for worms and fished them high and low without a strike. After three hours without so much as a single hit we decided to quit. The vote was 2-0.

We were halfway back down and just inching our way through a thick copse of aspens when Su let out a yelp and did a perfect little jump from her seat into mine. "Hey!" I shouted as I struggled for control.

"A bear!" she said. "Step on it!"

"I'm not going to step on any bear," I said.

"The gas, stupid! Step on the gas!"

I tromped the floor pedal, and the Jeep lurched forward, its gears grinding, and just then the bear crossed the road at a blinding speed of some two or three miles an hour. "Come on," I said, "they're fun to chase!" We jumped out and followed the porcupine into a stand of pine trees. He waddled about another hundred yards before climbing up a spruce tree and glowering down inhospitably at us, and just as I turned to begin the walk back to the Jeep I caught a glint of blue through the trees. "Water!" I said, and stumbled through the woods with Su stumbling after. We quickly came upon a tiny lake hidden in the deep forest, its waters held back by an earthen dam and its borders edged by willow brush and kinnikinnick and thick patches of iris and dandelions.

"A pond," Su said. "Don't get excited. It's just a pond."

"It's a pretty little place," I said and just then something came rocketing out of the water in the middle of the lake and made a splash the magnitude of which had not been seen since the launching of the *Ile de France*. My knees started to give way, and Su, an old hand as a trout fisherman's wife, quickly grabbed me. "Take it easy," she said. "It was just a muskrat or a beaver."

"Yeah," I said, my voice trembling. "Musta been a muskrat or a beaver." Then a similar splash came from the far edge of the lake. "That beaver gets around," I said, beginning to shake again. Hardly were the words spoken when a fish spurted out of the water, performed a one and a half with a full twist in the layout position and splashed back in, throwing droplets of sun-speckled water in a fine rainbow spray.

"What was that?" Su said.

I rapped my forehead and fell to my knees and inhaled gallons of air and rolled my eyes and performed half a dozen other involuntary spasmodic actions that only another trout fisherman would understand, and when I finally regained control of myself, about five minutes later, I said, "A trout! A three- or four-pounder! A brook trout! They don't come that big anymore! It's impossible! I'm dreaming!"

Even Su seemed impressed, and this was the first time I had seen her impressed by a fish since a succulent serving of turbot hollandaise at the Poularde Bressane in Grenoble (one star in your *Guide Michelin*). "Let's get the rods!" she said, and we raced back through the woods toward the Jeep. But by the time we reached the car sanity had returned. "Listen," Su said, "we can't fish that lake."

"Why not?" I said, knowing full well why not.

"Because it's obviously man-made, and it's obviously been stocked for some special purpose."

"We found it, didn't we? Nobody told us not to fish it."

"You know how Perk is. If he'd wanted us to fish this pond he wouldn't have sent us up to Waterdog."

"Yeah," I agreed, "and up the Gunnison headwaters and up the mountain and up to the Deer Lakes and every place in Hinsdale County except here."

"There's only one thing to do, and that's go down and ask him for permission," Su said.

"Yes," I said, "and if he says no, what then?"

Su thought for a moment. "If he says no," she said, "you hold him and I'll strangle him."

So that's how we came to learn the secret. Afterward Perk admitted that he had been almost ready to tell us anyway. "You just about passed my test," he said.

"What test is that?" I asked.

"My personal test for who can fish the upper lakes," he said. "I got my own standards. Don't ask me what they are, but I can list at least one United States Senator who didn't make it and a couple of millionaire oilmen from Texas and a very prominent attorney from Oklahoma. They'd give ten thousand dollars apiece to fish those ponds, but they haven't got a chance."

"Why not?"

"How would I know?" Perk said. "There's no rule about it. I don't even understand the rules myself. Two-thirds of the people that come here never see those upper ponds. Not one person in twenty qualifies. I got people who've been coming back for thirty years and they've never wet a line in those lakes."

Perk told the story of his homemade upper lakes. "It was just about the same time we were asking the government to let us make the Deer Lakes," he began, drawing on a black cigar and waving lazily at the foul smoke in front of him. "I'd ride up to the upper ranch on my horse, and I'd always say, 'Boy, when the good Lord made this he really did a job.' All those meadows and woods and little streams running down and golden eagles and badgers and bobcats and all kinds of wildlife up there. It always seemed to be the prettiest place on earth to me. But this whole countryside's pretty out here, and people were beginning to realize it, and they were swarming into here in the summertime and fishing that lake fork to a frazzle, and I began to realize that public fishing wouldn't always take care of the demand. And what about the people that came up here when the river's high and discolored? Shouldn't they be allowed to fish, too?

"Well, I had made those four ponds down below and stocked them with trout that I bought by the pound, and then I realized that we could make something extra special up on the upper ranch. There's a little stream that drains the whole upper ranch — Park Creek, it's called, and it's about a foot wide. The beavers were always damming it up and making these little lakes, and then they'd wash out and cause all kinds of damage. So as soon as I got some money together I rented a bulldozer and went up there and made a good, solid earthen dam where the beavers had worked. I didn't build any spillway because this was late summer and I knew the pond wouldn't fill up over the winter.

"The next spring I'd almost forgotten about it. I was working in our gold mine and somebody came running into the tunnel and told me to get out, my dad said it looked like the whole upper ranch was washing away. The pond had filled and the dam had burst and the water was coming down the mountainside. So the next thing I did, I learned how to build a rock spillway and I was in business. From then on every chance I got I built another pond up there and planted it with fingerling brook trout and cutthroat. I'm up to eight ponds now, and I'm building more all the time. But I take certain precautions. Only one of those eight ponds is anywhere near a road — and that's the lowest pond and nobody knows how to catch fish out of it except my son Larry. The rest of those ponds — you could drive all over the upper roads and never get a glimpse of one. *You* wouldn't have seen one either if it hadn't been for that porcupine."

I told Perk I would like to fish one of his ponds and asked him if I qualified. "I think so," he said. "I been watching you. You're not a fish hog. You release fish and we don't find wasted fish in your garbage can in the morning."

"You've been checking?"

"We keep our eyes open," Perk said, relighting the smelly old stogie. "Sometimes we'll find a garbage can with thirty or forty trout in it not even cleaned. I don't care if those fish come out of Lake San Cristobal or the Gunnison or Crystal Lake or our own ponds or where — those people don't come back. We're full up when they call the next time."

"Do any local people poach?"

"Once some fellows from Lake City went in and cleaned out one of our ponds, and we found out about it because there's not that many people in Lake City and all of a sudden they're all eating big brook trout. So we put out the word that anybody caught poaching our ponds would suffer the death penalty. They must have believed us. Nobody's been poaching up there since, I hope."

"How about the guests?"

"Well, by the time they pass my test I'm pretty certain about 'em. They'll take a few trout — enough for dinner — and they'll return the rest and they'll obey my rules about flies only and no bait or lures. Nothing scares trout more than lures and nothing kills 'em worse than bait. If you fish with bait you can't return 'em. But a fly just catches a trout's lip and you can let him go and he doesn't even know it happened.

"The worst experience we had in the upper lakes was with five old customers — lawyers from Texas. I watched 'em for years and they seemed like perfect sportsmen, and one day I gave 'em permission to fish Vickers Lake, which is where we keep our biggest and wildest brook trout and cutthroat. Well, sir, my brother Bob went up to see how they were coming along that day, and they had gunnysacks full of trout from two to five pounds. Our prize fish!

"Bob rode back down and told me, and when those men finished fishing I was waiting for them. We counted: they had one hundred twenty-five. Prize brooks and cutthroat, weighed about three hundred, four hundred pounds. I looked at the fish and I looked at those lawyers, and not a word was spoken. They looked like they were gonna burst out crying. Later on one of them told me they were going to have an attorneys' convention back home and they wanted to furnish enough fish for a trout fry."

"So that was the end of them as guests here?" I asked.

"The end of them?" Perk said. "Why, hell, no. They come back every year. They're my prize customers. But they know they'll never fish one of my ponds again. Never! They can fish the public water all they want, and that seems to satisfy them. They've never asked to fish the ponds again. They know better."

The next morning Perk gave us *sotto voce* instructions on how to get to one of his best fisheries: Alden Pond. The instructions were Stengelesque: "Go up that road and open the gate. Up about a mile take the right-hand prong past the little fork and keep on going till you come to one, two, three switchbacks. On the third switchback veer off to the left. If you don't you'll wind up at our gold mine. After a while there's a pond. Drive just under the dam and cross the spillway and follow a grove of trees. Keep outside the timber till you come to a fence, and then follow the fence till you come to a gate. Open the gate, and the road goes through some heavy timber and through a meadow, and then you make a right turn around some beaver ponds and follow a little stream till you can't go any farther, and then you walk straight ahead through the woods and over a barbed-wire fence, and there's your lake, full of brook and cutthroat."

"Simple as that, eh?"

"Simple as that," Perk said.

Thirty minutes later we came to the end of the dirt road, walked a few steps through a deep woods, slid like snakes under a barbed-wire fence, walked a few more yards and came into sight of a crystalline mountain lake.

The pond was about three acres in all, with borders ranging from semitundra, where almost nothing grew, to a thick slice of woods that marched right down to the water's edge and deposited large trunks like toothpicks in the water. Everywhere else there was the low kind of brush that I have personally renamed bear-brush, partially because I don't know its name and partially because I find it almost always associated with bears, who can root around on all fours and not be seen as they move from bush to bush. Indeed, there was bear sign around, but I did not bother pointing it out to Su. She would only have become hysterical.

In advance I decided to keep two trout for our dinner. All the rest would be released and we would be welcome to fish another day. I started out with a mayfly, and to my astonishment nothing hit it. "O.K.!" I shouted to the fish. "I'm ready! You can start now!" The big brown mayfly sat out there on the water like a hot fudge sundae, but nothing stirred.

"I thought this was going to be so easy," Su said.

"It will be," I said, "as soon as I get the formula. If it was all that easy these wouldn't be trout."

At least an hour went by without a semblance of a strike. Every now and then a big fish would break water, but never near my flies. "Do you want me to start digging for worms?" Su said.

Soon I had worked my way around to the place where the timber lay helter-skelter in and out of the water. I tied on a tiny Kelso nymph, let it sink between two jagged tree trunks and began retrieving slowly. On about the third pull, something hit and snapped off the 6X leader. After this happened twice more I switched to a 3X leader, let the water rest for a few minutes and cast out my last Kelso nymph. Whack! Something hit it with a thump and took off under a tree trunk. I put on all the pressure the leader would hold and steered the fish back toward the open water, and after about five minutes of fight the trout made its first jump and sent me into a state of total puzzlement. This wild mountain trout, living in a pond that was fished only three or four times a year, had gone into a coloration phase that would have put many a tropical bird to shame. It looked more scarlet than anything else as it burst from the water, but its fins and belly appeared to be an apricot color that I previously had seen only once: on brook trout caught in a little stream in Nova Scotia.

I played the fish carefully, and Su came running over as I

finally slid it up on the bank. Biologists will scorn, but the fish had the pronounced purplish stripe of a rainbow trout, the large, open spots and high coloring of a brook trout and the bright orange-red slashes of a cutthroat. Such a three-way hybrid is impossible — according to the textbooks — but we were looking at one. We also looked at several more as the day went on, plus a few fish that were obviously pure brook trout and a few that were pure cutthroat. We took a pair of fat two-pounders and released another twenty or so. When I ran out of Kelso nymphs I switched to Alder quills, which are similar, and the trout didn't seem to mind. Just before the sun dipped below the mountains to the west, we laid our two fish on the grass and walked up the slope for a better view of the sunset, and when we returned about twenty-five minutes later we couldn't find our catch.

"Don't be silly," I said to Su. "They're not lost. Dead trout can't walk."

"They were right here," Su said. "Right here where the grass is trampled down."

"Trampled down?" I said, and walked over for a better look. I could see where my own feet had crushed some of the grass, but I could also see where other blades had been flattened along a narrow corridor that led into the bearbrush. "My God!" I said. "It must have been — . . . ."

"It must have been what?" Su said, gripping my arm with fingernails of steel.

"Nothing," I said. "I was just thinking out loud."

"What took our fish?" Su said, her voice cracking slightly.

"Probably an elk," I lied. "An elk, I guess."

"Elk eat fish?"

"Under certain conditions," I said. "Yes, they will. They have been known to do this." I took my wife's arm and led her gently but firmly through the shadows toward the fence and the Jeep. "It's nothing," I said in my jolliest voice. "After all, elk have to make a living, too. Ha, ha! We'll come back tomorrow and catch some more trout."

All the way down the mountain I kept looking in the headlight glare for the lousy, bleeping bear that had stolen my two rain-brook-throat trout, but the only wildlife that turned up was a pair of sleepy-eyed does and another porcupine. Each time I turned to the side I noticed that Su was staring at me. "Why are you staring at me?" I asked.

"What really stole our fish?" she said in her most accusatory voice.

"Roll your window up," I said.

"What kind of an answer is that?" she said as she rolled the window up.

"A bear," I said softly. The rest of the way down the mountain we both occupied the same seat.

Driving home one week and 137 trout later (we kept six and released the others with slight shaving nicks in their jaws), I got to thinking about Perk Vickers and some of the other fishing-resort operators I've known. The main thing Perk had going for him was the lake fork of the Gunnison River, as famous among Western trout nuts as the Esopus and the Beaver Kill are to Easterners. But Perk wasn't content to rest on his river's reputation, to exploit the vivid imaginations and great expectations of his clientele. I thought back on other resort operators and on miserable trips to famous trout rivers like the Allagash in Maine and the White in Arkansas, and I remembered being told so many times that I should have been there the week before or I should come back the next week, when fishing would be fast and furious. But when a man is fishing, it is always this week, and in a long life of chasing trout I can remember no other resort operator who worked as hard as Perk Vickers on the task of providing trout fishing this week instead of cheery predictions for next or fond remembrances of last. To be sure, his four lower ponds are full of hatchery trout and suitable only for the tenderest of tenderfeet. The Deer Lakes are overfished and underproductive, like many lakes around the eleven thousand-foot mark. And the eight ponds on Perk's upper ranch are a caution to get to — even if you're invited — and no one without a sturdy four-wheel-drive vehicle or a horse need apply.

But so what? Taken together, all of these man-made fishing spots increase the odds for the fisherman and diminish his dependence on the river alone. Rivers, like the trout that live in them, are highly unpredictable, and even so magnificent a stream as the lake fork of the Gunnison can turn into a wet desert, roily and high and fishless. Should the sportsmen who invest large sums to come there have to sit in their cabins and wait the river out? Perk doesn't think so. And it may be that his place, despite its cornball name and its fish-stealing bears, is the trout resort of the future.

To tell you the truth, I wouldn't mind a bit.

The King

Edwin Lewis Peterson

As I started out of the water, I looked at my fingers. They were puffy and wrinkled. I ached all over. But as I stepped up on the shore, I had a feeling of exultation — I had made the Prince rise to a fly. Even George had not been able to do that, and to succeed where George had failed was cause enough for pride.

In the morning sunlight, her hair gleamed golden. I was not surprised.

"You did splendidly," she said. Her voice was very calm and mature. "My father will be glad to know. He would have come himself, but . . . There was an accident, and he could not come, not just now. You must be very cold. How long did you stand there?"

"I don't know," I said. "Since before daybreak. How long have you been here?"

"I was here, too, before daybreak," she said, "for I wanted to see you. I want to show you the King, while I may."

I should have been overjoyed, but the quality of her voice disturbed me. It was hurt and troubled. When I looked at her closely, I saw that her eyes were bloodshot.

"While you may?" I asked. "There is nothing wrong is there? Your father . . . ?"

"Not really," she said in an even tone. "Nothing can ever be wrong. It is only we who are wrong. You believe that, you know that, do you not? Nothing is ever wrong, except us."

"Yes, of course, but sometimes . . . What was the accident?"

"It does not matter. Only I wanted to show you the King. It is hard for any of us to tell what may occur tomorrow. Your friend is ill. You may be ill. I may be gone. The sky may drift about our ankles. It is hard to tell. That is why I want to show you the King, before anything can happen."

"There is something wrong," I said. "Tell me first about that."

From far off, it seemed to me that I could hear the sound of screaming. A man's voice, wild and hurt. I looked at her sharply. I was sure that she, too, heard the screams, but her face did not lose its composure and no look of fear came into her eyes. When she spoke, she spoke steadily, as if she were part of the permanence she talked of.

"There is nothing wrong," she said, "except with us. Sometimes we lose our power, and when we do, we think the stars have varied. But they have not. We are hurt, but the fault is our own. It is we who are weak, not the years that are wrong. Only, for a moment we have forgotten the bright equation. Terrible things may happen then, things that make the flesh quiver, but nothing is ever wrong. I hear, but I am not afraid. We will overcome."

"Is your father injured?" I asked, persistent.

"No, not my father. You would not understand. We can live here, you should know, all three of us, only because two of us have power. My father is a powerful man. He is very strong. But his brother is weak and foolish. Sometimes my father must hurt his brother. It is unfortunate, and it is painful to all of us. It has come to be a great trial. Perhaps it will end soon. The weak perish because of their weakness, and when they go down, the strong must sometimes go on and on, like a bear pursued by yelping dogs. That is why we cannot tell what may occur tomorrow or the next day. That is why there is uncertainty of location though not of truth. That is why, if you wish to see the King, it would be wise to do so soon."

"You know how much I wish to see the King," I said. "I have looked for him for many years. I used to think I wanted to see him more than anything else in the world."

"But now?"

"Now I am confused. You are bright and bewildering. I do not know what to think, but I know that if you are in trouble, I should like to help you, and you must let me. That is all."

For a moment her face softened, and she laid a quick brown hand on mine.

"You are kind," she said, "but kindness is not always a virtue. Do you really think you could help?" She took her hand away but I could still feel its coolness.

"I might," I said.

"You know you could not. Only the strong can help the weak, and I am stronger than you. Much stronger. There are things you do not know of, or only dream of. The mandrake root can be got with child, and the falling star can be caught. Overhead, overhead, rushes life, and the father and the daughter, and the owl is with the moon, and the strong they call crazy, and the weak scream out their weakness and die. It is unfortunate, but the wrong lies with them, with the weak, and in the end the equation is clear and bright."

Her beaded moccasin tapped slowly on the wet ground. I did not look at it directly, but I was conscious of it, of the glitter, of the little thud. Her eyes were hard again. I looked away.

"Tonight," she said, "you will see the King — if you wish."

"You know I do," I said, almost defensively. I found myself staring between rhododendron leaves at a bright pebble. The leaves glistened darkly and the pebble was translucent. I could see little blue veins in it. As I looked at it, I could hear her speaking.

"Directly above the riffle," she was saying, "is a small, deep pool. Go there tonight after the moon has risen. Moonlight is a good time. Sit on the flat rock on the other side of the stream from here. Sit there and look across the pool. Do not look back. Look at the pool in the moonlight. After a time, I shall come to you, and you will see the King. You will never forget that. I must go now. I must go back to my father. If I have talked unwisely, please forgive me. Good-by."

Lightly she made her way through the thicket. I watched her go. The branches seemed to part before her and to make a clear path into the hemlock grove beyond them. Again I heard the screaming, but it seemed subdued and less terrifying. Then, for some reason which I do not yet understand, I looked for the pebble with the blue veins. I could not see it. Still peering, I took two or three steps in what I thought to be the right direction. Far off I saw something bright. It was ten yards or more away. When I got to it, I saw that it was a bright pebble with blue veins. The veins made the identical pattern I had seen clearly when standing thirty or forty feet away. I know it was the same pebble, but I shall not attempt to explain how, at that distance, I had been able to see the blue veins. I cannot explain it.

When I got back to the cave, George was gone. I ate the oatmeal he had left, drank some coffee, and washed the dishes. Then I started up the stream with a dry quill Gordon on the end of a light leader.

II

I was gloriously happy. That night I was to see the King. That night I should have proof that the legend I had believed in since childhood was true. And moonlight was a good time. The golden moths would be out, the golden moths with ruby eyes, and the whippoorwills would be singing from the dark. I should stand there alone for a time, looking and listening, and then she would step from the shimmering laurels and come to my side. She would be lovely and real and true. Her hair would be like a bright mist and her voice like the murmur of gentle waters. She would point with a slim brown arm, and out of the mystery of shadows and moonlight would come the King.

Night would have seemed far away, separated by loneliness and years, except that in the meantime there was the joy of a June afternoon on Shade Creek. Surely the trout would rise as my spirits had risen; the sun would be bright, the hemlocks fragrant. Fishermen are the happiest of human kind, I thought. What other class of men can find such happiness in such variety? "No life, my honest scholar, no life so happy and so pleasant."

In the catalog of angling there are many pleasures — day-long, blessed idleness beside a frothy pool while we fish with a Walton worm; minnow fishing under overhanging brush for the monster trout whose evening meal is a smaller brother or two; streamer fishing in cloudy water; nymph fishing with a twelve-foot leader and a 4X tippet while we watch the floating cobweb for a sign; the wet fly in turbulent rapids where gray shadows and scarlet flashes revive our hope. There is a type of angling for every mood, for every age, for every philosophy and disposition. But for most of us, in the whole bright galaxy of pleasures, there is nothing quite equal to the laying of the dry.

Success with the dry fly, it is true, demands long practice and much patience. It demands a will for perfection, an insistence on the correct performance of every phase of the cast from the perfect pickup to the delicate dropping of the feather. It demands attention to tackle, to the contour of the stream, to the currents, to the habits of trout, to the condition of light, to the type of insect on the stream at the moment the cast is made. And finally, it asks for an understanding of brown rocks, black shadows, yellow buds, a swirling thorn blossom, and the mist that starts and closes the perfect day of angling. Understanding? Even more. It is love and interpretation and a belief in the existence of things never seen but always sought.

I began wading slowly and cautiously. The laurels were in blossom, and the air was filled with their fragrance. As I walked, I felt like someone other than myself, lighter, gayer, and more certain. Early morning sunlight dazzled on the water and threw changing shadows on white sand at the bottom of the creek. A thrush warbled a June melody and the water sang over stones.

There were no dusty answers and many mysteries. Was there a trout beside the black log that lay along the shore? If there were, could he be reached? The pink and white blossoms and the shimmer of dark leaves blocked the cast from below, and the riffles above the log made drag inevitable should the fly come from above. If there were any entrance, then, the fly would have to come directly across from the opposite shore.

The angler, who was no longer I, did not hurry. The morning was young, his legs were strong, the rod in his hand was airy lightness. He came out of the stream, and as he raised his booted knee, he was surprised at its shiny cleanness. The ground under his feet was spongy. It felt good after the hardness of rock. He made a half circle back to the stream, but slowly enough to notice a rugged scrub pine, to see a brown caterpillar on a glossy leaf, to look for a saucy catbird, to smell the blossoms and the faint fragrance of damp hemlock. "Fishermen," he sang to himself, "are the happiest of men."

Six feet away from the stream, he stopped and looked ahead. If the backcast could be made, the forward cast could be made, too — over the tops of the bushes and down to the mossy log. He looked behind. A hard, high backcast (the books, he remembered vaguely, called it a steeple cast) would clear the dangerous branches behind. But if the fish were hooked, how could it be netted? There was a way, though, through the bushes, a way in which he could eventually get to the stream and use his net. Since the sun was in his eyes, there was no danger of his shadow or of the shadow of his rod falling across the water. And since he had stepped lightly ever since leaving the stream, there was little fear that vibrations had traveled through the ground to the trout — whose existence was merely conjectural.

The angler who was not I inspected the hook, tried it on his forefinger. He blew at the hackles to see that they were dry and fluffy, and he pulled the fly to test the knot. Then, raising his head only enough to see the upper end of the log, he tilted the rod back over his shoulder to get the fly started. Two short casts added six feet to the line. Ten more were needed for the final cast. He stripped them from the reel while the fly was in the air. Four of them went out on the hard, high backcast — only this time the rod stopped when it reached a perpendicular position. Then a swift downward cast, at the end of which the remaining six feet whistled through the guides and shot out over the laurels. The fly stopped its forward motion directly over the moss-covered log and spun back a foot or so. Like thistledown, it dropped to the water.

There was a wild churning, then a quick twitch to the rod. Two bubbles floated down from where the fly had been taken. The rod was pumping solidly, and the angler picked his way through the bushes toward the shore. The trout had turned down. It was fortunate for the fisherman that it did so, for if it had come across, the angler would have lost it in a tangle of line and bushes. By the time the fisherman had got to the edge of the water, the trout was thirty feet downstream. It turned suddenly and came up. As the angler tried to loop up the slack, something bright streaked past not more than ten feet away. The trout was back under the log, but there was no snag, for the rod throbbed with his short plunges. When he started for the riffles, a slight pressure on the rod turned him. He was tired, by then, and sulky. The dashes grew shorter and shorter and less frequent. For a moment he lay on his gorgeous side on the top of the water, and the angler prepared the net. The trout went easily where it was led and drifted into the net. With a sparkle of drops, the trout came into the air, its tail quivering above the rim.

Without hurry, the angler stepped back into the bushes. Hurry, he remembered, sometimes loses trout and is bad for the nerves. Good fishermen do not hurry. He took the tiny hook from the trout's jaw and laid the bit of rainbow on a bed of ferns and moss.

He was flushed with victory. The air smelled sweeter than before. Victories come seldom in life; on the trout stream they come often. He had placed the fly in a pool that ordinary anglers would have passed by as impossible, and he had been rewarded. Victorious in a duel that was poetry from the first smell of laurel blossoms to the golden shadow beneath the water and the damp ferns that lined the willow creel, he knew, as he had never known before, that all things were possible.

He was part of the pleasant world about him. A chickadee, hanging upside down from a pine twig, chopped at a pine cone. A blue flower twinkled at the tip of a blade of star grass. A butterfly fluttered from sunlight to sunlight. Overhead, light clouds raced across the blue; yet on earth there was no wind, only audible stillness. He heard the language of water, of a gray leaf, of wings that whirred among shadows, and it was not strange. It seemed for a moment that it was his language, familiar and native, reminiscent of another place in a far distant time.

In a small way, he felt within himself the mystery of earth, but he could not explain it. The wind glided over ancient mountains, and the sunlight beat through the trees as it did in Eden. The river Jordan flowed softly, and a girl, in tears, stood amid the alien corn. He remembered a boy in short trousers. The boy believed in butterflies and bent pins and a rabbit's nest, in the goodness of all things, of other boys and strawberries and the hills behind his home. He knew some words about the goodness, faraway words, for it was long ago, as long as death, as long as the Jordan and sunlight, but the words began to come back. "He maketh me to lie down in green pastures . . . in green pastures . . . Surely goodness and mercy . . . all the days of my life . . ."

It had happened long ago, but it had come back.

III

When I left the cave that evening, the moon had not yet risen, but there was a blurred glow in the sky and the stars were beginning to show against the blue. The frogs had begun booming a heavy background for the indeterminate treble of the crickets. The air was warm and sweet.

As I picked my way toward the upper pool, I felt vaguely uneasy. George was really sick, so sick that even when I told him about Elaine and her promise to show the King, he took no interest in the matter. His face was swollen, and he was running a fever. In the firelight, as I looked at him when I was leaving, his eyes seemed on fire and his face was drawn and haggard. We should have to leave in the morning, there was no doubt of that, and I wondered how he would ever be able to make the trip. I had given him dionol to quiet his nerves and a teaspoonful of spirits of niter to break his fever, but how much they would help I did not know.

I circled the laurel thicket and skirted a grove of pines that grew back from the stream. The ground beneath them was soft underfoot. A rabbit bounced away in front of me, his white tail bobbing in the dark. In the distance an owl shrilled and another answered. Everything seemed still and expectant, as though the woods themselves had paused to await the coming of moonlight.

It was a strange journey we had been on, I thought, everything about it, from Solomon croaking in the dark cabin to my last attempt to see the King. All day I had been thinking of the screams I had heard in the morning and of the hard pathos in Elaine's voice when she talked of them. Her father's brother was weak. That was why he suffered. There was nothing else to do about it, and, of course, there was nothing wrong. But I could still hear those agonized screams.

Ahead of me and to the left, I caught a glimmer of the upper pool. I came down from the pine grove and made my way through the low laurels. Up there, they were not so thick, and I had no difficulty getting through. I saw the large rock at the head of the pool and went to it. It was about ten feet from the edge of the water. I climbed on it and waited for the moon.

In the east, the sky was growing lighter, and a few wisps of cloud had already caught the light of the moon. They looked ghostly and white. The stream flowed smoothly in the pool, patches of froth floating in gentle curves. The water, I thought, must be very deep. I peered into it but could see nothing. A moth fluttered close to the surface, dipped its wings. Momentarily, I found myself expecting a rise from the mysterious fish, but the moth rose a few inches higher and zigzagged across to the other shore.

Though there was not a breath of wind, the air was not close. Near me, a katydid repeated his two notes with monotonous regularity. I tried to locate him, but no matter in what direction I moved, he seemed to be ahead of me or to the right or left or behind me. There were dancing reflections in the pool, and when I looked up, there, over the edge of the mountain, was the rim of a moon, a rich, clear yellow, almost orange. I watched it climb with perceptible motion, watched its lower rim clear the mountain, watched it rise above the lowest trees, and on, like a copper penny, into the sky.

As it rose, the night noises increased in volume — crickets, katydids, the distant hooting of owls, occasional flutterings in the trees above, and strange scratching sounds as mice, raccoons, rabbits, foxes, and a hundred other inhabitants of the woods began their moonlight search for food. The stream, too, seemed to come to life. In places it shimmered with brightness; in spots, shadows drifted across it; and from along the shore came the sound of splashing and of little feet as mink, otter, and weasel began to stir.

Leaves rustled behind me. I turned, but, half blinded with the moon, I could see nothing. The rustling continued, close to me, then slowly moved away. After a time, I heard a few pitiful chirps, frightened and half smothered, and I knew what had caused the rustling in the leaves — a black snake in search of his evening meal. The sound of a bird trapped by a snake is the most pitiful sound of the woods. It is plaintive and helpless, the struggle lost before begun, but the end takes a long time. I tried not to think about it.

A golden moonpath shone across the pool and ended in the darkness of the laurel on the other side. I looked deeply into the water. This was the home of the King, the realm of the trout I had heard about since childhood. It seemed incredible that I was to see him this very night, for that I should see him I never doubted. There were no flashing lights from silver sides, but deep in the pool a white rock shimmered, a white rock or a stretch of sand, I could not tell which. On the floor, grasses and water weed seemed to waver, but perhaps they were only shadows.

To look at water in the moonlight, to look at it intently and for a long time, is actually painful. You strain your eyes even when you are looking for nothing. You twist your head to get small objects into the moonpath, and then try to determine how far away they are from you; but you can never tell, for moonlight on water annihilates distance and perspective. Moths flash into the light for a moment and disappear. You look for them but seldom see them again. A bat whirs close to your head, and you turn quickly. You can almost hear each separate beat of its leather wings. You imagine you can see the red spots above its eyes. You see it blur across the moon, which is now high and round, lighter in color than when it rose. The stars have faded. No matter where you look or what you think of, your eyes and thoughts come back to the moonlight. Sometimes you try to forget about it, to ignore it, but a sliver of light takes you off guard and you are back to it again, straining your eyes against your will.

I do not know how long I had been sitting there when I heard the sound of her moccasin on the rock. Though it startled me, I did not turn around. She sat down beside me. For a long time she said nothing, and I stole a glance at her. She was dressed in blue, the same blue I had seen, days before, glimmering from behind low hemlock boughs, on the edges of rhododendron tangles, in out-of-the-way places where shadows lurked. Her hair was bright and misty, and the beads on her moccasins glittered. She was looking out across the pool, her arms wrapped about her knees. The ring on her finger sparkled. Sitting there, she seemed to become part of the mystery and permanence that hung about us, part of the eternal secret of the earth.

"It *is* beautiful," she said, almost regretfully, as though she might never look upon it again. "That is what you were thinking, is it not? As beautiful as men and women could be, sometime will be."

"Yes," I said, "it is strange and lovely. Everything is tonight. I have been sitting here a long time, just looking. And now you are here to make it complete."

"If you look at it long enough," she answered, "you think you almost possess it. You cannot really possess it, though, for it possesses you. In a way, there is not much difference, for we are part of it, and so possess ourselves."

"When I was looking into the pool," I said, "I saw a white rock on the bottom, or white sand."

"It is white sand," she said. "In the spring and fall you cannot see it. Only in summer when the water is clear and there are no leaves on the bottom. When I was a little girl, I thought it was gold and silver. Now I know it is more. I still have a dish of it at home. I have had it a long time. When I let it run through my fingers, it feels clean and bright and hard. I cannot crush it even when I put it between my two thumbnails and grind it. It scars my nails, but I cannot crush it."

I heard a soft thump behind me and turned around, but I could see nothing.

"It is the black toad," she said. "I heard him, too. He lives under this rock. Sometimes on bright nights he comes up here to catch insects. If you do not disturb him, he will stay. He will even come up close to you. He is friendly and very old. Once he followed me all the way to our house, but that is a long journey for him."

I could see a black lump, then, on the rock, though I could not have told that it was a toad. It was quite motionless.

"Is there anything in these woods," I asked, "with which you are not personally acquainted? You speak of them all as though they were members of your family."

"But they are," she said. "We are friends with all things. They do our bidding. It will be hard to leave them."

"Leave them? You are not going away? Not soon?" As I spoke, I was surprised at my own agitation. Was it the loneliness of the woods and water, the loneliness of hour after hour on the stream, that had made me depend so upon her presence, or was it something more impelling and necessary, out of life and death, and the living and the dying of it?

"Yes, I think my father and I will go away soon. It seems best. But someday we will return. It will be the seventh spring, I think. Yes, in the seventh spring, I will be here again, and we shall search for each other and find each other, for you will be here too."

"But you have lived here most of your life. Why would you leave it now, after all this time? Unless, of course, you must."

"It seems best," she said, hesitantly. "But we love it so. I should like to tell you where we are going, but I am not sure. I am sorry to disappoint you. I do not want to leave. Oh, I do not want to leave you. I am glad you came here — to go fishing. It has been good, for both of us."

She was rocking slowly back and forth, her hair shimmering

in the moonlight. She looked beautiful and unreal. Beside her, something moved. It was black and formless, a tremendous creature with drooping white throat. He sat, unconcerned, not more than a yard away from her. If she noticed him, she did not seem to.

"When will you leave?" I asked. The finality of the question shocked me, and the old memories crowded into my mind. Astolat had been so near.

"I do not know for certain," she was saying. "Perhaps tomorrow, perhaps not. It will be hard to go, to leave them all. I have a squirrel with a broken leg. If I leave, he will die. He will be killed. Then there are the birds. They, too, will miss me. Will you?"

She rubbed a brown hand across her forehead, the ring making a green streak. "I should like to tell you more," she continued, without waiting for an answer, "but I cannot. You would not understand. There are many things you do not understand, things that are bright and almost terrible. My father can do things other people only dream of. That is why they do not want him in the world. He makes them feel uncomfortable and inferior. He frightens them, and fear is the one thing dreadful. That is why my father's brother . . ." She stopped.

I remembered the screams that came through the morning sunlight. Tonight it seemed that nothing could be hurt. Then I remembered a bright blade hanging from an old man's belt, and I remembered the smothered chirping of the bird.

"The weak perish," she went on. "It is glorious because it is the law. In the world, they try to forget the law, but it is still the law, earth's law, nature's law, of death and life. That is why my father and I are unconcerned about it. But we shall be sorry to go. I wanted to stay so much, but my father thought it best to go. He said that sometime we should come back, in the seventh spring, perhaps, back to the cardinals and little creatures, to the owls, and the King, and you. It will be hard to leave, so hard, but it is best. I have more than a bushel of sunflower seeds. I am going to leave them outside the door."

I could have touched her with my hand, she was so close, yet we were worlds apart and centuries and all the distance of the stars. She was still swaying back and forth, her hair cloudy in the moonlight, the side of her face in shadow, but chin, lips, nose, and forehead in bright outline. The toad opened his wide mouth and gulped. The toes of her moccasins rose and fell as she swayed. They shot out little spears of colored light.

"Have you looked into the pool, here, close to the edge?" she said. She had lowered her voice until it was almost a whisper.

I looked quickly. The pool was like a mirror except for crisping ripples of light. It was hard to see the bottom of the stream because of the reflections, but I looked hard into it.

"Not now," she said, "but soon. Keep looking. The King is there. Shortly he will begin moving. Not now, but soon, and you must watch, keep on watching until you see him. I want you to see him, to see the King. You will remember him always with me."

"I am looking," I said in a low voice.

"Look, keep on looking," she answered, "and do not speak. I can speak, for he is not afraid of my voice. I have known him a long time. I have seen him often, in April when the willow buds were yellow, in November when the water was brown like old grass, in winter when there was ice on the edge of the water, but the best time is in moonlight. Moonlight is a good time."

I had heard those words before, many times, but they had come from a croaking old voice. Now I was hearing them again from a voice gentle and low as wind at the foot of a hill. It was bewildering and unreal.

I kept staring into the pool, though the brightness hurt my eyes.

"You will see him tonight," she was saying as she rocked slowly back and forth. "You will see him soon. Do not be alarmed when I leave you. Do not move when I go. Keep looking for the King and you will see him. But you must see him alone. With glory, it is always so. To know the King, you must be alone, alone and cold. You must feel like the last man left on earth and the last night almost over. That is why I must leave you. I should like to stay here, touching your hand or hair, feeling the pulse of your body, while you look upon the King. Then you would remember me, forever, so. But I must not. Do not look for me tonight. Do not look to see which way I go."

"You cannot go," I cried. "You must not." The stream mumbled in my ears, loud and confused, and there was a higher note, like the flute song, sharp and clean, like the sound of high wind in winter. I felt dizzy.

"When I go, you will not see me for a long time. But there will come a seventh spring, and we shall meet again. I shall love you then as I do now, as you do me, in the seventh spring, in the spring of heaven. Now, look for the King. He is at the head of the pool. He is coming down, now, now. Good-by." She put something into my hand, kissed my lips, and fled.

Though I heard her go, I did not see her. At that instant, there was a great flash in the water, a broad streak, a shadow on fire. It swirled as it came to the shore and sent up a shower of spray. Ahead of it fled another trout, skimming the surface of the water, but the inexorable shadow flashed behind it. The whole pool was on fire, moonlight sparkling on the waves, and the great trout shining red under water.

This was the King, King of the legend, beautiful, unbelievable. I could see him clearly now, lying on the bottom of the pool over the white sand. The sand was clean and bright. I could see it as though above it was no water. Sand of childhood, sand that could not be crushed between fingers, moonlight made tangible, home of the King and of hopes come back. Through my mind flashed disconnected thoughts, images, moods. A soft voice, gentle as dusk, telling of things strange and beautiful, telling of songs that come in the night, of sunrise and sunset, of wood moss and the scent of hemlock, of clear water and deep nights, nights that are filled with the shadows of things true, true and everlasting, living in the pulse of man, in the heat of a rock, in a vision of fire beneath water.

Where are the still waters that all men seek? In a pool, luminous in moonlight, in the touch of a hand, in lips upon lips, in the sound of a voice heard no more, in a moth wavering across the moon, in wind over mountains, in a quest of no ending, of no ending before death or after. But if there were an ending, she would be there, she, and the girl with the pony, and a stone that turned into a rabbit, there in the place of still waters and wind overhead.

In the wind, in the place of still waters and fast, is the singing of voices gone, of hopes long vanished, of David and Walton, of a dream by a blackberry bush, of Bach and a man in Cremona, of a voice that choked. It is the singing of earth and of crickets and a melody, and somewhere, far off, is the song that is never heard again, and it is man wandering down ages with a torn hand and forlorn, and a dog that limped with bleeding teats, and a dead owl, and a rusted shotgun. It is an old fishing rod and a boy with a pole and a man who left one night and did not come back. All the lost causes are there, all the lost hopes, and the heart of man is on fire, burning, singing, singing of hatred and love and desperation and a girl with a pony and a little dog that was loved.

They are all there, in the singing of the wind over still waters and fast, of the wind at night, at night when there is no sorrow or joy so deep as the earth's, the earth's that bleeds and is barren, is barren of youth, is cut by the loggers that die in the dust of their axes, is earth in the old twilight, is all that matters, is life and breath, is God and still waters, still, still, and sad. Does the locust crawl along the bark of the maple? Is the lichen red at the tip? Is there a man on the earth, or only a bird dipping in the dark, in the dark of music, of death and life, of the earth? Somewhere there is singing, and the song is life and death and hope and the earth.

In the shadows on the other side of the pool, the fiery sweep of the square-tail had died. I stood up, for I had lost sight of him. Somewhere among the laurel roots, he must have been struggling still with the captured trout. I did not care. I had seen the King, had felt a mystery I had searched for since childhood.

My head ached and my hands were numb. When I opened my right fist, there was blood on the palm and running down my fingers. From the blood I picked out something small. I held it up against the moon. It was a green drake, I thought, badly tattered, but I stuck it in the lining of my hat.

Standing on the rock, cold in the moonlight, I thought again of George, and I knew that I could never tell him. In this world, even anglers do not always believe stories of trout that feed at moonlight and turn a pool into dazzling streaks. There are other things they do not believe, too, but faith is still the substance of things hoped for, the evidence of things unseen. Some stories one keeps to himself.

But occasionally, in these barren days of eight-inch trout with no color, I meet an old-timer, an old lumberman from the second growth; and when he tells me in broken sentences of the time he saw the King, I say nothing. The truth is in his eyes. I notice the green drake in the lining of his hat. When he sees that I believe though I have said nothing, his eyes light up and he says, "Ah, you have seen him too, I think," and we are friends thereafter.

Perfidia

Dana S. Lamb

Spring, that year, came slowly to our valley but it came exceeding fine. There were two pairs of bluebirds in our apple orchard and more orioles than ever before swung their cradles from the swaying branches of the elms. The maple leaves burst joyously from their buds to shade the nesting robins and the catbirds and the wrens sang their simple songs in the lush-blooming lilacs by the kitchen door.

It was good to be alive; to be fifteen and catcher on the Wolfville baseball team. It was good, too, to have Uncle Ken's old Thomas rod and Hardy reel and Mother's Easter present of a brand-new line from Orvis over in Manchester, and a stout gut leader and a spare and half a dozen bucktails — the same kind, Dad said, they used down on the Esopus.

Spring was particularly fine down by the river where the violets vied in loveliness with the swamp iris and the scent of mint was strong and sweet. The river held trout galore; not the brilliant little brookies of the millpond, but big brown and yellow busters — some of them two pounders or better. And though they were suspicious of shadow or motion and easily put to flight by the trembling of the bank under the tread of incautious booted feet they were less chary of a well-worked streamer fly than of the worms dunked by other local fishermen.

Thus, though I was far from a star on the local nine and owed my position rather to lack of competition than to heavy hitting, I soon was recognized as the most successful fisherman in the village. "That kid," they said, "can catch them where they ain't." This should have satisfied a carefree country boy, but for two reasons it did not. The first was Holly Finch who seemed somewhat indifferent to the obvious fact that I was head over heels in love with her. Holly was just my age; the most beautiful girl in the junior class — senior too for that matter. The second was Old Mose, the biggest brown trout in the whole North Branch, who since nearly wrecking Uncle Ken's rod when he hung me up under Slant Rock had disdained all my offerings.

Somehow the two were in my mind and heart bound up together. Always when I sought to catch Old Mose I thought of Holly. Often when I sat on Holly's porch I thought and sometimes talked about Old Mose. As a matter of fact they were not far apart. From Holly's front gate you could look downstream and see the pool where Old Mose lived, blasé and hard-bitten. But no one knew this and I was resolved that no one should.

Equally distant upstream and on the other side of the river was the finest house in town, the home of Baxter Rogers. Baxter, going on eighteen, was away at boarding school, but in the Finch dwelling he was not out of mind. I'd seen with pangs of desperate jealousy the eagerness with which Holly awaited at the Post Office in Smith's general store the letters postmarked Andover. I'd been almost rude when Mrs. Finch asked if I weren't excited at the news that Baxter had passed his entrance examinations for Cornell.

Neither a lucky home run in the final game against Antwerp nor the sartorial splendor of a new Sunday suit served to arouse in Holly an awareness of the merits of her adoring classmate. Soon Baxter would be home for the summer and the competition for her favor — already keen — would become formidable indeed. Desperate measures were in order and I was resolved to shoot the works. I would take her fishing for Old Mose.

Every trout fisherman knows that a champion must cover his tracks if he expects to remain a champion. If he confides in just one friend or goes directly to his secret places he will never fish alone again and his favorite holes will soon be fished out.

When I went after Old Mose I drove Dad's Model T across the bridge in the center of town and took the river road to the old Schoolhouse Pool where I hid the car in a grove of pines. Until I was certain that no one was watching I fished from the shallows at the head of the pool and then, if the coast was clear, I'd wade across and take a deer trail downstream through the woods. This trail led around the town until, by the graveyard, it crossed the road to Pawley. Here, for fifty yards, you might be seen from the road, but if you carried your rod low and horizontal it was hidden by the stone wall and the only time I'd been noticed by a passing neighbor I'd dropped the rod and pretended I was looking for wild strawberries. Once across the road the trail led on to Basket Brook which in turn flowed down on the east side of Holly's house to Old Mose's private pool.

It took some time for me to summon sufficient courage to ask Holly to go fishing with me for this particular fish since it must have been obvious to her that an offer to share Old Mose was the equivalent of a declaration of undying love. I stammered badly when I did. I told her that if we didn't catch him his location must remain forever a secret except for just us two. For a girl Holly was quite interested in trout fishing and although she said she couldn't wade across the river or walk way up the hill to the graveyard she did agree to saunter down the road and, if unseen, to slip into the protecting copse of alders that guarded Slant Rock and to wait there for me.

I made certain she'd have but little time to wait by running the full two miles from the Schoolhouse Pool to Slant Rock and although she failed to heed my warning against quick movement or showing herself too close to the water, so that my hope for making contact with Old Mose was dim, it was nevertheless well worth the effort. The intoxicating excitement of standing very close and guiding her arm as she cast, being alone together by the river, and sharing as we parted a great and wonderful secret were more than ample compensations for an empty creel. I lived for the moment when we would again fish together in secret. I extracted a promise from Holly to fish with me again the following Saturday.

This time we planned to throw outsiders off the scent by taking our lunch and fishing here and there without regard to Old Mose until well after sunset. But when I reached the Finch house to keep our appointment I was unpleasantly surprised to see a shiny new Pathfinder parked by the woodshed. Baxter had arrived. He and Holly came across the lawn to greet me, Holly bubbling with excitement. "What a wonderful surprise," she said. "Baxter's just as interested in fly fishing as you are and I've asked him to come with us today."

"Dry fly fishing," Baxter said.

He said he'd just been fishing with his uncle at his club in Pennsylvania and he wore an outfit such as I had never seen before: waisthigh waders, a wading jacket fancy enough to wear to the school dance, hobnailed brogues, a landing net, a wicker creel, and in his hand he held the most beautiful fishing rod I'd ever seen, a four-ounce Payne.

I was not pleased by the sight; less so by the prospect of his company for a full day on the river. Nevertheless we started out and I was distressed to observe how well Baxter could cast, how gently and naturally his fly floated downstream toward him and that he seemed to know just where to place it. Evidently Holly noticed too for she showed great interest in his method comparing it, no doubt favorably, with mine. This grew and I determined to put an end to what was becoming an ever more painful performance. I said I'd just remembered that I had promised Dad to help him do some work on the barn. I said I'd get my lunch at home and they could have my share of the sandwiches. I left and spent a mournful afternoon.

Before dusk I sneaked up to the graveyard and took my secret path down toward Old Mose. I prayed hard as I walked along that this time I might have luck and, with a really mammoth fish, show up this stuckup college boy. I approached the pool cautiously but I never reached it. Sitting on Slant Rock holding hands were Holly and Baxter and at their feet, although the light was now becoming dim, I saw Old Mose, all four pounds of him, glistening in the light of the rising moon.

The Sun Stood Still

Arthur R. Macdougall, Jr.

It was past sundown, and a moment to twilight. A spell of lazy light moved over the lake, while a distilling tint of yellow passed in the west.

The sense of well-being that follows the satisfaction of hunger possessed me. If the calm on Dud's lean and kindly face was evidence, the same sense of tranquillity dwelt in him. And as for our guest, Dick Lord, he had been unrestrained the livelong day in declaring his continual pleasure. The cup — the angler's cup — was full to the brim.

I stood up to light a lamp. Its yellow light softly invaded the log camp. And outside, the ancient quiet of the night possessed the world.

Dick Lord slid down a bit in the chair he occupied, and wiggled the toes inside the sock on his right foot. "I presume," he said, "that each of us has some eventful fishing trip that stands out in his memory, a day, to borrow from the King James Version, when the sun stood still. I hope that I shall not sound like a schoolteacher assigning topics for discussion, but I do wish that Dud would tell us about the day's fishing that comes back to him most often in memory."

Dud smiled. "That's a big order, young feller. 'Fraid my memory ain't that selective. I've done consid'able fishin' in my time, fust an' last When I begun, we useter hoss 'em in on a stiff pole. The idea was to get as many as yer c'ud as quick as possible. The trout was as plentiful as good wishes at a wedding. That's all I remember erbout the fishin' in them days — the bounty of the wilderness.

"Since them days, I have fished more waters than I can rec'lect, offhand. I've caught, an' seen catched, some really *big* trout — the best one was a 'leven-pounder who had lived a long time on the fat of the land. I've been elated, an' I've been pooched. I have been blessed, and I've been practically frozen to death. I have hooked an' netted three trout at the cast — I mean, that I had 'em on from start to finish, an' that they struck so near at a time that I c'udn't have told which was fust. An' I have lost trout so large that I never fergot them, an' the pervokin' sense of defeat is with me yit.

"And now yer want me to name the top day out of all these years! Wel-el, b'crotch, I'll go yer. The day an' its fishin' took place no more 'n eight miles above our town on the old Kennebec. I was born beside it, an' I love it above all the rivers God uses to fill the sea. This partic'lar day, I know that I never did see more trout, size fer size, in one place.

"Tell the good truth, the trout fishin' is only soso on the Kennebec, becuz the log drives plow an' scour the life out of one of the best trout rivers in the world. How it happens that thar are any trout left I d'know, unless we have the hundreds of lakes, ponds, bogs, an' streams that feed it to thank.

"Anyhow, the time I'm thinkin' erbout was jist before an' durin' a thunderstorm. Now Mak is beginnin' to rec'lect. At least, I sh'ud be surprised if he has fergotten that afternoon."

"Do you mean above the Gut, below the Ed Berry place?" I asked.

Dud nodded. "That's it. An' I mean that I never saw anythin' to beat that show in all my life. When I got home that night, I told Nancy that I bet heaven an' hell was one an' the same place. Nancy said fer me to go on bettin', and I'd be apt to find that thar was a clean-cut distinction. Anyhow, if Mak an' me sh'ud fish until we're a hundred, we w'ud never see the beat of that ag'in."

"How many fish did you get?" asked Dick.

"They was *trout,*" replied Dud. "I can't remember how many we caught."

"Five," I said, for the whole event was coming back to me.

"Did we?" asked Dud, indifferently. "I c'udn't have told to save a winter's pay, but I know that it all happened quick, an' that lightnin' struck twice — once up on Pleasant Ridge an' ag'in over in back of us. . . . Say, Mak, what ever did become of that feller, what's his name?"

"But there's something I don't get," interrupted Dick. "It has always been my experience that fish will not rise in a thunderstorm."

Dud chuckled. "Thunder an' lightin' usually bother," he conceded. "I've seen the time when they was comin' good, an' a little bluff of a storm 'ud blow up to ruin the fishin' fer the rest of the day. Most always a low glass is thumbs down on a fisherman. But I have known exceptions among thunderstorms. To tell the truth, if I knew all erbout fishin' fer trout, I w'ud give it up an' tackle sunthin' more int'resting.

"And my advice w'ud be that if yer happened to be fishin' when Gabriel blows his horn, to keep right on fishing. The trout might begin to rise that very min-it. But why don't yer git Mak to tell erbout this special fishing? He'll remember it, becuz that was the time he busted off short the best rod he ever owned."

"How? Big trout?" asked Dick.

"No. He stepped on it hisself. Say, Mak, the more I think on it, the more I want to tell this yarn myself. Um . . . how the years come an' go. . . . Before a man can hit 'em, they're in kingdom come. So a man's motto sh'ud be, Go fishin' *now!* An' then go later on, if yer get the chance. Let's see, what was that feller's name, Mak?"

"McComick."

"Aya, that was his name. Seein' as how he was a friend of Mak's, he was prob'ly Scotch."

"He was not."

"No? Crotch, this yarn starts uphill, don't it? Wel-el, this man McComick come up to visit Mak. It was in August, becuz I 'member that I warned 'em that at sech a season thar warn't much use to go fishin' anywhere, an' less in the river. However, I finally agreed to go. But by crotch, when I met Mrs. McComick, I felt like backin' out. Anybudy c'ud see that she didn't favor fishin' much.

"They had a brand-new car that was almost as long as a string of hoss sheds, an' she was seated in front.

" 'How d'yer do?' she asks me, when she was interduced.

" 'Fair to middling,' I says, but of course I knew she didn't care a durn. Her face showed that she was one of them persons who don't take no int'rest in anythin' but their own comforts.

"When Mak started to git in the back seat, she took one look at his old boots an' britches, an' says, 'Spread that robe out over the cushion.'

" 'Thanks,' says Mak, 'but we won't need it, this weather.'

"She ignored that. 'Spread it out on the seat,' she says. 'It's the one we use fer the dog.'

"Maybe yer don't know it, Dick, but this feller Mak can be danged perverse, if he feels that way. So he c'udn't understand. 'Where is the dog?' he says, lookin' over the back of the front seat. I took the robe an' spread it out over the cushion.

"Then we told McComick where to drive, an' started out. In them days, the old road ran close to the Kennebec. If a man didn't have better manners, he c'ud lean over an' spit in the river in some places. Now, that road is under Wyman Lake. The Dugway, as we called it, give Mrs. McComick the jitters. But I think she was the sort of person who w'ud kick erbout the road to Glory — and w'ud have turned back, most likely.

"Her husband was built like an elephant. His neck was wide an' short. Thar was three upholstered rolls on it, an' they got redder 'n redder as his wife talked. After a while he said a few words that was as red as his neck, but the lady never wavered.

If thar is anythin' in all the world tha's more uncomfortable than listenin' to somebudy else's family row, I'm glad that I have missed it, so far.

"Bineby we drew up opposite the Gut. Thar was a little field next the road, where folks landed logs sometimes. The Gut was a run of water off the main river, eround an island. It ran shallow an' fast by a p'int of intervale land an' then swung down to the river ag'in, like a kid that had run away from home an' was glad to git back. Once in a while we useter get some nice trout in the Gut. An' once I got a nice mess on the other side of the island in the main river. But it was off the p'int, in the main river, where we usually had the best fishing. On an' off, I've seen some nice trout thar.

"When we got out of McComick's car, we agreed that him an' Mak 'ud try the Gut, an' then wade over to the p'int, while I was to go up to the Berry place, which was erbout a fourth of a mile up the road. I was to fish down the river until I met them at the p'int.

"McComick suggested that his wife w'ud drive me up thar, but I said not to bother — an' she didn't. When I was leaving, she spoke up an' said that it was surely goin' to rain. An' although Mak said sunthin' optimistic, I agreed with the lady. It was goin' to rain.

"However, the water in the river was jist right. Thar had been a head earlier in the day, but the river was back to a normal pitch. I started out 'ith wet flies, but somehow they didn't raise a trout. Thar was a queer run of natural flies on the water. They was erbout number sixteen, an' all of a reddish brown. The strangest part was that they all seemed to be dead. An' they was floatin' high and dry. I was puzzled becuz I c'udn't figger where they all come from. Evidently from up the river somewheres. Near as I observed, thar warn't a single fish, all the way down to the p'int, that paid attention to the naturals. An' nary a one did I raise to my flies.

"Consequently. I warn't long goin' from the Berry place to the p'int. Now, remember that fer a ways above the p'int thar was several oak trees. At the head of that stretch at 'bout the fust oak, the water ran fast over some big rocks an' through a couple of turn-in-and-out pools. Right thar them brownish flies was uncommon plentiful. They was comin' down at a fast clip. An' it was thar that I noticed the fust signs of trout. In fact I hooked two little fellers erbout ten inches long.

"Thinks I to myself, 'Might's well keep them, becuz it is goin' to be scant fishing,' as Doc Brownin' said, the time a feller offered him a bunch of skunk skins fer services rendered. An' it was while I was bent over unhookin' the second trout that one of them wide-open blasts of thunder let go, like a crack of doom. I warn't exactly surprised, becuz it had been grumblin' up on Pleasant Ridge fer ten min-its er more. But I *was* taken 'back when that woman of McComick's opened up. The river makes a lot of noise in a place like that, but the yell she let out of her carried like the report of a ten-gauge gun.

" '*Harry! Harry!*' she screams.

"Crotch, yer w'ud have thought she had been hit, until it come to yer that she c'udn't make so much noise if she had been struck. I looked down the river an' see McComick drop his duffle an' dust out of thar as fast as a man wearin' rubber boots c'ud run. I reeled up an' went down thar, becuz I figgered we'd prob'ly be leaving, if we went back to town 'ith the McComicks. But Mak was castin' as if thar hadn't been any thunder er commotion.

" 'Guess the lady was scared,' I says to Mak.

"Mak looked up, an' it was the fust notice he'd taken of me bein' thar. 'Dud' he says, 'this river is full of trout, old codgers!' And then he went back to castin' ag'in, like mad.

"Crotch, when I looked at the water erlong thar, I see that it was full of feedin' trout. It's likely thar warn't a million, but they was thick as hens on a roost, an' big fellers. They laid thar in two er three feet of water, takin' them brown flies as they come down to them.

"Jerusalum! It really looked like all the trout in the Kennebec had congregated in that place. Fust ye'd see a big, flat-sided cuss roll up. Then Mak w'ud cast in the boil. Next, maybe twenty feet up, er out, another 'ud rise, an' Mak w'ud switch to him. By jumpin' horn pout, it was some performance. An' I was jist so long as it took me to wade out erbout gittin' in on it, myself.

"I fergot all erbout the McComicks. An' Mak had never remembered them at all. But it didn't do me any good to join that party. A man might jist as well have been castin' in a haymow. Them trout simply w'udn't look at a wet fly. But don't think that we stopped trying!

"Purty soon a trout that was five pounds old sprung up out of the water, and says, 'Hello, hayseeds!' And I reckon that was too much fer Mak, becuz he reeled in his line, an' stumbled ashore.

"Out of the corner of my eye, I see him goin' through that old duck's-back huntin' coat of his'n that holds half a ton of stuff. After he had pulled out a fistful of last year's shotgun shells, a tin cup, and an old felt hat — in fact, erbout everythin' but a prayer book — he hauled out a little box erbout four inches square.

" 'Dud,' he shouts, 'come in here.'

"When I got thar, he says, 'Now pick out a dry fly that looks like those naturals.'

"All the time we was gittin' fixed up 'ith lighter leaders an' them dry flies, the thunder got louder an' the sky blacker. When we begun to fish ag'in, the rain come. It came at us in a straight wall, like ye've seen it sometimes. An' it come at us so evenly that yer w'ud have thought the devil hisself was drivin' a sprin-'klin cart at us. At a hundred feet away, the river was a-pelt with big drops, but thar warn't a sprinkle touchin' us. Then it hit. At sech times a man knows that all this talk erbout controllin' nature is nothin' but danged foolishness.

"I had made a few cast b'fore the rain hit us. When it got thar, it sunk that fly like a stick of pulp in white water. I was disap-p'inted, but when I started to lift the line, I felt a big, wide trout take that fly from underneath. Crotch, one of them size sixteen hooks gits lost in a real trout's mouth. I don't use number eight shot fer ducks, and I don't plan to use number sixteen hooks fer really big trout — not when I'm doin' the choosing. But of course, jist at that moment thar warn't nothin' as per *my* specifications.

"When I set that hook, it took hold good, an' that trout rolled over as mad as a skunk at a tea party. So I let him run until he had taken practically all my line out inter the river, an' then I tried to turn him, while he was rollin' crossways of the current. Wel-el, thar's some things we jist can't do, although it may be up to a man to try.

"That give me a chance to git the rainwater out of my eyes. I made out that Mak was also fast to a heavy trout. His line was slicin' the water like a knife drawn through a sour-milk cheese. Up an' down it went, until finally Mak got him back in near shore where I c'ud git the landin' net under him. That trout was mighty beautiful in that wild half light. A trout is purty in any light. An' they're firm an' pink-meated inside, which gives the lie to that old sayin' that beauty is only skin deep.

"Wel-el, what a spell of weather we had after that! When the wind an' the rain had passed over us, it looked like it might clear up, so we waded out ag'in. But that was jist a lull before the decks was cleared fer action, an' in a min-it the heavens turned loose a broadside that rumbled an' roared an' exploded like all hell was on a drunk. Once thar was a crack of white-hot light, as wide as a door, that run from the top of the universe to the bottom. An' either I had some wet matches in my pockets, er I actually smelled brimstone.

"Three er four times it looked like a hand that we c'udn't see had cut a slit a hundred miles long in the black sky. An' them slits let through the most uncomfortable yeller light a man ever see. Then streaks of lightnin' w'ud go dodgin' down the sky like a three-legged rabbit in front of a bowlegged hound."

Dud paused. And Dick asked, "Do you mean to say that the trout were rising in all that inferno?"

"No, no. I don't say that. I really don't know what them trout was doin' jist then. Y'see, fer the fust time in my whole life I had lost all int'rest in fishin' fer trout. Mak an' me was lyin' down flat. That storm was a little too much fer a man to stand up under. The wind 'ud blow like a cyclone, an' then the rain 'ud come on by spells. An' the thunder never missed a cue, by crotch!

"Wel-el, that sort of passed. So we raised up an' begin to

wonder erbout them trout. We fixed on some more flies an' was jist goin' out and at it when McComick appeared. He was as wet as we was.

" 'My wife insists on going home,' he says.

" 'I don't blame her a bit,' says Mak, an' he waded out inter the river ag'in.

"Then, by crotch a-mighty, it came! A flash of light as white as a frog's belly. I can remember jist how Mak looked, out thar in the river up to his knees. I can remember jist how everythin' looked, an' I thought I was lookin' at it fer the last time. That crash beat anythin' that ever happened, I guess. It hit a big pine up on the hill, on our side of the river.

"Now a quarter of a mile is a quarter of a mile, but when it's that near to a charge of lightnin' like that 'un, it's only a hair. McComick had jist picked up his own rod and basket, preparatory to leaving, but they fell out of his hands like sunthin' he w'ud never need ag'in. An' his face looked as if his soul had left him an' was already six miles down the road. But almost always in a time like that, sunthin' earthly happens to bring a man eround. An' it did then.

"Har-ry!'

" 'That's my wife,' says McComick, lickin' his lips.

"It's funny how differently we react to this an' that. Mak had his arm comin' up to make a cast when that crack came. Guess it scared him so he paralyzed right in the act. When it was over, an' his senses come back, nothin' c'ud be more natural than that he sh'ud finish the cast."

Dud broke off, turning to me. "You tell this feller what happened after that cast was completed. He'll never believe me."

"A trout hit it," I said.

"A trout hit it," reiterated Dud, with his heavy eyebrows drawn down and his gray eyes daring Dick to question the statement.

Dick didn't indicate belief or disbelief. Dud went on with the story.

"Now I wish that yer c'ud believe that I had been all prepared to go home like a gentleman, when Mak made that automatic cast. But thar he was, fast to a trout ag'in. An' at that very second, I seen another boil within ten feet of the shore. McComick seen it, too, but he jist moaned, 'My wife insists —'

"I'm askin' yer ag'in. What c'ud I do? C'ud I leave Mak in sech a perilous situation? 'By crotch,' thinks I, 'she's your wife, not mine.'

"And I waded out with the landin' net. We got that fish. But thar was signs of some more. I dropped erbout forty feet of line up the river an' watched my fly — tried to watch it. *Blub!* she goes. An' the fun was on. That felt like the best fish yit. That is, that's what I thought, until I discovered it was better'n that. It run clean to the end of my line, but it warn't two min-its after that till I was pullin' slack line — so much of it that it got out of my left hand an' trailed down the river. Jericho! That trout had it in his head to visit more places than a president's secretary c'ud keep track of. Yer understand that all this was goin' on in fairly quick water, an' at the end of a guess-and-by-gosh leader. Wel-el, thar's an end to all important things — one end or another — an' at last, I got that trout so licked it didn't care how it looked floatin' eround.

"Mak got hold of his landin' net. When he tried to git that trout inside, two-thirds of it hung over. I mean that the small half was inside. An' that's the way we started fer the shore, an' we got along fine, until Mak slipped. He didn't go down but pitched forwards, an' kept goin' that way. That's how it come erbout that he walked on his nice rod, which he had left on the shore when he got ready to net my trout.

"But we got that old-timer where he c'ud only flop a little. An' then danged if the sun didn't try to come out. Yer might say, Dick, that it had been standin' still. But it c'udn't seem to make a full go of shinin' through them clouds. Everythin' looked like a circus grounds after the circus has gone.

"We admired that trout. Then, all of a sudden, Mak remembered his McComicks. 'Dud,' he says, 'how are we ever going to face that woman?'

"Crotch, it did look like we was up ag'inst sunthin' worse than the thunderstorm. But it had to be faced. So we went eround the p'int, waded across the little brook that come down the intervale, an' then climbed up the bank to the car. . . . Thar warn't no car.

"But thar sot McComick on a rock. 'She's gone,' he says, 'with the car.'

" 'Man, man,' says Mak, 'we're sorry about this. Why didn't you go with her?'

"And then McComick begun to laugh, an' how he laughed. 'She must have left,' he says, 'jist after the last crack.'

"Gosh, we felt purty mean, but jist then I see a car comin' down the road, an' I waved my arms as a sign of distress. The driver was Albert Clark, an' he took us in."

"You haven't finished that story," I said. "Why don't you tell Dick what *you* did with that big trout?"

"Aya! I weighed him. That's what I done, b'crotch. Nine pounds an' two ounces!"

"And then — " I prodded.

"And then, like a danged fool, I sent him to that Mrs. McComick, erlong with my apologies fer the thunderstorm, an' all thunderstorms, past an' future. Sunthin' had to be done — didn't it? I never did blame her a mite, except . . . well, crotch? She — well, thar was them trout a-jumping."

Dick gave way to a hilarious reaction, as though he could stand it no longer.

"Did she, ha, ha, did she ever forgive you fellows?"

"Aya. She had sense enough, after all, to see I was in bad comp'ny. She sent me a nice little note of thanks writ on paper that smelled like them Lotus Islands, which Nancy says is a wicked place."

John Monahan

Paul Hyde Bonner

When Greta first saw the old man, he was wobbling precariously, clinging to a long pole, a willow sapling which he had obviously cut to use as a staff against the surge of the current in the stream, his short fishing rod waving like a conductor's baton as he struggled to keep his balance. She ran down the bank and waded out to him as quickly as she could, being none too steady herself on the round, slippery rocks in that fast water. By the time she reached him he was back on balance, shuffling slowly forward, jabbing the sapling ahead of him to feel out the boulders and get a firm stance.

"Here, let me carry that," she said, taking the rusty metal casting rod from his left hand and clutching his elbow to help him. At least, that was her purpose, but the contact also helped her to keep her own balance.

The old man emitted a short grunt. "Seems like you need

help, too," he said, as her grip on his arm tightened when her foot edged around a large rock.

"There! Now the going's easy," she said, when they had reached the shallows. But the old man still edged forward slowly, feeling out each step after poking his staff until he had found a firm hold for it.

Greta took her first good look at him and was more surprised than ever that he had risked the thigh-deep current of midstream. He was really old. His shrunken face was lined and seamed like the skin of a cantaloupe, and his scrawny neck, protruding from a faded gray shirt, was hung with pendants of loose skin, like the neck of a tortoise. A mustache that might have been silver had it not been stained with tobacco and coffee to a disorderly brown hung scraggily over his mouth. His small, watery, colorless eyes peered through a pair of steel-rimmed spectacles. His clothes, except for his khaki-colored hipboots, were old too, threadbare and patched.

Greta noticed that he was wheezing from the exertion of fighting the stream. "Aren't you getting a little bit old to wade the Gallatin?" she asked.

He stopped and looked at her sternly, one clawlike hand gripping the willow staff. "Been fishin' this river since I was a ten-year-old, that makes nigh onto eighty years, and I ain't quittin' yet awhile." He examined her carefully from wading shoes to felt hat. "You're a dude, ain't you?" he asked.

Greta smiled at him, and she could smile prettily when she wanted to, which was not often of late. "Yes, I'm a dude — a dude from New York."

"Humph! Mighty far to come fishin'. I ain't never been no further than Billings, and that was more'n ten years ago."

They had reached the sandbar of the bank, which was shaded by a row of tall cottonwoods. Greta pointed to a white cottage set in an orchard of apple trees near the rusty iron bridge, about a hundred yards from where they were standing. "You live there?" she asked.

"No'm. My ranch is up yonder a piece." He waved towards the wheat fields that clung to the lower slopes of the Gallatin Range. " 'Bout every day I ride me down here an' fish. My son-in-law an' daughter, they run the ranch now that I'm too old to work much." He gave a dry cackle of a laugh. "They're welcome to it. Ranchin' ain't what it used to be. It's all farmin' around here now — plows an' tractors an' wheat an' hay. No place no more for a cattleman. I can recollect . . ." He stopped abruptly and looked again searchingly at Greta. "I thought dudes come here to go ridin' the trails up in the canyon. That's what most of the lady dudes does. I seen 'em time an' agin, a whole passel of 'em followin' along after some kid wrangler all dressed up like he knew how to cut out a steer. Mighty seldom you see womenfolks tryin' to fish this river. When they does, they usually has a man along to catch 'em if they falls in. Ain't you got no man?"

"Yes, I have," Greta answered factually, coldly. "He's upstream, above the bridge."

"Likes to fish alone, eh? Most men is that way."

"No, it's just that he doesn't like to fish with me. I'm not good enough, I guess. Where's your horse?"

"Up to the road by the bridge. You go on with your fishin'. I'm goin' to set here a mite an' rest my knees. That cold water gets 'em to achin'. Rheumatiz. Come on after I passed eighty." He walked over to where the turf bent over the sandbank and sat down, stretching his legs out in front of him carefully, as if the knee joints were rusted.

Greta followed him, laying his old casting rod down on the grass beside him. She noticed now that it was rigged with a worm and a heavy lead sinker. "Did you have any luck?" she asked.

"No'm, not this mornin'," he replied.

"Neither did I — only a couple of tiddlers that I threw back. Do you mind if I sit here with you?"

"Dirt's free. You kin do as you like. Where's your fish pole?"

She turned and pointed. "Leaning up against the willows there."

He followed her gaze, appraising the light, split-bamboo rod. "Fishin' with them flies, eh?"

"Dry flies. My husband says that's the only way to catch trout."

"You don't look like you was married. Is he the fella fishin' upstream.

"Yes, he's fishing with Mrs. Sullivan. She's our hostess out here. Maybe you know her, she owns that ranch on Deer Creek, up where the canyon begins."

The old man smiled, nodding his head as if an ancient thought had come to life. "I knowed her since she warn't no bigger'n an April lamb. Jelly they used to call her, 'cause she was always laughin' an' shakin'."

"They call her Johnny now."

"Yeah, I know. Jelly Monahan she was till she married, and danged if she warn't a dead spit of her grandpaw, havin' her own way, gettin' anything she set her heart on."

"Did you know old John Monahan?"

The old man took the willow staff that was lying beside him on the bank and broke it in two with a snap. "I worked for John Monahan for forty years. Ain't no one knowed him better'n I did, knowed how hard he was, hard like a rock, trustin' nobody, not even hisself. Like I say, if he wanted somethin', nothin', nobody would stand in his way till he got it. That's how he come to get all the land from the Gallatin to the Madison. Had the boys homesteadin' for him. Build 'em a cabin, then, when the title was theirn, he'd have 'em deed it to him for a quart of whiskey. But I ain't a drinkin' man, never was, an' that's how I come to own my own section. When he come to me to deed over that land, I handed him one hundred dollars for the cabin an' told him I was quittin' to run my own ranch. Lady, I'm tellin' you he was the maddest Irishman I ever seed. He'd a shot me right there on my own doorstep, only I pulled faster'n he did an' told him to git off my section an' stay off. For three years after that he done his best to run me out, rustled my sheep, burned my hay, but it didn't do no good. For every sheep he rustled, I rustled two of hisn, 'cause the boys warn't none too loyal to him, an' they kinda liked me for standin' up to him."

"Mrs. Sullivan says that her grandfather was fearless," Greta said.

"She's right. He warn't scared of nothin' but his own meanness. That's what killed him, I reckon. He couldn't stand me havin' that section, which he didn't need any more than Jelly Sullivan needs another husband."

"What makes you say that?"

The old man turned his head toward her, his watery eyes twinkling. "What's your name, lady?" he asked.

"Mrs. Livingston, Greta Livingston."

"Well, Greta, I'm gettin' on to ninety an' I seen enough to know when a person ain't happy. Has your man taken a fancy to Jelly Sullivan?"

"She's a wonderful fisherman and he likes that."

"So he sends you off to slap a fly around by yourself, catchin' little ones in the fast water while Jelly is gettin' the big rainbows, makin' him think she's the smartest gal in Montana."

"Maybe she is," Greta murmured.

"Yeah, she's smart all right, too danged smart, just like old John, an' pretty, too."

"You're not very encouraging, mister . . . What is *your* name, by the way?"

"Will. Will Cross. I was aimin' to warn you."

"That's not necessary."

The old man picked the hook off the bar of his casting reel and scraped off the bits of dead, shriveled worm. "He wouldn't rise to me this mornin'," he said, as if to himself. "Gettin' too smart, won't grab the hook the way he used to, jest nibbles off the ends as is wrigglin'. Mighty cute old brown, that one. As cute as old John Monahan."

"Is it your special trout?" Greta asked.

"Yes'm. I don't go foolin' around with them ignorant fish they throw in from the hatchery. I only go after the big ones. This one I was talkin' about, this John Monahan, he's real big, go nigh onto five pounds. I've had him on twicet, but each time he broke me. But I'll git him yet, leastwise, I will if you don't happen to take him."

Greta laughed bitterly. "No chance of that. I never catch anything but tiddlers. Besides, he's your fish and I wouldn't think of taking him from you."

"Would you take him if it would show your man you was as good as Jelly Sullivan?" Will Cross asked.

Greta could feel an involuntary flush on her cheeks and she was ashamed and annoyed. "I don't even know where he lies," she said.

"He wouldn't take no dry fly," the old man said speculatively. "He's a deep feeder as don't like to show hisself on the top. That's why he's took over the hole and chased all the other fish out."

"Then he's safe from me. All I have are dry flies."

"Lemme see the one you got on."

Greta got up, fetched her rod and brought it back, sitting down again on the bank beside Will Cross. She unhooked the fly from one of the guides and handed it to him, still attached to a leader tapered to 3X.

Will examined it carefully. "What kind of a thing do you call that?" he asked.

"Out here they call it an Irresistible, but in the East it's known as a Rat-Faced McDougal."

The old man burst into a cackle of laughter. "Ratface McDougal, eh? That's a right smart name for him. By gum, if we could get him down fur enough, I believe old John'd take a fancy to him."

"He floats like a feather," Greta said. "You can't sink him."

"Mebbe there's a way to get him under." Will reached into his trouser pocket and brought out an ancient clasp knife with a bone handle that was worn smooth and yellow. When he opened it the blade, which was six inches long, shone clean and bright. "Hand me one of them flat rocks," he commanded, pointing to the water's edge.

Greta slid down on the sand and brought him one of the wet stones. "What are you going to do with my fly?" she asked.

"Never you mind." He placed his big, pear-shaped sinker on the stone and slowly carved a small slice of soft lead from its side. Taking the slice in his grimy fingers he rolled it skillfully around Greta's leader, about a foot above the fly. When he had it wound to his satisfaction, he laid the leader on the rock and pounded the lead gently with the handle of his knife until it was tight enough to the nylon not to slip. "Now, if that gut of yourn will holt, you might have a chance for him," he said, handing the fly back to Greta.

"You know I'll never catch him, that's why you're doing this," she said.

"Looky here, Greta, I want you should catch him," the old man said sternly.

"Why?"

"Never you mind why."

"Because Johnny's a Monahan?"

"Because she is fishin' in water as ain't hers." He gripped her arm so hard that she could feel his fingers like little steel bands through her fishing jacket. "See over yonder where that dead cottonwood stump sticks out over the river? See where underneath it there's a deep hole of black water? That's where he's lyin', right down on the bottom, near the bank."

"If I cast in there, it will only frighten him. The water is as still as a pond."

"Listen to me. Don't go castin' into that hole. Stand up this side of it an' flop your line into the fast water, lettin' it float down by itself. The current there takes a kind of a curl, like a rope on a saddle horn. If you leave it, it'll curl itself right down to the bottom where he can see it."

"I've got to wade across the middle of the river to get there," Greta said apprehensively.

"If I kin do it, you kin in them high waders," the old man urged. "Tain't nothin' to it if you take it slow." He picked up the stouter half of the long willow stick he had broken in two. "Take this to steady yourself."

Greta, gazing at the rushing river, was still fearful. "If by some wild chance I did hook him, I'd never be able to land him standing in that torrent," she said.

"Don't go horsin' him like he was a calf on a rope. That's my trouble, I keep callin' him John an' jerkin' him so hard I bust the line. Just keep enough holt on him to let him know who's boss. Bein' a brown he'll head upstream, an' that'll tire him quicker than it would one of them rainbows what runs downstream an' jumps."

"You talk as if I could really hook him."

"I'm tellin' you, you durn well better if . . ."

"If I want to keep my husband," Greta finished the sentence for him, then laughed bitterly. "Well, there's no harm trying. But if I fall in, I'm going to blame you, Will Cross."

She picked up her rod and the willow stick and waded out into the stream. Will watched her as she moved cautiously into the fast water, feeling for each step, leaning her weight against the force of the stream. As he knew, the worst, the swiftest and deepest part was the first she would encounter. After that the river was less than knee-deep, flowing smoothly in a fast, but not violent, glide. He held his breath when he saw her wobble once, clinging to the willow staff, but she regained her balance, rising at last to the shallow glide where she stopped to rest before moving on.

I'll never be able to get back to that bank, she thought. Negotiating the rapids once was enough. Whatever happens I'll get out on the bank that's nearest me. She examined the water ahead, concluding that above the pool where the old man said the big brown lay it was shallow enough to reach the shore. She decided that she had been an idiot to fall into the old man's plot. To begin with, the story of the monster trout was probably senile imagination, and, furthermore, why should she, Greta Livingston, be a party to an old cowpuncher's revenge on the long-dead grandfather of Johnny Sullivan? Johnny was a swell girl and she had been inclined to like her from the very moment they had arrived at Deer Creek Ranch. It had not been Johnny's fault that Tim Sullivan, who had invited them to come out for three weeks of fishing and who had been a classmate of Bob's at Yale, had had to rush back to San Francisco on some important business deal.

She and Bob had heard three years before that Tim had scored a bullseye when he had married the rich, beautiful and talented Johnny Monahan. But they had not known then that one of her accomplishments was an exceptional ability to present a dry fly invitingly on the fast waters of a mountain stream. That was what had captivated Bob. Ever since they had arrived he had been singing the praises of her prowess as a fisherman until Greta thought that she might have to throw up. Then Tim had left and Bob had informed his wife politely but firmly that she would have to fish on her own, as she could not be expected to spoil the sport of professionals. That was all right by her, she liked being alone on a stream. It was the reunions at lunch and at quitting time that infuriated her, when Bob, his face beaming like a fifth form schoolboy, would say, "Look, Greta! Look at this lunker Johnny caught!" He never once had asked to see the little fish in *her* creel.

She was standing now, full of righteous wrath, at the spot where she could cast into the run above the pool. She turned to look back at the bank she had left. The old man was still sitting there watching her. He waved his arm in an impatient casting gesture. Okay, Will Cross, she said to herself, I'll cast where you told me to, but pray for that trout to take with all the might that's left in that old head of yours.

She got her feet set in a good, comfortable stance, stuck the willow staff under her jacket where she could hold it with her left elbow, and started to false cast. The lead on her leader threw her timing off, causing the fly to hit the fast water behind her. It was awkward, but she got enough line out to reach the run, then, stripping a few yards more for the float, she cast forward. The lead hit the water with a plop. The Rat-Faced McDougal floated barely a foot before it was dragged under. In the gin-clear water she could watch it running down over the rocks until it reached the lip of the deep, dark pool where it disappeared into the depths. Holding her rod horizontal, she let the loose line she had stripped run through the guides. The leader had been swallowed up in the pool, but the greased line floated out over the black surface, the end of it curling backward as it was pulled by the descending fly. The whirlpool he was talking about, she thought. Then the knot that held the leader jerked suddenly downward. Instinctively Greta came up sharply with her rod tip. It was a solid, firm hold that bent her rod as the line came taut. A log, she thought, the same log that old Will Cross has for years mistaken for a huge trout.

She released the pressure, hoping the line would float downstream so that she could pull the hook loose. But instead of floating down, the line shot forward and again she came up sharply with the rod tip. But this time the reel screeched as the line whipped out of the pool and up through the run. Her heart stopped. It was a trout, and a big one. Holding the rod high, she felt for the little button on the reel and tightened the drag. Her small rod was bent double, but the fish swam on against the roaring current and the pull of the line as if nothing was deterring him.

Taking a deep breath, Greta recited to herself all the lore she had learned from Bob and the old man; keep your left hand off the line; hold your rod vertical; don't horse him, let him take his own lead; don't reel unless he stops or swims towards you; keep the pressure on, but never too much; let him kill himself. The line was almost down to the backing when he slowed up. But Greta, intent now on landing that trout even if it took all day, was in no hurry to start reeling. She shot a quick glance across the stream, hoping for the old man's applause, but he had vanished. He never waited to see, thought I'd never hook him, she said to herself.

The trout continued to cruise slowly, crossing back and forth from one side of the stream to the other, sometimes letting the current drift him back, then quickly ascending again in a determined plunge, as if trying to reach the big rock that came out of the river halfway between Greta and the bridge. But the pull of the lengthening line was always enough to stop him before he reached his goal.

After twenty minutes Greta's arm was beginning to tire. From time to time she shifted the rod to her left hand in order to ease the aching muscles of her right arm, but she could never do it for long as she had to be instantly prepared to reel in when the trout turned. She had no idea of its size other than the pull of it, for it had bored deep, never once coming near the surface. If I could only once get his head out of water, she moaned to herself, forcing her aching muscles to push the rod higher against her chest. At that moment the trout let the current take him again and she had to reel madly to keep tension on the line. It came drifting down almost directly towards her. Maybe this is it, she thought, wondering how she could reach the net and still keep reeling.

When the fish came in sight of her, it lifted its tail out of water and rushed off into the middle of the stream. She saw it, the whole of it, and the sight made her heart stop again. It looked to her as big as the monsters mounted on the wall of the tackle shop in Bozeman. She almost cried with the pain in her arms, thinking that it would take at least another half hour for a fish as big as that to kill himself.

"You're doin' fine," the old man's voice called from the near bank. "Jest keep on like you was doin'. He's killin hisself fast now."

"Oh, God, I hope so!" she moaned. "He's not as tired as I am."

"It won't be long. He's about ready to quit."

The trout was thrashing on the surface now, flapping his great tail in a vain effort to keep his head down. Greta switched the rod to her left hand and reached down with her right to unhook the net from her creel.

"Never you mind that net," the old man called. "He'll never fit in that corral. Jest you ease him over to the bank here. We'll beach him."

Reeling slowly, keeping the rod tip high to force the trout's head out of water, Greta inched herself backwards towards the bank. She thought of getting out the willow staff to steady herself, but realized that it had vanished long ago, probably when the trout made its first dash. Then she felt the clawlike fingers of the old man holding her arm.

"Steady now," he said in her ear. "You ain't goin' to fall while I got holt of you."

"How did you get over to this side?" she asked breathlessly.

"When I seed you had him hooked, I come across the bridge."

The trout was in close now, lying on its side gasping, but still strong against the leader.

"Keep acomin' back till you're leanin' agin the bank," the old man said. "Then jest hold him. I ain't goin' to fool with him till he's kilt himself."

Greta did as she was told, and was grateful for the backrest of soft grass. The water in which she stood was only a foot deep and the trout was slowly swinging toward her, gasping and thrashing. When the leader was close to the rod tip, she stopped reeling, taking the rod in her left hand and stretching her right to get the kinks out of it. It seemed a full five minutes that she and Will Cross stood there silently, watching the great trout until it finally shivered and lay still.

"Ease him over to me," the old man whispered, as if afraid to frighten the fish. He squatted down on his haunches, putting his hands under the water so that the dying fish slid over them.

Before Greta could see what had happened he had the trout as far back on the bank as the leader would stretch and scrambled up after it on his knees. Greta followed him, pushing the rod before her. There was no need to give the fish the coup de grace. He was dead — huge and magnificent. They both knelt there on the grass looking at him for a long while.

"Well, you done it," the old man said finally, turning his eyes to Greta. "You done what I been tryin' to do for three years." He returned his gaze to the fish. "Like I said, he'll go to five pounds or more — fat as a valley heifer. Wait till your man sees him."

"He'll never believe that I caught him," Greta said sadly.

"He's goin' to have to, 'cause I ain't goin' to be here." He struggled to his feet, cut a forked stick from a willow bush and hooked it through the trout's gills. "Come on, I'll carry him for you. He wouldn't set in that little basket of yourn, not if you folded him double."

Together they walked up the path to the bridge where Johnny Sullivan's car was parked in the shade of the cottonwoods. Greta opened the rear trunk and, with the help of Will, they laid the trout carefully down on some newspapers and covered it with green leaves.

"When are Jelly and your man fixin' to meet you here?" Will asked.

Greta looked at her watch. It was half past twelve. "In about a half an hour," she said.

"Well, I'll be gittin'. Past my dinner time anyway."

"Can I help you with your horse?" Greta asked, wondering how the old man could ever mount alone.

"No'm. He's most as old as I am an' right steady." He laughed, cackling like an old hen. "I shore would like to be watchin' Jelly's face when she puts her eyes on that brown."

Greta stood in the road and watched him as he crossed the bridge and hobbled into the bushes on the far side, his short rod trailing in the dirt behind him, the bow of his thin legs accentuated by the tight hipboots. In a few minutes he reappeared on the road leading a chunky piebald pony. They stopped on the crown of the road and the pony stood like a statue while the old man hitched the rod to the saddle horn with a halter rope. When this was done, he put both hands under his left knee, lifting his leg slowly until his foot reached the stirrup, then, catching a lock of mane with his left hand and the crupper with his right, he pulled himself halfway up the pony's flank. With another hoist he got his knee on the rump. The third heave got him into the saddle. Then taking the reins deliberately he turned and waved to Greta before kicking the pony and starting up the road in a rolling lope.

Greta went back to the rear of the car to gaze incredulously at the fish she had caught. The whole circumstance seemed to her puzzling and slightly unreal, like something out of a fairy tale. Now that Will Cross had vanished on his steed, she wondered, smiling to herself, if he were not some legendary knight, disguised as an ancient cowhand, who had come to rescue her from the wiles of the blonde Princess Johnny. Perhaps it was all a dream resulting from her apprehensions. She lifted the branch of leaves and touched the trout. It was solid and cool and slimy, and its black disc spots seemed to wink at her, as if to say, "I'm real."

Greta, who had taken off her waders and put on a pair of beaded moccasins which Johnny had lent her, was sitting in the car reading *Phineas Redux* when she heard the voices of Bob and Johnny as they crossed the bridge. She could not distinguish the words, but the tone was gay, bantering. Like a pair of courting magpies, she thought, with a pleasant mixture of bitterness and triumph. She looked at her watch. It was a quarter past one and she had hunger pains as well as the ache in her arms. She closed the novel and stepped out of the car.

"Sorry if we're late," Bob said to her as he strode up to the car, beaming under his battered felt fishing hat. "Johnny got into a big one just as we were about to quit. Wait till you see it!"

Johnny Sullivan, who looked stunning in any costume, with her honey-blonde, waving hair, her trim figure and her china-blue eyes, was particularly fetching in khaki shorts and wading shoes to frame her tanned, graceful legs. "He only weighs a pound and three-quarters on Bob's scales," she said modestly.

"Here, let me show you Johnny's catch." Bob said enthusiastically, propping his rod against the bushes and taking Johnny's creel from her shoulder, which entailed putting his arms around her. As his wife made no move, he had to bring the creel to her where she stood beside the car.

"Hmm. Three nice fish," Greta said, glancing into the creel which Bob held under her nose. "What did you get them on?"

Johnny looked rather surprised at the question, for up to this moment Greta had shown little interest in fly patterns. "The two little cutthroats on an Adam and the big rainbow on a Wulff."

"I caught mine on a Rat-Faced McDougal," Greta said casually.

"So, you got a fish, did you?" Bob said. He was sitting on the grass pulling off his waders. "Good for you," he added patronizingly.

"I actually caught three, but I only kept one," Greta said.

"Good kid!" Bob said, full of well-being. He yanked the waders off, tossed them on the bush, and stood up in his stocking feet. "How's about an ice-cold Gibson? Any takers?"

"I've been waiting for one for three-quarters of an hour," Greta said.

"Coming up!" Bob sang and lifted the rear trunk cover of the car. His eyes caught sight of the leaves and his hand, reaching for the cocktail shaker, stopped in mid-air. "What the hell is this?" His hand descended, lifting up the branch. "God Almighty! Who killed that?" he yelled.

"That's the one I kept," Greta said. "Hurry up with that cocktail, I need it."

Bob stared at the trout as if hypnotized. "You actually caught that trout, Greta?" he said hoarsely, his voice trembling with amazement. "On that little three-ounce rod? With a 3X tip? It's a miracle! It's the greatest thing that's ever happened!"

Johnny Sullivan walked over to Bob's side, put an arm over his shoulders and looked at the trout. Her first glance was one of astonishment, but that changed to one of sober contemplation. Finally she turned slowly and looked at Greta. "Did you get him in that deep hole by the dead cottonwood?" she asked.

"Yes," Greta answered, still trying hard to appear casual about her triumph.

Johnny came over and put her arm through Greta's. "Then you got him, you got John Monahan," she said, in a tone which implied that it was a prodigious feat.

Bob pushed Johnny to one side and grabbed his wife. "You're a wonder, sweetie!" he said, hugging and kissing her.

When the outburst was over, Greta straightened her hair and said to Johnny, "Why did you call him John Monahan?"

"Because that's what old Will Cross calls him," Johnny answered. "He does it to tease me. Will's an old man who lives on a ranch back there." She pointed to the mountains. "He has tried to catch that trout for years, but never succeeded."

"What has your grandfather got to do with it?" Bob asked. He was holding the fish on his hand scales and straining to read the marker.

"Oh, that's a long story," Johnny replied, gazing at the great trout.

"Five pounds seven ounces!" Bob exclaimed. "I'm going to have him mounted."

"Oh, no you're not!" Greta said firmly. "I'm going to cook John Monahan myself, poach him and serve him cold in jelly."

Johnny shot her a quick, startled glance. "You win, Greta. He's yours, to do with as you like."

The Hunchback Trout

Richard Brautigan

The creek was made narrow by little green trees that grew too close together. The creek was like 12,845 telephone booths in a row with high Victorian ceilings and all the doors taken off and all the backs of the booths knocked out.

Sometimes when I went fishing in there, I felt just like a telephone repairman, even though I did not look like one. I was only a kid covered with fishing tackle, but in some strange way by going in there and catching a few trout, I kept the telephones in service. I was an asset to society.

It was pleasant work, but at times it made me uneasy. It could grow dark in there instantly when there were some clouds in the sky and they worked their way onto the sun. Then you almost needed candles to fish by, and foxfire in your reflexes.

Once I was in there when it started raining. It was dark and hot and steamy. I was of course on overtime. I had that going in my favor. I caught seven trout in fifteen minutes.

The trout in those telephone booths were good fellows. There were a lot of young cutthroat trout six to nine inches long, perfect pan size for local calls. Sometimes there were a few fellows, eleven inches or so — for the long distance calls.

I've always liked cutthroat trout. They put up a good fight, running against the bottom and then broad jumping. Under their throats they fly the orange banner of Jack the Ripper.

Also in the creek were a few stubborn rainbow trout, seldom heard from, but there all the same, like certified public accountants. I'd catch one every once in a while. They were fat and chunky, almost as wide as they were long. I've heard those trout called "squire" trout.

It used to take me about an hour to hitchhike to that creek. There was a river nearby. The river wasn't much. The creek was where I punched in. Leaving my card above the clock, I'd punch out again when it was time to go home.

I remember the afternoon I caught the hunchback trout.

A farmer gave me a ride in a truck. He picked me up at a traffic signal beside a bean field and he never said a word to me.

His stopping and picking me up and driving me down the road was as automatic a thing to him as closing the barn door, nothing need be said about it, but still I was in motion traveling thirty-five miles an hour down the road, watching houses and groves of trees go by, watching chickens and mailboxes enter and pass through my vision.

Then I did not see any houses for a while. "This is where I get out," I said.

The farmer nodded his head. The truck stopped.

"Thanks a lot," I said.

The farmer did not ruin his audition for the Metropolitan Opera by making a sound. He just nodded his head again. The truck started up. He was the original silent old farmer.

A little while later I was punching in at the creek. I put my card above the clock and went into that long tunnel of telephone booths.

I waded about seventy-three telephone booths in. I caught two trout in a little hole that was like a wagon wheel. It was one of my favorite holes, and always good for a trout or two.

I always like to think of that hole as a kind of pencil sharpener. I put my reflexes in and they came back out with a good point on them. Over a period of a couple of years, I must have caught fifty trout in that hole, though it was only as big as a wagon wheel.

I was fishing with salmon eggs and using a size 14 single egg hook on a pound and a quarter test tippet. The two trout lay in my creel covered entirely by green ferns, ferns made gentle and fragile by the damp walls of telephone booths.

The next good place was forty-five telephone booths in. The place was at the end of a run of gravel, brown and slippery with algae. The run of gravel dropped off and disappeared at a little shelf where there were some white rocks.

One of the rocks was kind of strange. It was a flat white rock. Off by itself from the other rocks, it reminded me of a white cat I had seen in my childhood.

The cat had fallen or been thrown off a high wooden sidewalk that went along the side of a hill in Tacoma, Washington. The cat was lying in a parking lot below.

The fall had not appreciably helped the thickness of the cat, and then a few people had parked their cars on the cat. Of course, that was a long time ago and the cars looked different from the way they look now.

You hardly see those cars anymore. They are the old cars. They have to get off the highway because they can't keep up.

That flat white rock off by itself from the other rocks reminded me of that dead cat come to lie there in the creek, among 12,845 telephone booths.

I threw out a salmon egg and let it drift down over that rock and WHAM! a good hit! and I had the fish on and it ran hard downstream, cutting at an angle and staying deep and really coming on hard, solid and uncompromising, and then the fish jumped and for a second I thought it was a frog. I'd never seen a fish like that before.

God-damn! What the hell!

The fish ran deep again and I could feel its life energy screaming back up the line to my hand. The line felt like sound. It was like an ambulance siren coming straight at me, red light flashing, and then going away again and then taking to the air and becoming an air-raid siren.

The fish jumped a few more times and it still looked like a frog, but it didn't have any legs. Then the fish grew tired and sloppy, and I swung and splashed it up the surface of the creek and into my net.

The fish was a twelve-inch rainbow trout with a huge hump on its back. A hunchback trout. The first I'd ever seen. The hump was probably due to an injury that occurred when the trout was young. Maybe a horse stepped on it or a tree fell over in a storm or its mother spawned where they were building a bridge.

There was a fine thing about that trout. I only wish I could have made a death mask of him. Not of his body though, but of his energy. I don't know if anyone would have understood his body. I put it in my creel.

Later in the afternoon when the telephone booths began to grow dark at the edges, I punched out of the creek and went home. I had that hunchback trout for dinner. Wrapped in corn-meal and fried in butter, its hump tasted sweet as the kisses of Esmeralda.

The English Exposure

Edward Weeks

At the end of the Second World War, when the new transatlantic planes made the flight to Europe so much more comfortably than the old flying boats, I planned on an annual visit to England to scout for articles and authors. Someone told me that the month of April has the highest incidence of sunlight in the British calendar, so I came then and stayed until early May, tasting their spring before I returned to ours. I took with me a trout rod, and a set of waders with heavy underwear which I checked in my London hotel at the end of each visit. This proved to be opportune, and in time the same rod went with me on speaking trips to California and on my "cultural" visits to the Soviet Union and to Yugoslavia.

Edward R. Hewitt, the Aristotle of American anglers, had a number of magnificent prejudices which, given an audience, he would proceed to harp on at length, and one of them was his distrust of the British diet, which in his view had in it more than enough starch to deplete the Empire-builders. Well, I confess I had my own troubles with the London menu, which left me feeling like a snake that had swallowed a tennis ball, but this surfeit was due to an excess of hospitality. When I arrived I was asked the traditional question by my friends in the publishing houses and literary agencies: "Are you here for pleasure or here to read?" I was there to read, and my wife too on many occasions and in no time our suite at the Stafford would be heaped with galley proofs and advance copies of English books still needing an American sponsor, and with shorter manuscripts for the *Atlantic* from diverse sources, also four daily newspapers and all the weeklies including *Punch*. For a visiting editor the London regime admits of at least five opportunities for the giving and receiving of food and drink: breakfast, lunch, tea, drinks (6:00–7:30 P.M.), and dinner or supper, either before or after the theater. The closer one comes to departure the more they all are utilized, and the impact on the digestive system is terrific.

I doubt I should have survived without the antidote of my fly rod. Each week from Monday on I was seeing people, talking, persuading, reading or listening until Friday afternoon when, talked out and jaded, I had thoughts only for the country, simple food, a stream and a comfortable friend who would not mind my distraction.

The first author to be my fishing companion was Geoffrey Household. Geoff is a master of suspense in fiction, and his many fine short stories which we featured in the *Atlantic* and novels such as *Rogue Male* and *Watcher in the Shadows* put him on a par with John Buchan and have all eventually been published in book form under the Atlantic–Little, Brown imprint. Although he has worked everywhere, as a bank clerk in Bucharest, selling ink in Latin America, as an infantry officer in Greece, and on mysterious missions in the Levant later in the war, Geoff is first and last a countryman whose ruddy complexion, trim figure, close-cropped mustache and general air of command are the portrait of a Brigadier. At war's end he, Ilona, his Hungarian-born wife, and their children went to live with Geoff's father in an old schoolhouse in Dorset, close by the Thomas Hardy country, and here while England was still on short rations we came to visit. From Canada I had air-mailed a rib roast and a steak timed for our arrival Easter weekend, and little Nyusi, the nine-year-old son who had never seen that much of a steer and had been told it was flying over from America, kept looking anxiously up in the sky for it to appear.

Fishing is not in Geoff's book but he had wangled permission for me to try his neighbor's brook on Saturday afternoon and he and Nyusi came along for the sport. There wasn't any. Green as I was to the habits of the brown trout, I fished all the wrong places, the open water instead of letting my fly ride over the dark submerged grass, and we came away with an empty creel. As we trudged home across the meadows, all thoughts of a trout supper gone glimmering, I can still hear Nyusi's little treble saying, "Papa, Mr. Weeks must be a wretched fisherman, not to catch even one." But in our absence the beef had arrived and I was excused.

Easter morning, and a cold one, we attended service and early afternoon when we set out for the river Piddle a cutting wind was blustering down from the north. Geoff had secured a two-day permission for me to fish Sir Ernest Debenham's waters lying — I remember the quaint wording — "between the village of Puddleton and the Chamberlain's boundary." We first paid our respects to Sir Ernest, an octogenarian, who made us welcome and presented me with a little blue permit book, stipulating among other things: "Dry fly only; no wading whatever; First Brace for the master; thereafter an even division until the limit of four brace have been taken." White-haired and hearty, he led me to the big window where from his couch he could see the lovely, curving course of the chalk stream, every pool of which held memories. "The fish should be in prime condition," he said. "A March Brown is all you need, and be sure to fish the center of the stream. My bailiff will show you to the good water. I wish I could join you!"

It was so cold the girls stayed in the car, but Geoff and Nyusi, with his bare legs, insisted on watching, huddled in the lee of some blackthorn. So, after a bit, did a young couple who stopped their motorbike near the bridge while I was netting. Things happened so fast that I fought the wind instinctively, changed flies only when the first became waterlogged, and in little over an hour when we were again at Sir Ernest's door, I asked the butler for a platter and on it presented to the master my largest trout, which was just under three pounds. "God bless us!" he said. "Your limit in that space of time!" and his delight was as warming as his sherry and the open fire.

From the Stafford Hotel it is but a few steps to St. James's, the street I most relish in London. Here is every delight but one to please the male: wine from Berry Brothers, whose cellars deep under the pavement were first reinforced to support the coronation coaches of Charles II; hats from Lock's, whose shop has been swept but otherwise unchanged from the days they were shaping a cocked hat for Lord Nelson; from Prunier's delectable bisque homard and Dover sole; from Webley's a fowling piece or rifle to match your build, and at the upper level, those clubs, Boodle's and White's, Brooks's and Pratt's, whose banter and decorum are a perpetual surprise to the American visitor. Around the lower end of St. James's on Pall Mall and across from the Palace is Hardy's Fishing. Hardy's is the cornucopia of English angling; the shop is run with a quiet air of authority and it has everything: the long rods the English prefer and need for their streams; flies from the tiniest, exquisitely tinted drys to the big Salmon flies for heavy water, as large as the bowl of a serving spoon but much more deadly; nets and leaders (in England "casts"), the latest word in fishing hats and waterproofs — everything, including good advice proffered by the clerks in their dark clothes required for town wear. One of the most considerate of them all was Mr. Beauchamp, who became my tutor.

I got him to pick out an assortment of dry flies such as he himself might use on the chalk streams and to write their names in his precise script in the little square on the inside cover of the fly box, and approximately in the order that I might need them as the day advanced, beginning with the Iron Blue and Gray Olive, passing on to Lunn's Particular ("Good anytime, that one, sir"), and coming down to the late evening flies, the Orange Sedge and the Houghton Ruby.

I could not spend every Easter with the Households, and since few of my publishing friends would be in their offices from Maundy Thursday until the Tuesday after, it seemed to me on my next trip that here was a heaven-sent opportunity for a fishing adventure on my own, and I asked Mr. Beauchamp where to go. He consulted the big ledger in which Hardy records the latest news from the most fishable streams from the north of Scotland to Land's End, and then recommended the River Tamar in South Devon. "The salmon should be running at this time of year," he said. "There are plenty of trout in those waters and if there's a room for you in the Arundel Arms, you will be comfortable indeed." I telephoned the inn to ask for reservations for four and then I telephoned my oldest friend in England, H. R. Creswick, with whom I had shared rooms in Great Court, Trinity, in 1922–1923. Dick as an undergraduate was interested in rare books which he purchased from Old David, the secondhand bookseller in the Market Place; it was a lifelong interest which led him on to be Director of the Bodleian, Oxford, and then for twenty years Director of the University Library, Cambridge, the only bookman in history to achieve both offices. We spoke the same language.

"Dick," I said, "I've got some trout fishing reserved for us down in Devon for the long Easter weekend. Do say you and Agnes can join us!"

He seemed slightly incredulous but willing, and in the upshot we joined them in Cambridge and motored down, pausing to pay our respects to the rustic beauty of Stratford and Broadway, and pausing again to stretch our legs and take early tea at Bath. Motoring with Dick is not an endless race as it is on our American throughways; the bookman in him keeps looking for signs of the past and in Bath we found them in the Roman remains which put me in mind of Kipling's story "A Centurion of the Thirtieth." ("Dick," I asked, "how do you think they reacted here when they heard that Rome had been sacked and that no more legions could be spared for Roman Britain?"); we also found something of the more graceful past in those immaculate crescents which we tried to people as in Beau Nash's day. With one thing and another we reached the Arundel Arms in the tiny hilly hamlet of Lifton barely in time for sherry and dinner.

This was my first experience at a fishing inn and I was much taken with it. The Arms and the water on the three streams it controlled were the property of a benign manufacturer of powdered milk; he liked fishing and reserved for himself certain salmon pools; he also liked eating, and his chef at the Inn had a reputation for roast chicken with skin that crackled, Yorkshire pudding as light as a popover and crème brulière of which Trinity College would be proud.

After a day on the Tamar and its tributaries the guests assembled to compare notes over drinks before dinner; the catch, brown trout and occasionally a salmon, were displayed on a vast platter (they would later be iced and sold by the inn), and after the meal, without apparent haste or greed, the anglers signed up in the Book for the beats they would fish on the morrow. You could not hold on, day after day — or even every second day — to the more desirable stretches; it was reasoned that those here for a long stay would have their share and that the brief-comers should be given fair chance. Threading his way through the banter and recitals was a quiet-spoken colonel (ret.) who supervised the fishing and had flies or boots for those in need. Dick and I turned to him for tips as the water was exceptionally high and we wanted to know where the trout would best respond to the dry fly ("The slow run behind the schoolhouse," he said) and where I should try my salmon rod. Dick was fishing only for trout.

For my first day I drew a rather deep stretch at such a distance from the inn that we took with us what the Colonel called "a packed lunch." Dick drove us to a little lane sunken between blackthorn in bloom which finally became so narrow the car couldn't pass; here he left us saying he'd be back at five o'clock, and I entered the stream by the small white stake which bounded my domain, with Fritzy, loaded with lunch and camera, trailing along above me on the bank. As we approached the railroad bridge there seemed to be a good shaded run close to the left: I inched my way, working up to the dark water under the bridge in short quartering casts; one moment I was wading waist-deep, the next there was nothing to tread on and I quietly, coldly submerged. Watching from above, Fritzy saw me sink until only my hat was above the surface; undecided, torn between the impulse to photograph and the apprehension that she might have to plunge in, she was relieved when the hat began to rise and I under it as my boots caught hold of the bottom the other side of a deep hole. Breathless and damp from the shoulders down I squelched up the bank. It was much too far to think of walking to the Inn in wet boots so I stripped, wrung out my heavies and let the April wind and what *The Times* in its forecasts refers to as "an occasional bright interval" dry me and my garments. The cows in the next meadow were unconcerned, there was no one else in sight and what with Fritzy's hoots and a nip of Scotch I was back in action in an hour and quite dry by noon. "I meant to warn you about that hole," said the Colonel when I told him that evening. "Actually there are two of them, made when the bridge was built — which did you choose?"

Dick got our best fish that year and a fine sight it was on the white platter. Time flies when spring days are as happy as ours at Lifton and I still smile over one incident which illustrates that English angling does not always run true to form. It was understood that an angler lucky enough to hook a salmon had the choice of bringing it to the net or beaching it but under no circumstances should he use the gaff, a stout pole with a sharp, wicked hook on the end. Among the guests were a sprinkling of officers who had retired after the war and the largest and ruddiest of whom we nicknamed "the General," as he may well have been. He was deferred to for his knowledge of the place and in his bland way he expected and received certain privileges. In my effort to lure a salmon I thought it sensible to follow his choice of beats and one morning as I was casting a pool in which the General said he had risen a salmon the day before I came on a weapon lying on the bank which brought me to a halt. It was certainly a gaff but an outsize one, more like a halberd that might have been borrowed from the Tower of London. Any fish, fighting for its life, impaled on this would soon expire. At day's end I brought the trophy home and showed it to the Colonel.

"Yes," he said, "it belongs to the General. I'd return it to him but perhaps not at drinks." When I did so, the great man said simply, "Thank you, my dear boy."

I set no records on the Tamar; I think my finest moment came on the run behind the schoolhouse when at dusk, with the Colonel watching, some veteran trout, to judge by the size of the rings, began feeding hardly a foot from the opposite shore. I was well below them but my problem was complicated by the giant beech on either bank whose branches almost interlocked overhead: I had to make a sidearm cast to keep my fly out of the branches but with enough length so that it would drop above the rings, short of the bank, and drift languidly downstream. After some thirty false casts this happened: the little Orange Sedge rode placidly six inches from the bank; there was a roil, I waited, then cocked my wrist, felt the strength of the fish, and the leader broke. "Well done!" said the Colonel. "You had him well hooked. He was a good fish. Too bad."

What I began to learn in Devon — from the Colonel, if not from the General — was the etiquette of British angling. I was impressed by the respect which the Colonel and the guests both had for the beats they were fishing. There were no bottles or tin cans carelessly tossed into the stream, no fragments of a picnic shoved under a bush. I don't mean the riverbanks were manicured, simply that they were left in a state of nature. I was impressed by the absence of competition when the time came to select one's fishing for the next day. There must be fish hogs in England as there are in America, but I did not chance to meet them at the Arundel Arms. Finally, I was impressed by the nicety, even the elegance with which these people dressed for their fishing. Not for them the Sloppy Joe hats and greasy lumber shirts in which we throw off the tedium of business. The English in their hats, tweed jackets and waterproofs are professionally trim.

There is something to be said for the innocence of the eager. When I gave Mr. Beauchamp a grateful report of our trip to the Tamar I went on to ask whether there wasn't a trout stream closer to London which I might fish for a day or two at a time, the Test, for instance?

He looked at me gravely, "You're asking for the best chalk stream in Britain," he said. "But because you're an American they might just make an exception for you. Call up Miss Kay Potts at Leckford and throw yourself on her mercy." I did so only to be told that they were booked solid through June; then her voice relented, "If you care to come down for a single afternoon and evening on April nineteenth," she said, "I can put you on beat five. But I must warn you that the farmers will then be cutting the banks and the river will be heavy with vegetation." I blessed her for the chance and on the morning of the nineteenth took the two-hour train trip to Andover and a cross-country taxi to that glorious valley in Hampshire which is today the most cultivated school of fishing in the world. The pools I was being admitted to were directly upstream from those of the famous Houghton Club.

I checked in at the Leckford Abbas, bolted down a slice of fruit cake with my tea, said hello to Miss Potts, who was cordial and direct in her welcome as she told me where Mr. Mott, the head keeper, would meet me on the stream, and in my Wellingtons, down I clumped to beat five, a bundle of anticipation. The afternoon was cold and overcast, the downriver wind strong in my face and the water looked like the floating gardens of Babylon. The farmers had indeed been cutting and the problem was to drop a fly in the clear spaces between the drifting brush when a trout was rising. My beat consisted of a broad deep stretch of the Test and angling off from it some narrow, shallow canals known as "carriers."

"You're standing rather close to the water," said the quiet voice of Mr. Mott, a tall lean countryman with fine eyes, in his gray tweeds and cap, a friendly advisor I was to depend on in days to come. We shook hands, he looked approvingly at the Blue Upright which I had on my line and with disgust at the clotted stream. "When the river's clear," he said, "we stand or kneel well back of the bank so the fish won't see us. That means a high retrieve to keep the fly out of the rushes behind you — which is why we favor the longer rod." Then he stood by watching and I became more and more inept, as one does in the face of an expert. "Be sure to fish the carriers before dusk," he cautioned, with just a hint of encouragement before he turned away. When he had departed and I was convinced that this was one day the fish could not see me, I not only returned to the edge, I ran along it, dapping my fly in any available opening. Twice, at dusk, I had a fish on — but not for long. That was my first day.

I was, of course, being looked over and my eagerness if not my skill may have tipped the balance, for Miss Potts seemed genuinely sorry that she had no other beat to offer when I paid my fee the following morning. "Well," I said, facetiously, "I shall be praying that one of your members will sprain an ankle while I am still in London. If that does happen, Miss Potts, will you please be sure to telephone me? I shall be praying hard." That was on a Tuesday and on Friday morning a call came through. One of the partners had gone off to the hospital for a checkup, releasing four days the first week in May. They were at my disposal. Conscience forbade my taking all, so I compromised on two, beat eight for my first day and number three for my second.

The conditions which were awaiting me a fortnight later were quite different and more difficult. On my first morning as I crossed over the little railroad bridge that led to the top of my beat I paused to savor my surroundings. The Test as it approaches the village of Stockbridge is a quick, deep stream rarely wider than forty yards; it is controlled by a system of weirs which keep the depth constant and the water tumbling with life, while breaking off from the main current are the narrow carriers, some as straight as a canal, others curving away for half a mile through shaded banks before they rejoin, forming succulent pools at their reentry. On this particular day the windows of the sun as they opened through the high clouds lit up the whole valley in different planes, the landmarks, the white chalk cliff, the beechwoods, the steeple at Longstock being now in sunlight, now in shadow. Ahead of me was the little thatched hut in which I would park my sandwiches and raingear, and beside the bridge waiting to greet me, Mr. Mott.

I had that blissful feeling of trout impending and the whole day ahead. Looking upstream Mr. Mott pointed to some of the hot spots: the deceptive quiet stretch to the right of the great willow, and the fine pools to the right and left of the point of the island, formed by the carrier; then turning about he studied the turbulent water below the bridge: "There are some very strong fish in this pool," he said. "See, there's one feeding now!" (Peering at the sunpoints dancing on the fast water I could distinguish nothing.) "But it's not easy to fish — you have but a second or two before the fly is drowned. Best save it till dusk when the big ones drift down to the quiet end."

On my own I started up the left bank toward the willow where I could see a fish coming regularly to the surface. The hatch was on, flies were in the air and on the water, and I thought my Blue Upright a fair replica. The river was clear as a martini and the banks, now cut, were so damp and tremulous that even at three feet from the brink my tread sent fish arrowing into midstream. Brown trout seldom move far from their favorite lair unless fright sends them but once startled it will be some time before they resume their feeding ground. From then on I picked my way at the base of the high grass which seemed to have grown a foot in my absence.

By now fish were feeding up and downstream. I saw the big one by the willow, his green and silver perpendicular beauty as he rose close to the bank for my fly — and then saw me, or rather the drag in my line, and turned away. I was learning that the largest fish survive in the Test because they grow wary and because it is so darned difficult for duffers like myself to keep a fly from dragging or drowning in that powerful current. I began looking for more protected pockets.

The hatch is short-lived in the spring and I thought I was beginning to see a new batch, flies of a yellowish hue, so I changed to a Gray Olive and had three good strikes in the next twenty minutes, each one of which I missed.

Mr. Mott, who has the eyes of a falcon, had been watching from afar and now came up. "You've been striking too soon, Mr. Weeks," he said. "These browns are more deliberate than your brook trout. You have to wait until they take the fly and go down. We say to ourselves: 'God Save the Queen!' and then strike. Now let me show you. You're using the right fly."

And show me he did. He pulled up his boots and he got me down on my knees and since my Wellingtons were short and the banks very wet I was soon soaked (yes, three days of stiff rheumatism were worth the cost). From his kneeling position he took the line off the water with a steeple cast, then snaked it out straight as a rule above a feeding fish; the fly drifted slowly, was sucked under and — "God — Save — the — Queen!" — he cocked his wrist and the trout was on. Together we took a pair, his, the first, going over two pounds. I have always thought that the striking of a fish was the most delicately timed act in angling. Now I was watching a master working with a rhythm and restraint I had still to acquire.

Sometime towards three o'clock the river quieted down and I retired to my hut to a chicken sandwich washed down with tea and an apple — but with the door open so that I should know as soon as a new hatch reanimated the stream. Boots off, toes flexing. I wondered what to use in the afternoon light — Lunn's Particular? Greenwell's Glory? Certainly a Houghton Ruby on the pool below the bridge.

But my feeling when the fish began feeding again at five was of abundance and futility. All about me was an abundance of strong and challenging trout and such was their cunning there was little I could do to lure them. At the top of the island was a rowboat moored to the bank and close to the gunwale a fish was making large rings, but I despaired of reaching him from below for the wind either blew my fly into the cockpit of the boat or too far to the left. "In my country," I explained to Mr. Mott, who had rejoined me, "I should go above him and drift the fly down."

"Oh, that wouldn't do, sir; Miss Potts wouldn't like it," he commented. "The Test is for upstream dry fly only."

I had my reprieve at dusk when the cuckoo was calling, and when I took another two-pounder on the Ruby at the tail of the pool. Lightheaded and pleased with myself — I had been on the water nine hours — I left the fish lying in the net after having put the priest to him, and wandered along the bank, false casting to dry my fly. There was a small commotion in the carrier to my right; I tiptoed up and let the fly drop; there was an explosion and from the feel I was into something bigger, with my net hopelessly beyond reach. We played each other up and down the narrow stream until my neighbor from the beat below chanced by on his way home and rescued me. "But you really should carry your net," he admonished as he weighed my prize, "otherwise you may find it rather awkward."

The two brace that day were beginner's luck and on my return visits I have never done better. Back home in Boston I told all this to Ferris Greenslet, whose fishing expeditions were coming to an end, adding for his editorial approval that when my two days were over I drove on to Oxford, presenting one brace of trout to John Masefield at Abingdon and the other to Sir Isaiah Berlin. That Christmas Ferris gave me a copy of the English classic *A Summer on the Test* by John Waller Hills and this wise and leisurely book with its lovely plates by Norman Wilkinson deepened my appreciation of a river where the artificial fly was fished upstream by men who might have seen and talked to Shakespeare, and where in early times lines made especially for fly fishing were tapered down to a single horsehair. "How," Mr. Hills writes, "would you like to kill a four-pounder on a single horsehair with no reel?"

On subsequent visits it pleased me to think that I was on a stream men had loved and struggled with for centuries, where Sir Humphry Davy cast his fly, where Landseer and Turner fished and then sketched for the Houghton Club journal their favorite pools, where Palmerston, Lord Grey, Andrew Lang and even perhaps Izaak Walton may have felt a little of the futility that was mine. Thus far my longest stay at Leckford has been two days and a half and always in early spring but a man may dream and mine is to have a week on the Test when the mayflies are hatching.

In my exuberance on the Test I am often treading my beat before the first hatch of flies has brought any fish to the surface and it took many defeats before I learned that the wise trout will be frightened down by any one of several warnings in the brightness of noon: by the flash of the rod or by the angler's shadow close to the bank, or by awkward casting which produces a drag in the line or sends the leader like a gleaming arrow across the fish's window. The magic hour comes with the dusk when there may be such an abundance of flies that the water almost seems to boil with the avidity of the feeding fish. The old and crafty angler will take advantage of this. I observed a retired colonel, rather gimpy in the leg, who conserved his strength for the fading light. He made his first appearance after tea when with his landing net as a cane he would pace his beat, not softly but stamping his heels at the water's edge. This had the effect of driving out the fish that had been loitering under the bank; he would mark the location of the larger and return to the lodge for his early supper and when he reappeared with his rod and evening flies of a large enough pattern for him to see he netted as fine trout in ninety minutes of this gloaming as we who had been at it all day.

I was never introduced to this character who lived to himself and his memories as some anglers prefer to do. The habitués at Leckford who went out of their way to befriend me were Miss Charyl-Hinton of the peaches-and-cream complexion and Captain Dunlop, a hearty veteran of the First World War. She was the most graceful dry fly caster of her sex I have ever watched, she had fished the Test since childhood as a companion to her father, himself an expert, and proposals of which she must have had dozens did not lure her from the river. The largest trout in our fridge were invariably those she had netted. Captain Dunlop was an exemplar of English hospitality: if I had no car, which was usually the case, he would drive me to my beat before he went off to his own and would of course pick me up when dark fell; he made up the deficits in my fly box with flies he had tied himself and he gave me invaluable tips. "You'll be fishing beat 11" he would remark. "Lovely water, lovely water and the swans won't bother you. The bigger fish come from the reeds directly across from the hut and they won't show till the evening. Then put on a Houghton Ruby and don't fret, my dear boy, if it sinks a little. They sometimes like it that way."

Beat 11 is at some distance across the valley from the lodge and it offers the widest variety: very fast water holding some stout rainbows, a long stretch through the water meadows that must be fished from far back and the wide swan's bay opposite the hut which I purposely saved till the last. It fell out as the Captain predicted: in deepening dusk I put on a Houghton Ruby and when, to be honest, it had become a little waterlogged I felt the strong down pull of a heavy fish, and set the hook. I couldn't move him. With my rod bent double I got below him, to add the current to my persuasion, but he had gone to grass and his hold on it and his weight made him immovable, though I could feel his bulling. I thumped the butt of the rod against my palm, which sometimes gives shivers to a sullen fish, but not to this one. And then came the Captain's horn tooting for me to join him on the road at the top of the ridge. I didn't want to call; fish are sensitive to sound and it might make this one strain the harder. Again a long note from the horn. "Coming!" I shouted, involuntarily. "Coming." It would be such a triumph for both of us if I could bring this big boy to the net. But I mustn't keep the Captain waiting; slowly I forced the bowed rod above my shoulders. Would he come up? Would the fly hold? . . . No. The sudden slackness told the story and I reeled in.

My visits to Leckford, never for more than forty-eight hours, always presented me with something memorable: now it would be the high bank above the drive with masses of cream and yellow daffodils, now at dusk the elastic colloquy of whippoorwills across the valley; once on a warm bright day when I had fished too long in rubber pants I was seized with cramps in both legs and lay writhing on the meadow till they passed, and again, the moment when knowing I could not be in England when the mayflies came I decided to experiment with one prematurely — and was happily surprised when a good trout came up for it greedily and was hooked. I even encouraged my English authors to work with me at the lodge on their manuscripts, and on my desk in Boston is a photograph in color of my favorite beat sent me for Christmas by Joan Bright Astley. How it invites the mind.

One Sunday evening as I was on my way back to Andover and the City I asked the driver about the upper reaches we were then passing — was the fishing here as good as at Stockbridge.

"Oh, no, sir, the stream hereabouts is filthy and polluted." "The Test?" I said, incredulously. "Yes, sir." By such a narrow margin does even the greatest river survive.

Much of the best fishing in Britain is in private hands and the pleasure of staying in a well-served country house and visiting the family pools at will has been repeatedly conferred upon me by two Conservative Members of Parliament, long good friends of each other who came to be good friends of mine. Sir Frederic Bennett, the younger of the two, has his favorite domains at opposite ends of the islands which suits his temperament as he loves to be in motion: his nine-gun castle at Kingswear, built in the fourteenth century to command the entrance to the River Dart, is his seat in his constituency, which embraces Torquay and Dartmouth, whereas his country estate Cwm which he hungers for in recess is far to the north, high in the Welsh hills. Freddy has the powerful legs and torso of a sprinter, which he was in school; he is one of the best shots of his generation and with his gun and his beloved Labrador, Twist, he could spend all day on the Welsh moors and never tire. He is an impulsive, warm-hearted collector, of guns, dogs, houses, rare birds, and of motors each one faster than the last — but not of fish. The little lake at Cwm which he assures me he stocks for my benefit (and that of his nephew David) is apt to be glacial and windswept when I am there in April and like most non-anglers Freddy soon grows impatient; whether he is rowing me or accompanying me to the water of a friend his attitude becomes that of a mother forcibly feeding Junior some spinach: the trout are there and it is plainly willful of me not to heave them in without all this dither, fly-changing and delay. The fish know this: "Old Fred is above," they say. "Let's skulk and annoy him," and they send a boy to do a man's job.

There may be a good hatch of flies at Cwm in the heat of July but I am never there to see. When I push out on that rhododendron-bordered pond the trees are not yet in leaf and the surface, slightly warmer than ice, is disturbed only by the wind from the Arctic. In the distant past Fred's father, a member of Lloyd George's cabinet, stocked Cwm with brown trout and rainbow which, it is assumed, have grown to great size. Pointing out the spot where little David last summer "caught a really good trout on a worm," Fred shoves me away in the canoe and with irrepressible energy goes forth to feed the peacocks, Canada geese, and jungle fowl, to build a fox-proof pen for the Muscovy ducklings or to discuss with his farmer the possibility of liberating on the wildest down his small herd of Bagot goats.

It is my private suspicion that in this forty-degree water with so little feed of any kind, the fish shrivel, but I go about my business, casting a March Brown into the shallows where the vinegar sunlight may have attracted a little life, knowing full well that two hours later I shall be summoned with "God's teeth, nothing but that tiddley? What *have* you been doing! Well, come on up and have some tea with my mother." And seated on the floor, boots off, reaching now for the warmth of the coal fire, now for the plum cake, I shall have this solace from Lady Bennett: "Freddy's father couldn't catch them either; it used to make him *so* annoyed!"

(Actually — a word the English employed with special emphasis — the trout did shrink. After years unnumbered a sudden violent hurricane burst the dam at the outlet and the nine million gallons of water and its contents surged down the valley, into the river Angle, and thence in the tumultuous Dovey. Within the fortnight the natives were capturing strange fish with monstrous heads, which an expert identified as rainbows, whose skulls but not whose bodies had grown during the decades, gaunt souvenirs of the elder Sir Frederic's planting.)

I was saved from total defeat by Freddie's neighbor Ralph Beaumont, who had converted two tarns for his own amusement: into the small blue bowls of mountain water on the very crest of the tawny downs he had introduced grass and brown trout; there was not a tree or bush to grant protection and here on one noon picnic, under leaden clouds and a northeaster that cut to the bone, we had to form the traditional British square to preserve any warmth in the women and children in the center. But on clear eves when the wind had dropped Rafe and I had good sport, using a black Zulu, and returned with enough for a full platter. For Freddy, loving his heritage as he does, it is a grievance that I come so early, two months before the sea trout begin to fill the pools of the Dart and the Dovey. By late June, he swears, Edwards, his eighty-year-old-gillie, and I could catch them with our hats; yes, but by then the Atlantic salmon are coming upstream in eastern Canada, and that is the closer call.

But as I have already told, it is quite a different story in Hampshire where my other cordial host, Sir Hugh M. Lucas-Tooth, has his unique estate, on the Avon, one of that noble trio of rivers, the Test, the Ichon, and the Avon, all of which empty into the Southampton estuary. In 1945, looking for a place not too far from London — two and a half hours, by road — where Laeta, his wife, could garden and he could fish or shoot on weekends, they found their heart's desire at Fordingbridge. I call it a water house for it stands as close to the river as the banks allow and the sound of water rushing through the weir is music to my ears. The foundations of the house are very old and the weirs themselves are weathered and immemorial. There may have been a dwelling here in Roman times; the Romans were fond of fish and oysters, indeed it was the discovery of a mass of oyster shells plowed up by a nearby farmer that led to the excavation of a large-scale Roman villa.

Sir Hugh can never tell when the salmon will arrive: he has killed a thirty-four-pounder on March 4, yet a year later no fish appeared until early May when he killed two each day he fished until the run was through. The run is a short one, some fish lingering on to spawn in his waters, most after a day or so moving on to the redds upstream. The take on his five pools, which are twenty miles in from the sea, varies with the height of the water and those I have hooked in the early spring hang in the Upper Weir Pool, at the point of suction where the water surges through, or down and around the corner in Willow Run where they lie close to the undercut bank or right across the stream where a large fly so eagerly clings to the brambles on the bank. In a good year Hugh and his guests will account for forty fish; a more moderate run yields twenty-five, and he apologizes for the fact that my largest was only twenty-three pounds.

Lady Laeta has a green thumb and her flowerbeds flourish, daffodils and grape hyacinth, bordering the paths to the water's edge. It is not uncommon to watch from her guest bedroom a salmon indolently disporting in the slack water of her rock garden.

Hugh is an erect and sandy Scot; he tops me by four inches and it is always a surprise, considering his breadth of shoulder, to find that his extra pair of fishing trousers have a tighter waist than mine. Whether he is fishing a Golden Sprat with his greenheart rod or casting a fly with his fourteen-footer of cane, from the first cast to the final gaffing he is an angler alone. He will tolerate no gillie here and watching him dominate his fish is a picture and a lesson in competence. "You must dominate your fish!" he calls to me as I come scrambling after mine, and remembering how he does I try to imitate.

When the salmon are gone and the river is down he wades upstream dry flying for the brown trout; his log shows an average of just under three pounds with a few going above six. In June with his cousins he fishes the prime salmon rivers in Scotland, including the Dee and the Spey; grouse shooting calls him in August and when Parliament convenes in the autumn he goes down to Fordingbridge for the weekends for the ducks that will be flying till January. Not a bad calendar.

There are times, especially in his lowest pool at the tip of the woods, where the wading is sticky, when Hugh has his hands full. Laeta, a Scot herself, tells it with her mischievous smile. "Hugh was very late so I went to find him and there he was down by the trees, mucking about, saying that he'd had the beastly fish on for almost an hour and he didn't know how much more of this he could take. 'I have my garden shears,' I said. 'Shall I cut the line?' That seemed to fetch them both."

The Fisherman

Martin Armstrong

The road, diving downwards off the bridge, slid away to the left; but tucked into a low recess on the right, so that it looked down upon the river and up at the high, foreshortened mass of the bridge, the George Inn opened its comfortable, L-shaped front, thick with climbing greenery. Behind it a flourishing kitchen garden stood embanked above the river to which steps descended under a canopy of ancient elm trees.

Michael Dunne, having finished his breakfast, appeared in the doorway and stood looking up at the sky. Then he lowered his eyes to the scene before him and slowly drew in his breath. It was delicious to be in the country again. The trees, loaded mound upon mound with fresh young green; the pervading hush of the river; the soft clean air tinged with the smell of wet earth and standing water breathed up from the river edge, thrilled him with indescribable delight. He glanced again at the sky. It was bright, too bright, at present, but there were light clouds in the blue and a gentle breeze: there would certainly be intervals of dullness. Not, on the whole, a bad day for fishing. He had made up two fishing casts overnight, seated in the bow window of the sitting room with half a dozen trout flies hanging from his mouth. When the gut was sufficiently soaked, he drew out the flies one by one and carefully knotted them onto the cast. He had decided to use nothing but March Browns, and old Wales, the landlord, had entirely agreed when Dunne had mentioned it to him.

He was ready to start now at any moment, and he stood there in the doorway with his hands in his breeches pockets, impatiently waiting for the sun to stop shining. From time to time in the inn behind him footsteps tapped along the stone-floored passage and died away. But at last he was roused by some that came closer and closer still and finally stopped just behind his back. He swung round. Somebody was waiting to be allowed to pass: a young woman. With a quick apology Dunne moved out of her way and she came out, thanking him with a smile as she passed him, and moved away along the front of the inn, a slim figure in a brown coat and skirt. A white-handled umbrella hung from her left arm: her right hand carried a camp stool and a satchel.

Dunne stood watching her. It was as if in its flying course an invisible flame had swept over him, for the brief glimpse of her face had thrilled him suddenly and profoundly. Only two or three times before had that curious experience befallen him, for he was not easily attracted by women. He stood now, immovable, gazing after her with flushed face, till she vanished around the corner of the house: then he turned back into the inn, his sense resounding with the impression of her. In a few minutes, he reappeared, preceded by the slim point of his rod. He had put on his waders and an old cap stuck with one or two gaudy salmon flies; a creel hung at his left side. His emotion at the sight of the beautiful girl had died down; he was calm again, and now he began to make his way down the little garden path under the elm trees, carefully pointing the wavering tip of the rod into the spaces between the thick hanging foliage. At the river's edge he paused to survey again the gray and golden bridge whose four stone arches towered above him a stone's throw away to his right. Under the two nearest, at this time of the year, there was nothing but dry gravel, thickly overgrown near the bank with a jungle of wild rhubarb. Under the third, the water, brown and clear as ale, babbled shallow over the pebbles. It was only under the fourth, where it washed the farther bank, that the water was deep.

Dunne clambered down, holding his rod carefully in front of him, and began to push through the great funnel-shaped rhubarb leaves. Then, crunching across the gravel bed, he waded through the shallows to a little island within a short cast of a round pool, the very place for a trout. He had watched them rising there on the previous evening as he stood, an hour after his arrival, leaning idly over the parapet of the bridge. It was a deep, round pool, slowly stirred by a circular eddy which swung the streaks of floating spume into narrowing whorls, so that it looked, from above, like a huge polished ammonite. He had decided to fish upstream from that point.

It was years, four years at least, since he had last had a day's fishing, but as he began casting up to the head of the pool, he recovered at once that delicious mood peculiar to the fisherman — a mood composed of conscious craft, expectation, and at the same time a quiet passivity laying the mind open to streams of thoughts and ideas which flow through the brain easily as the flowing of the river, washing it clean of complexities.

The breeze had almost died down. Not a fish was stirring. And, moving slowly upstream, he worked leisurely on for half an hour without getting a single bite. But just as he reached the lower end of another promising pool — a gently swirling pool fed by a narrow and copious flow — the breeze freshened again and the day clouded over. It was ideal now — gray, and with just the right purl on the water.

The fish were beginning to feed. A small one rose in the pool a few yards from where he stood; then, just under the bank, another, a larger one. The sudden musical splash sounded clear and sharp above the monotonous babbling of the water. Then, as though his line were a nerve identifying the finger that held it with every movement of the floating fly, he felt three electric tugs. The end of his rod curved into a hoop, and he began to play the trout.

It was only, he knew at once, a small one — something over a quarter of a pound perhaps; and, though it fought gamely, as a trout always does, Dunne landed it at once. It lay for a moment motionless on the pebbles with helpless, gaping mouth: but as he stooped to take hold of it, suddenly it began to twist and wriggle, tense as a steel spring. Dunne caught it, grasping the firm, wincing body in his left hand while with his right he began to work the hook free of its mouth, twisting and wrenching the pale, talc-like flesh. Then, stooping again, he struck its head against a stone. It lay motionless in his palm now, a limp, exquisite shape of silver, gold, and brown. The delicate cucumber scent of it rose to his nostrils. Between a quarter and half a pound he thought, and dropped it into his creel.

A few minutes later, soon after he had begun to cast again, Dunne experienced a curious repetition of the physical sensation of striking the soft, unresisting creature against the stone. A little shudder ran through his vitals. Curious! Could it have been something disagreeable in the sound of it, or in the sense of the too hard striking the too soft? He shuddered again, but less perceptibly, and then the ceaseless tinkle of the water smoothed the faint scar from his mind. Peaceably, incoherently his thoughts swirled with the swirling clusters of bubbles.

But soon he was thinking coherently again. What was it that happened when he struck the trout's head against the stone and all its exquisite mechanism stopped forever? Was it nothing more than that he broke the delicate motor housed in the little box in the skull? No more than the smashing of a watch? Years ago, old Mr. Worston, the peppery old gentleman who always gave him a sovereign when he went back to school after the summer holidays, smashed his watch against the wall in Hexham station because it was slow and had made him miss the express. Smash! Swinging it the full length of the heavy gold chain. A pulp of little gold wheels and broken glass. Delightful thought! It had delighted him as a boy and it delighted him still. But a watch is hard. To smash something hard . . . a bottle or an egg against a wall . . . how satisfying! But to hit a fish . . . a limp, soft fish . . . and alive! Another faint shudder. All the leaves on the riverbank hissed and rustled suddenly: hurrying gray spearheads shot along the surface of the stream. The wind was freshening.

A twitch. A palpitating tug. He had hooked another; and a few minutes after that there was another, and then another — a much larger one. Such a game one it was that Dunne thought for a moment that it must be a salmon trout. When he landed it, the hook was fixed in the extreme tip of the lower jaw: it was a wonder it had held. A fine fish, fully a pound, the tarnished silver sides spotted with rose. Dunne gazed at it fascinated, curiously inspecting the staring, expressionless eyes, set like the work of a master jeweler in the subtly molded bronze of the head. The slippery body thrilled and stiffened spasmodically in his clenched fingers. Its slipperiness was beginning already to grow viscous against his palm. The foolish mouth gaped patiently, sufferingly, and Dunne suddenly recalled the blanched, tight-lipped mouth of a dying man whom, years ago, he had visited in hospital. He felt his heart contract under his ribs. Then, throwing off his morbid fancies, he stooped down and struck the trout's head against a stone, as he had struck the other. The body stiffened: the tail curved up tensely like a spring. He struck it again and then loosened his grip. The second blow had done it: the body was limp and flaccid now: the life was gone.

Gone where? Could the life be something distinct from the body it actuated . . . could it fly out and escape from the killed fish? A shadow . . . a little puff of cigarette smoke, detaching itself from the fish's mouth . . . floating away? Life must be the same as what some people call the soul . . . The immortality of the soul . . . A fish's soul . . . Jesu, lover of my soul. A flood of the emotion which that hymn always produced in him as a boy. Ancient memories . . . sentimental . . . absurd!

A touch on his face, soft, fluttering. Here he was, standing up to his thighs in water, fishing. A gust of wind was furrowing the water and blowing his line along in a great bow. He reeled in a few yards of it. The breeze stiffened: all his fisherman's skill was needed now, and for the next few minutes his attention was concentrated on throwing a clean line in defiance of the breeze. But it had only been a momentary flurry: soon it had swept on downstream and with the return of calm Dunne dropped back into his former line of thought. . . .

Fishes are cold-blooded creatures without feeling. A comforting idea, but false — mere metaphor and simile drawn from human experience. We know nothing outside our own narrow circle of experience, can never escape into the universal where everything is true and equal. A simple thing to beat the life out of a trout; and yet, when we have done it, what have we done? A mystery. A tremendous act of whose consequences we know nothing. Who can tell? Perhaps the death of a fish changes irrevocably the whole hidden scheme of things. And yet, wherever there is life, there must be death. All life devours life, even the sheep and cows that munch grass. Life feeding on life. Life destroying life that it may live. An endless process . . . process . . . progress . . . progression . . . the scheme of things . . . stream of things . . .

The stream had caught his mind again, caressing it, floating it safely away from all those jarring, sharp-edged thoughts. But now the fish had stopped taking and during the next hour Dunne caught nothing. Yet he fished on, soothed by the peacefully sliding river, his mind sliding with the water over rough and smooth, deep and shallow. Then, discovering that he was hungry, he looked at his watch and began to wade towards the bank.

There he sat down and took out his flask and sandwiches. But before beginning to eat he opened his creel, tumbled out the contents, and arranged them in a row on the grass. They were a nice lot — seven fish ranging from a quarter to half a pound and, at the end, the noble one-pounder. They were dull and gummy now; their clean slipperiness was gone, their iridescence faded. Dunne gazed at them until his mind slipped out of the grooves of habit and again he was gazing at fish for the first time in his life. Strange, unbelievable creatures; mysterious slips of life, swift and spearlike, marvelously designed and colored. He stared at their eyes; for a man, baffled by man or beast, always stares at the eye, that smoldering window of the spirit, and there finds some partial answer to his question. But these quaint metallic disks, stark as the painted eyes of a mask, told him nothing except that their secret was undiscoverable or that there was nothing to discover. They did not even rebuke him, like the eye of a dead bird or animal, for snatching them from their secret world and slaughtering them. Dunne sighed and next moment shrugged his shoulders. After all, such questions as he was asking have no answer. Neither philosophy nor religion casts any light on them. To what category, then, can they belong? To poetry, perhaps: and Dunne, being no poet, but a solicitor and a fisherman, threw the trout back one by one into the creel and began to eat his sandwiches.

The sun came out. He looked anxiously at the sky: this would play the devil with his afternoon. But meanwhile it was delicious to feel its warmth on his back, stealing through coat and shirt. He finished his last sandwich, lit a cigarette, and leaned back full length on the grass. Although the sun was still shining, clouds covered more than half the sky: there was certainly some hope, now, for the afternoon. A luxurious drowsiness overcame him: he closed his eyes for a moment then opened them again. Then he closed them again and this time they remained closed. The cigarette fell from his fingers and lay twining a blue spiral among the tall green grass blades. . . .

He was still fishing. The little brass rings on his rod had sprouted into green leaf-buds. He was fishing in a stream of liquid gold, the Gulf Stream. All at once he noticed that his line was running out noiselessly . . . longer . . . longer . . . longer. He clasped it to the butt of the rod, gripped it with all his strength. When he had almost given up hope, he succeeded at last in holding it. Then slowly he began to reel in, and as he did so the reel tinkled a little tune like a musical box. It was a heavy fish — a pound at least. He reeled away strenuously until he had reeled the cast right out of the water.

A beautiful wooden fish, streaked with scarlet and blue, hung from the end of it. A Chinese fish. Each eye was a gold disk with a daisy in the center of it. He began to sway the rod so that the fish swung to and fro. When it was at the top of its swing he suddenly dipped the rod and the fish dropped on the bank. But the moment it touched earth it began to cry — a horrible human cry. "No! No!" it cried. "No! No! No!" He stood staring at it, appalled, not daring to touch it. Then, bracing himself, he suddenly put his foot on it and immediately swooped upon it to remove the hook. The fish did not move, but its mouth opened and shut spasmodically like an automatic toy and, to his horror, it began to cry again. But soon its voice flagged, died away, fainter . . . fainter . . . It had become almost inaudible when suddenly, as if summoning its last strength, it shouted aloud a single sharp "Ah!"

Dunne awoke. A shaggy dog stood looking at him, wagging its tail. He held out his hand to it and sat up, but the dog flounced away and trotted off along the bank with its tail down. Dunne looked about him. The sun had gone in: conditions were perfect once again. He felt refreshed and clear-headed after his sleep and, scrambling to his feet, he pocketed his flask, took up his rod and creel, and began to work slowly downstream.

During the afternoon he added eight good fish to his catch, and by five o'clock he had got back to the point from which he had started. He reeled in and, securing his cast, waded to the bank. He was looking forward to showing the fish to old Wales. Mrs. Wales would fry the best of them for dinner: she knew how to fry trout perfectly, rolling them first in oatmeal and serving them with melted butter. He climbed up the bank to the little path and, with his rod pointed in front of him, began to make his way cautiously under the elm trees. In the creel behind him a trout not yet dead kept up a dry, persistent rustling.

As he came out in front of the inn he became aware of something unusual. A little group of people was moving towards the door. They were stooping as if carrying something. A few yards from the bridge an empty motor stood at the roadside.

When Dunne came up with the moving group they had reached the inn door. They were carrying something laid on a large sack, as on a stretcher, and with a sudden constriction of the heart he caught sight, between two of the bearers, of an end of brown skirt hanging over the edge of the sack. Hardly knowing what he did, he propped his rod against the house wall and, turning his back on the door, walked away towards the standing car. His instinct had been to escape from something unbearable. Then, pausing dazed where the road dipped from the bridge, he saw lying at the roadside between him and the car a white-handled umbrella. He stooped and gently picked it up and began to carry it to the inn. He felt vaguely that he had found something that he could do for her.

The bearers had vanished indoors. Dunne entered the stone-flagged hall with its pleasant, humble smell of beer and sawdust. A group of women — Mrs. Wales and the three servants — stood with their backs to him at an open door, their heads craning into a great bare room. It was a room unused except in summertime when large parties came to the inn for lunch or tea. Several people were inside. A table was being moved. Dunne, still holding her umbrella, paused beside the women.

"What happened?" he whispered.

One of the maids turned a white face to him. "The car knocked her down," she replied. "It must have come on her when she was crossing the road."

Another turned. "They come so unexpected over that bridge," she said.

Old Mrs. Wales was leaning against the doorpost with her apron to her eyes. Dunne touched her arm. "Is she . . . is she much hurt?" he asked.

The old woman raised her bleared face from the apron and stared at him vacantly. Then her chin began to tremble. "Hurt? She's dead, poor thing!" she whispered.

Twenty-five years later Dunne himself died. He was a bachelor, and his things went to his nephews. They had spent several days in his house, going through cupboards and drawers. Last of all they looked into the attic. It was half dark, but one of them, rummaging among old hatboxes and portmanteaux, pulled out a creel and a fishing rod in a canvas case. Both the creel and the case were cloaked with the gray wool of cobwebs.

"I say, look at this!" the young man called to his brother. "I never knew the uncle was a fisherman."

A Fight with a Trout

Charles Dudley Warner

Trout fishing in the Adirondacks would be a more attractive pastime than it is, but for the popular notion of its danger. The trout is a retiring and harmless animal, except when he is aroused, and forced into a combat; and then his agility, fierceness, and vindictiveness become apparent. No one who has studied the excellent pictures representing men in an open boat, exposed to the assaults of long, enraged trout flying at them through the open air with open mouth, ever ventures with his rod upon the lonely lakes of the forest without a certain terror, or ever reads of the exploits of daring fishermen without a feeling of admiration for their heroism. Most of their adventures are thrilling, and all of them are, in narration, more or less unjust to the trout: in fact, the object of them seems to be to exhibit, at the expense of the trout, the shrewdness, the skill, and the muscular power of the sportsman. My own simple story has few of these recommendations.

We had built our bark camp one summer, and were staying on one of the popular lakes of the Saranac region. It would be a very pretty region if it were not so flat, if the margins of the lakes had not been flooded by dams at the outlets, — which have killed the trees, and left a rim of ghastly deadwood like the swamps of the underworld pictured by Doré's bizarre pencil — and if the pianos at the hotels were in tune. It would be an excellent sporting region also (for there is water enough) if the fish commissioners would stock the waters, and if previous hunters had not pulled all the hair and skin off the deer's tails. Formerly sportsmen had a habit of catching the deer by the tails, and of being dragged in mere wantonness round and round the shores. It is well known, that, if you seize a deer by this "holt," the skin will slip off like the peel from a banana. This reprehensible practice was carried so far, that the traveler is now hourly pained by the sight of peeled-tail deer mournfully sneaking about the wood.

We had been hearing, for weeks, of a small lake in the heart of the virgin forest, some ten miles from our camp, which was alive with trout, unsophisticated, hungry trout: the inlet to it was described as *stiff* with them. In my imagination I saw them lying there in ranks and rows, each a foot long, three tiers deep, a solid mass. The lake had never been visited, except by stray sable hunters in the winter, and was known as the Unknown Pond. I determined to explore it; fully expecting, however, that it would prove to be a delusion, as such mysterious haunts of the trout usually are. I confided my purpose to Luke, and we secretly made our preparations and stole away from the shanty one morning at daybreak. Each of us carried a boat, a pair of blankets, a sack of bread, pork, and maple sugar; while I had my case of rods, creel, and book of flies, and Luke had an ax and the kitchen utensils. We think nothing of loads of this sort in the woods.

Five miles through a tamarack swamp brought us to the inlet of Unknown Pond, upon which we embarked our fleet, and paddled down its vagrant waters. They were at first sluggish, winding among *triste* fir trees, but gradually developed a strong current. At the end of three miles a loud roar ahead warned us that we were approaching rapids, falls, and cascades. We paused. The danger was unknown. We had our choice of shouldering our loads and making a detour through the woods, or of "shooting the rapids." Naturally we chose the more dangerous course. Shooting the rapids has often been described, and I will not repeat the description here. It is needless to say that I drove my frail bark through the boiling rapids, over the successive waterfalls, amid rocks and vicious eddies, and landed, half a mile below, with whitened hair and a boat half full of water; and that the guide was upset, and boat, contents, and man were strewn along the shore.

After this common experience we went quickly on our journey, and, a couple of hours before sundown, reached the lake. If I live to my dying day, I never shall forget its appearance. The lake is almost an exact circle, about a quarter of a mile in diameter. The forest about it was untouched by ax, and unkilled by artificial flooding. The azure water had a perfect setting of evergreens, in which all the shades of the fir, the balsam, the pine, and the spruce, were perfectly blended; and at intervals on the shore in the emerald rim blazed the ruby of the cardinal-flower. It was at once evident that the unruffled waters had never been vexed by the keel of a boat. But what chiefly attracted my attention, and amused me, was the boiling of the water, the bubbling and breaking, as if the lake were a vast kettle, with a fire underneath. A tyro would have been astonished at this common phenomenon; but sportsmen will at once understand me when I say that the water *boiled* with the breaking trout. I studied the surface for some time to see upon what sort of flies they were feeding, in order to suit my cast to their appetites; but they seemed to be at play rather than feeding, leaping high in the air in graceful curves, and tumbling about each other as we see them in the Adirondack pictures.

It is well known that no person who regards his reputation will ever kill a trout with anything but a fly. It requires some training on the part of the trout to take to this method. The uncultivated, unsophisticated trout in unfrequented waters prefers the bait; and the rural people, whose sole object in going a-fishing appears to be to catch fish, indulge them in their primitive taste for the worm. No sportsman, however, will use anything but a fly, except he happens to be alone.

While Luke launched my boat, and arranged his seat in the stern, I prepared my rod and line. The rod is a bamboo, weighing seven ounces, which has to be spliced with a winding of silk thread every time it is used. This is a tedious process; but, by fastening the joints in this way, a uniform spring is secured in the rod. No one devoted to high art would think of using a socket joint. My line was forty yards of untwisted silk upon a multiplying reel. The "leader" (I am very particular about my leaders) had been made to order from a domestic animal with which I had been acquainted. The fisherman requires as good a catgut as the violinist. The interior of the house cat, it is well known, is exceedingly sensitive; but it may not be so well known that the reason why some cats leave the room in distress when a pianoforte is played is because the two instruments are not in the same key, and the vibrations of the chords of the one are in discord with the catgut of the other. On six feet of this superior article I fixed three artificial flies — a simple brown hackle, a gray body with scarlet wings, and one of my own invention, which I thought would be new to the most experienced fly catcher. The trout fly does not resemble any known species of insect. It is a "conventionalized" creation, as we say of ornamentation. The theory is, that, fly fishing being a high art, the fly must not be a tame imitation of nature, but an artistic suggestion of it. It requires an artist to construct one; and not every bungler can take a bit of red flannel, a peacock's feather, a flash of tinsel thread, a cock's plume, a section of a hen's wing, and fabricate a tiny object that will not look like any fly, but still will suggest the universal conventional fly.

I took my stand in the center of the tipsy boat; and Luke shoved off, and slowly paddled towards some lily pads, while I began casting, unlimbering my tools, as it were. The fish had all disappeared. I got out, perhaps, fifty feet of line, with no response, and gradually increased it to one hundred. It is not difficult to learn to cast; but it is difficult to learn not to snap off the flies at every throw. Of this, however, we will not speak. I continued casting for some moments, until I became satisfied that there had been a miscalculation. Either the trout were too green to know what I was at, or they were dissatisfied with my offers. I reeled in, and changed the flies (that is, the fly that was not snapped off). After studying the color of the sky, of the water, and of the foliage, and the moderated light of the afternoon, I put on a series of beguilers, all of a subdued brilliancy, in harmony with the approach of evening. At the second cast, which was a short one, I saw a splash where the leader fell, and gave an excited jerk. The next instant I perceived the game, and did not need the unfeigned "Damn" of Luke to convince me that I had snatched his felt hat from his head, and deposited it among the lilies. Discouraged by this, we whirled about, and paddled over to the inlet, where a little ripple was visible in the tinted light. At the very first cast I saw that the hour had come. Three trout leaped into the air. The danger of this maneuver all fishermen understand. It is one of the commonest in the woods: three heavy trout taking hold at once, rushing in different directions, smash the tackle into flinders. I evaded this catch, and threw again. I recall the moment. A hermit thrush, on the tip of a balsam, uttered his long, liquid, evening note. Happening to look over my shoulder, I saw the peak of Marcy gleam rosy in the sky (I can't help it that Marcy is fifty miles off, and cannot be seen from this region: these incidental touches are always used). The hundred feet of silk swished through the air, and the tail fly fell as lightly on the water as a three-cent piece (which no slamming will give the weight of a ten) drops upon the contribution plate. Instantly there was a rush, a swirl. I struck, and "Got him, by ———!" Never mind what Luke said I got him by. "Out on a fly!" continued that irreverent guide; but I told him to backwater, and make for the center of the lake. The trout, as soon as he felt the prick of the hook, was off like a shot, and took out the whole of the line with a rapidity that made it smoke. "Give him the butt!" shouted Luke. It is the usual remark in such an emergency. I gave him the butt; and, recognizing the fact and my spirit, the trout at once sank to the bottom, and sulked. It is the most dangerous mood of a trout; for you cannot tell what he will do next. We reeled up a little, and waited five minutes for him to reflect. A tightening of the line enraged him, and he soon developed his tactics. Coming to the surface, he made straight for the boat faster than I could reel in, and evidently with hostile intentions. "Look out for him!" cried Luke as he came flying in the air. I evaded him by dropping flat in the bottom of the boat; and, when I picked my traps up, he was spinning across the lake as if he had a new idea: but the line was still fast. He did not run far. I gave him the butt again; a thing he seemed to hate, even as a gift. In a moment the evil-minded fish, lashing the water in his rage, was coming back again, making straight for the boat as before. Luke, who was used to these encounters, having read them in the writings of travelers he had accompanied, raised his paddle in self-defense. The trout left the water about ten feet from the boat, and came directly at me with fiery eyes, his speckled sides flashing like a meteor. I dodged as he whisked by with a vicious slap of his bifurcated tail, and nearly upset the boat. The line was of course slack; and the danger was that he would entangle it about me, and carry away a leg. This was evidently his game; but I untangled it, and only lost a breast-button or two by the swiftly moving string. The trout plunged into the water with a hissing sound, and went away again with all the line on the reel. More butt; more indignation on the part of the captive. The contest had now been going on for half an hour, and I was getting exhausted. We had been back and forth across the lake, and round and round the lake. What I feared was, that the trout would start up the inlet, and wreck us in the bushes. But he had a new fancy, and began the execution of a maneuver which I had never read of. Instead of coming straight towards me, he took a large circle, swimming rapidly, and *gradually contracting his orbit.* I reeled in, and kept my eye on him. Round and round he went, narrowing his circle. I began to suspect the game; which was, to twist my head off. When he had reduced the radius of his circle to about twenty-five feet, he struck a tremendous pace through the water. It would be false modesty in a sportsman to say that I was not equal to the occasion. Instead of turning around with him, as he expected, I stepped to the bow, braced myself, and let the boat swing. Round went the fish, and round we went like a top. I saw a line of Mount Marcys all around the horizon; the rosy tint in the west made a broad band of pink along the sky above the treetops; the evening star was a perfect circle of light, a hoop of gold in the heavens. We whirled and reeled, and reeled and whirled. I was willing to give the malicious beast butt and line, and all, if he would only go the other way for a change.

When I came to myself, Luke was gaffing the trout at the boat side. After we had got him in, and dressed him, he weighed three-quarters of a pound. Fish always lose by being "got in and dressed." It is best to weigh them while they are in the water. The only really large one I ever caught got away with my leader when I first struck him. He weighed ten pounds.

Big Two-Hearted River: Part II

Ernest Hemingway

In the morning the sun was up and the tent was starting to get hot. Nick crawled out under the mosquito netting stretched across the mouth of the tent, to look at the morning. The grass was wet on his hands as he came out. He held his trousers and his shoes in his hands. The sun was just up over the hill. There was the meadow, the river and the swamp. There were birch trees in the green of the swamp on the other side of the river.

The river was clear and smoothly fast in the early morning. Down about two hundred yards were three logs all the way across the stream. They made the water smooth and deep above them. As Nick watched, a mink crossed the river on the logs and went into the swamp. Nick was excited. He was excited by the early morning and the river. He was really too hurried to eat breakfast, but he knew he must. He built a little fire and put on the coffeepot.

While the water was heating in the pot he took an empty bottle and went down over the edge of the high ground to the meadow. The meadow was wet with dew and Nick wanted to catch grasshoppers for bait before the sun dried the grass. He found plenty of good grasshoppers. They were at the base of the grass stems. Sometimes they clung to a grass stem. They were cold and wet with the dew, and could not jump until the sun warmed them. Nick picked them up, taking only the medium-sized brown ones, and put them into the bottle. He turned over a log and just under the shelter of the edge were several hundred hoppers. It was a grasshopper lodging house. Nick put about fifty of the medium browns into the bottle. While he was picking up the hoppers the others warmed in the sun and commenced to hop away. They flew when they hopped. At first they made one flight and stayed stiff when they landed, as though they were dead.

Nick knew that by the time he was through with breakfast they would be as lively as ever. Without dew in the grass it would take him all day to catch a bottle full of good grasshoppers and he would have to crush many of them, slamming at them with his hat. He washed his hands at the stream. He was excited to be near it. Then he walked up to the tent. The hoppers were already jumping stiffly in the grass. In the bottle, warmed by the sun, they were jumping in a mass. Nick put in a pine stick as a cork. It plugged the mouth of the bottle enough, so the hoppers could not get out and left plenty of air passage.

He had rolled the log back and knew he could get grasshoppers there every morning.

Nick laid the bottle full of jumping grasshoppers against a pine trunk. Rapidly he mixed some buckwheat flour with water and stirred it smooth, one cup of flour, one cup of water. He put a handful of coffee in the pot and dipped a lump of grease out of a can and slid it sputtering across the hot skillet. On the smoking skillet he poured smoothly the buckwheat batter. It spread like lava, the grease spitting sharply. Around the edges the buckwheat cake began to firm, then brown, then crisp. The surface was bubbling slowly to porousness. Nick pushed under the browned under surface with a fresh pine chip. He shook the skillet sideways and the cake was loose on the surface. I won't try and flop it, he thought. He slid the chip of clean wood all the way under the cake, and flopped it over onto its face. It sputtered in the pan.

When it was cooked Nick regreased the skillet. He used all the batter. It made another big flapjack and one smaller one.

Nick ate a big flapjack and a smaller one, covered with apple butter. He put apple butter on the third cake, folded it over twice, wrapped it in oiled paper and put it in his shirt pocket. He put the apple butter jar back in the pack and cut bread for two sandwiches.

In the pack he found a big onion. He sliced it in two and peeled the silky outer skin. Then he cut one half into slices and made onion sandwiches. He wrapped them in oiled paper and buttoned them in the other pocket of his khaki shirt. He turned the skillet upside down on the grill, drank the coffee, sweetened and yellow brown with the condensed milk in it, and tidied up the camp. It was a good camp.

Nick took his fly rod out of the leather rod case, jointed it, and shoved the rod case back into the tent. He put on the reel and threaded the line through the guides. He had to hold it from hand to hand, as he threaded it, or it would slip back through its own weight. It was a heavy, double tapered fly line. Nick had paid eight dollars for it a long time ago. It was made heavy to lift back in the air and come forward flat and heavy and straight to make it possible to cast a fly which has no weight. Nick opened the aluminum leader box. The leaders were coiled between the damp flannel pads. Nick had wet the pads at the water cooler on the train up to St. Ignace. In the damp pads the gut leaders had softened and Nick unrolled one and tied it by a loop at the end to the heavy fly line. He fastened a hook on the end of the leader. It was a small hook; very thin and springy.

Nick took it from his hook book, sitting with the rod across his lap. He tested the knot and the spring of the rod by pulling the line taut. It was a good feeling. He was careful not to let the hook bite into his finger.

He started down to the stream, holding his rod, the bottle of grasshoppers hung from his neck by a thong tied in half hitches around the neck of the bottle. His landing net hung by a hook from his belt. Over his shoulder was a long flour sack tied at each corner into an ear. The cord went over his shoulder. The sack flapped against his legs.

Nick felt awkward and professionally happy with all his equipment hanging from him. The grasshopper bottle swung against his chest. In his shirt the breast pockets bulged against him with the lunch and his fly book.

He stepped into the stream. It was a shock. His trousers clung tight to his legs. His shoes felt the gravel. The water was a rising cold shock.

Rushing, the current sucked against his legs. Where he stepped in, the water was over his knees. He waded with the current. The gravel slid under his shoes. He looked down at the swirl of water below each leg and tipped up the bottle to get a grasshopper.

The first grasshopper gave a jump in the neck of the bottle and went out into the water. He was sucked under in the whirl by Nick's right leg and came to the surface a little way downstream. He floated rapidly, kicking. In a quick circle, breaking the smooth surface of the water, he disappeared. A trout had taken him.

Another hopper poked his face out of the bottle. His antennae wavered. He was getting his front legs out of the bottle to jump. Nick took him by the head and held him while he threaded the slim hook under his chin, down through his thorax and into the last segments of his abdomen. The grasshopper took hold of the hook with his front feet, spitting tobacco juice on it. Nick dropped him into the water.

Holding the rod in his right hand he let out line against the pull of the grasshopper in the current. He stripped off line from the reel with his left hand and let it run free. He could see the hopper in the little waves of the current. It went out of sight.

There was a tug on the line. Nick pulled against the taut line. It was his first strike. Holding the now living rod across the current, he brought in the line with his left hand. The rod bent in jerks, the trout pumping against the current. Nick knew it was a small one. He lifted the rod straight up in the air. It bowed with the pull.

He saw the trout in the water jerking with his head and body against the shifting tangent of the line in the stream.

Nick took the line in his left hand and pulled the trout thumping tiredly against the current, to the surface. His back was mottled the clear, water-over-gravel color, his side flashing in the sun. The rod under his right arm, Nick stooped, dipping his right hand into the current. He held the trout, never still, with his moist right hand, while he unhooked the barb from his mouth, then dropped him back into the stream.

He hung unsteadily in the current, then settled to the bottom beside a stone. Nick reached down his hand to touch him, his arm to the elbow under water. The trout was steady in the moving stream, resting on the gravel, beside a stone. As Nick's fingers touched him, touched his smooth, cool, underwater feeling he was gone, gone in a shadow across the bottom of the stream.

He's all right, Nick thought. He was only tired.

He had wet his hand before he touched the trout, so he would not disturb the delicate mucus that covered him. If a trout was touched with a dry hand, a white fungus attacked the unprotected spot. Years before when he had fished crowded streams, with fly fishermen ahead of him and behind him, Nick had again and again come on dead trout, furry with white fungus, drifted against a rock, or floating belly up in some pool. Nick did not like to fish with other men on the river. Unless they were of your party, they spoiled it.

He wallowed down the stream, above his knees in the current, through the fifty yards of shallow water above the pile of logs that crossed the stream. He did not rebait his hook and held it in his hand as he waded. He was certain he could catch small trout in the shallows, but he did not want them. There would be no big trout in the shallows this time of day.

Now the water deepened up his thighs sharply and coldly. Ahead was the smooth dammed-back flood of water above the logs. The water was smooth and dark; on the left, the lower edge of the meadow; on the right the swamp.

Nick leaned back against the current and took a hopper from the bottle. He threaded the hopper on the hook and spat on him for good luck. Then he pulled several yards of line from the reel and tossed the hopper out ahead onto the fast, dark water. It floated down towards the logs, then the weight of the line pulled the bait under the surface. Nick held the rod in his right hand, letting the line run out through his fingers.

There was a long tug. Nick struck and the rod came alive and dangerous, bent double, the line tightening, coming out of water, tightening, all in a heavy, dangerous, steady pull. Nick felt the moment when the leader would break if the strain increased and let the line go.

The reel ratcheted into a mechanical shriek as the line went out in a rush. Too fast. Nick could not check it, the line rushing out, the reel note rising as the line ran out.

With the core of the reel showing, his heart feeling stopped with the excitement, leaning back against the current that mounted icily his thighs, Nick thumbed the reel hard with his left hand. It was awkward getting his thumb inside the fly reel frame.

As he put on pressure the line tightened into sudden hardness and beyond the logs a huge trout went high out of water. As he jumped, Nick lowered the tip of the rod. But he felt, as he dropped the tip to ease the strain, the moment when the strain was too great; the hardness too tight. Of course, the leader had broken. There was no mistaking the feeling when all spring left the line and it became dry and hard. Then it went slack.

His mouth dry, his heart down, Nick reeled in. He had never seen so big a trout. There was a heaviness, a power not to be held, and then the bulk of him, as he jumped. He looked as broad as a salmon.

Nick's hand was shaky. He reeled in slowly. The thrill had been too much. He felt, vaguely, a little sick, as though it would be better to sit down.

The leader had broken where the hook was tied to it. Nick took it in his hand. He thought of the trout somewhere on the bottom, holding himself steady over the gravel, far down below the light, under the logs, with the hook in his jaw. Nick knew the trout's teeth would cut through the snell of the hook. The hook would imbed itself in his jaw. He'd bet the trout was angry. Anything that size would be angry. That was a trout. He had been solidly hooked. Solid as a rock. He felt like a rock, too, before he started off. By God, he was a big one. By God, he was the biggest one I ever heard of.

Nick climbed out onto the meadow and stood, water running down his trousers and out of his shoes, his shoes squelchy. He went over and sat on the logs. He did not want to rush his sensations any.

He wriggled his toes in the water, in his shoes, and got out a cigarette from his breast pocket. He lit it and tossed the match into the fast water below the logs. A tiny trout rose at the match, as it swung around in the fast current. Nick laughed. He would finish the cigarette.

He sat on the logs, smoking, drying in the sun, the sun warm on his back, the river shallow ahead entering the woods, curving into the woods, shallows, light glittering, big water-smooth rocks, cedars along the bank and white birches, the logs warm in the sun, smooth to sit on, without bark, gray to the touch; slowly the feeling of disappointment left him. It went away slowly, the feeling of disappointment that came sharply after the thrill that made his shoulders ache. It was all right now. His rod lying out on the logs, Nick tied a new hook on the leader, pulling the gut tight until it grimped into itself in a hard knot.

He baited up, then picked up the rod and walked to the far end of the logs to get into the water where it was not too deep. Under and beyond the logs was a deep pool. Nick walked around the shallow shelf near the swamp shore until he came out on the shallow bed of the stream.

On the left, where the meadow ended and the woods began, a great elm tree was uprooted. Gone over in a storm, it lay back into the woods, its roots clotted with dirt, grass growing in them, rising a solid bank beside the stream. The river cut to the edge of the uprooted tree. From where Nick stood he could see deep channels, like ruts, cut in the shallow bed of the stream by the flow of the current. Pebbly where he stood and pebbly and full of boulders beyond; where it curved near the tree roots, the bed of the stream was marly and between the ruts of deep water green weed fronds swung in the current.

Nick swung the rod back over his shoulder and forward, and the line, curving forward, laid the grasshopper down on one of the deep channels in the weeds. A trout struck and Nick hooked him.

Holding the rod far out toward the uprooted tree and sloshing backward in the current, Nick worked the trout, plunging, the rod bending alive, out of the danger of the weeds into the open river. Holding the rod, pumping alive against the current, Nick brought the trout in. He rushed, but always came, the spring of the rod yielding to the rushes, sometimes jerking under water, but always bringing him in. Nick eased downstream with the rushes. The rod above his head he led the trout over the net, then lifted.

The trout hung heavy in the net, mottled trout back and silver sides in the meshes. Nick unhooked him; heavy sides, good to hold, big undershot jaw, and slipped him, heaving and big sliding, into the long sack that hung from his shoulders in the water.

Nick spread the mouth of the sack against the current and it filled, heavy with water. He held it up, the bottom in the stream, and the water poured out through the sides. Inside at the bottom was the big trout, alive in the water.

Nick moved downstream. The sack out ahead of him sunk heavy in the water, pulling from his shoulders.

It was getting hot, the sun hot on the back of his neck.

Nick had one good trout. He did not care about getting many trout. Now the stream was shallow and wide. There were trees along both banks. The trees of the left bank made short shadows on the current in the forenoon sun. Nick knew there were trout in each shadow. In the afternoon, after the sun had crossed toward the hills, the trout would be in the cool shadows on the other side of the stream.

The very biggest ones would lie up close to the bank. You could always pick them up there on the Black. When the sun was down they all moved out into the current. Just when the sun made the water blinding in the glare before it went down, you were liable to strike a big trout anywhere in the current. It was almost impossible to fish then, the surface of the water was blinding as a mirror in the sun. Of course, you could fish upstream, but in a stream like the Black, or this, you had to wallow against the current and in a deep place, the water piled up on you. It was no fun to fish upstream with this much current.

Nick moved along through the shallow stretch watching the banks for deep holes. A beech tree grew close beside the river, so that the branches hung down into the water. The stream went back in under the leaves. There were always trout in a place like that.

Nick did not care about fishing that hole. He was sure he would get hooked in the branches.

It looked deep though. He dropped the grasshopper so the current took it under water, back in under the overhanging branch. The line pulled hard and Nick struck. The trout threshed heavily, half out of water in the leaves and branches. The line was caught. Nick pulled hard and the trout was off. He reeled in and holding the hook in his hand, walked down the stream.

Ahead, close to the left bank, was a big log. Nick saw it was hollow; pointing upriver the current entered it smoothly, only a little ripple spread each side of the log. The water was deepening. The top of the hollow log was gray and dry. It was partly in the shadow.

Nick took the cork out of the grasshopper bottle and a hopper clung to it. He picked him off, hooked him and tossed him out. He held the rod far out so that the hopper on the water moved into the current flowing into the hollow log. Nick lowered the rod and the hopper floated in. There was a heavy strike. Nick swung the rod against the pull. It felt as though he were hooked into the log itself, except for the live feeling.

He tried to force the fish out into the current. It came, heavily.

The line went slack and Nick thought the trout was gone. Then he saw him, very near, in the current, shaking his head, trying to get the hook out. His mouth was clamped shut. He was fighting the hook in the clear flowing current.

Looping in the line with his left hand, Nick swung the rod to make the line taut and tried to lead the trout toward the net, but he was gone, out of sight, the line pumping. Nick fought him against the current, letting him thump in the water against the spring of the rod. He shifted the rod to his left hand, worked the trout upstream, holding his weight, fighting on the rod, and then let him down into the net. He lifted him clear of the water, a heavy half circle in the net, the net dripping, unhooked him and slid him into the sack.

He spread the mouth of the sack and looked down in at the two big trout alive in the water.

Through the deepening water, Nick waded over to the hollow log. He took the sack off, over his head, the trout flopping as it came out of water, and hung it so the trout were deep in the water. Then he pulled himself up on the log and sat, the water from his trousers and boots running down into the stream. He laid his rod down, moved along to the shady end of the log and took the sandwiches out of his pocket. He dipped the sandwiches in the cold water. The current carried away the crumbs. He ate the sandwiches and dipped his hat full of water to drink, the water running out through his hat just ahead of his drinking.

It was cool in the shade, sitting on the log. He took a cigarette out and struck a match to light it. The match sunk into the gray wood, making a tiny furrow. Nick leaned over the side of the log, found a hard place and lit the match. He sat smoking and watching the river.

Ahead the river narrowed and went into a swamp. The river became smooth and deep and the swamp looked solid with cedar trees, their trunks close together, their branches solid. It would not be possible to walk through a swamp like that. The branches grew so low. You would have to keep almost level with the ground to move at all. You could not crash through the branches. That must be why the animals that lived in swamps were built the way they were, Nick thought.

He wished he had brought something to read. He felt like

reading. He did not feel like going on into the swamp. He looked down the river. A big cedar slanted all the way across the stream. Beyond that the river went into the swamp.

Nick did not want to go in there now. He felt a reaction against deep wading with the water deepening up under his armpits, to hook big trout in places impossible to land them. In the swamp the banks were bare, the big cedars came together overhead, the sun did not come through, except in patches; in the fast deep water, in the half light, the fishing would be tragic. In the swamp fishing was a tragic adventure. Nick did not want it. He did not want to go down the stream any further today.

He took out his knife, opened it and stuck it in the log. Then he pulled up the sack, reached into it and brought out one of the trout. Holding him near the tail, hard to hold, alive, in his hand, he whacked him against the log. The trout quivered, rigid. Nick laid him on the log in the shade and broke the neck of the other fish the same way. He laid them side by side on the log. They were fine trout.

Nick cleaned them, slitting them from the vent to the tip of the jaw. All the insides and the gills and tongue came out in one piece. They were both males; long gray-white strips of milt, smooth and clean. All the insides clean and compact, coming out all together. Nick tossed the offal ashore for the minks to find.

He washed the trout in the stream. When he held them back up in the water they looked like live fish. Their color was not gone yet. He washed his hands and dried them on the log. Then he laid the trout on the sack spread out on the log, rolled them up in it, tied the bundle and put it in the landing net. His knife was still standing, blade stuck in the log. He cleaned it on the wood and put it in his pocket.

Nick stood up on the log, holding his rod, the landing net hanging heavy, then stepped into the water and splashed ashore. He climbed the bank and cut up into the woods, toward the high ground. He was going back to camp. He looked back. The river just showed through the trees. There were plenty of days coming when he could fish the swamp.

Trout Widows

Corey Ford

The papers were filled with the details of the Twitchells' divorce last week. You may have noticed it, because it was rather an unusual case. All the wife did, according to the story, was to send her husband's felt hat to the cleaner. "Absolutely all I did, your Honor," she explained to the judge, in filing suit on the grounds of desertion, incompatibility, and cruel and unusual punishment, "was just to take this dirty old hat that he'd been wearing for years, with grease stains all over it and the top crushed in like a muffin and the hatband practically ripped to pieces where he'd kept trout flies in it, and send it around the corner to be cleaned and blocked. And then he came home, and took one look at it, and began smashing the furniture and throwing it at me, and setting fire to the house in several places."

I knew the husband in this case pretty well, as it happened. His name was Herbert Twitchell, and he was as mild-mannered and considerate a chap as you would ever want to go fishing with. He belonged to the Mayfly Club on the Beaverkill, and he was one of the most popular anglers on the stream. I never saw him lose his temper when his backcast caught in a balsam, or a heavy shower came up just in time to spoil the evening hatch, or when he got pebbles down inside his waders. We all thought a lot of Herbert, but I must admit none of us was particularly surprised when things sort of blew up with him at home. We had seen it coming for a long time.

"In fact, I wouldn't be surprised if it happened any day now," Mac was saying at the Mayfly Club, only the other evening. We had all dropped into Charlie's room as usual after we had come off the stream, to have a quick one and hear Charlie tell how the barb came out just as he had his trout at the net or it would have gone easily three pounds, maybe four or five, and the conversation had drifted around to Herbert. "I mean, he hasn't shown up here at the club for several days," Mac said, leaning back in Charlie's chair and crossing his boots on Charlie's pillow, "and you take the way he's been acting so funny lately and all, I personally wouldn't be at all surprised if she — " He paused just a moment on the word "she" — "had been getting at him again."

"She's going to get at him once too often," Cliff nodded darkly, pouring himself another drink from Charlie's bottle. "You mark my words."

"When a nice quiet fellow like Herbert lets go," said Tom, "he lets go all of a sudden. Like a one-horse sleigh."

We all paused and looked at him expectantly.

"What is it, Charlie?" asked Tom.

"I just said 'shay,' " said Charlie sullenly. "Herbert's like a one-horse shay."

"That's just what I was saying," said Tom. "She's got him to a point where sooner or later he's bound to let go."

"You'd think a wife would more or less encourage her husband if he had some healthy outdoor hobby like fishing," said Mac, borrowing one of Charlie's cigarettes. "I mean, you'd expect that a wife would make some effort to share her husband's interest a little. Like you take my own wife, the other day she actually objected to cleaning some fish I brought home. She said she was sick of the smell of fish."

"I know how it is," Tom nodded. "My wife objects like that sometimes to my fishing coat."

"Speaking of fish," Charlie began eagerly, "I had hold of one today — "

We all looked at Charlie for a moment, and looked away again.

"Anyway," said Mac after a pause, "I wouldn't be at all surprised if something happened with Herbert almost any time. You can drive a man just so far."

"He's bound to crack sooner or later," said Tom.

Cliff nodded. "You mark my words," he said solemnly.

I guess that Herbert was pretty much on my mind, because I remember mentioning him to Mary when I got home from the Beaverkill that night. Mary is my wife and she is really what you might call the fisherman's ideal wife. That is, she never asks me whether my feet are wet; she never questions my alibis; she never objects if I borrow several choice feathers from her hat to tie some special pattern of fly, and in all the years that we have been married she has never asked me whether I wouldn't catch more fish if I used a worm. Other wives, like Herbert's wife, for instance, are forever nagging their husbands and complaining about minor details like getting up at four in the morning to fix him a little light lunch; but Mary has invariably displayed a sympathetic attitude toward my fishing, and she has never, so far as I know, exhibited the slightest symptom of malignant anglerphobia, or an acute dislike for trout, which gets to bother so many women who marry fishermen. That is, up to this same night I happened to mention Herbert.

As a matter of fact, the subject of Herbert arose in a rather curious manner. I was having a late supper. I know some men's wives get pretty wrought up when their husbands are late for supper, and fold their arms, and tread around and around the kitchen with little puffs of smoke rising from the soles of their feet; but Mary always has everything piping hot, and serves it without a word of complaint, and then sits and watches me eat it with a sad sweet smile. Sometimes she murmurs, "I know those popovers are ruined, John; you don't have to pretend to eat them," or "I worked on that pudding for you all afternoon, but of course it's all dried out now after being in the oven three hours," and occasionally she will borrow my handkerchief to dab at her eyes a little — I have never understood why women who cry never carry their own handkerchiefs — but all I have to do is to pat her hand and tell her to go buy herself another bureau. Mary is very fond of antique furniture, and I can always fix things up by telling her to buy another old chair or bureau. In the course of the past ten years, I have probably bought enough chairs and bureaus to furnish a sizable summer hotel. As I was saying, I was enjoying my supper, and regaling her between mouthfuls with various items of news that I thought would be of interest.

"Like, for instance, you take a day like today," I told her, "all lowry and overcast, the average person would say under those conditions that a bright fly, like a Coachman or even a Pink Lady, would be the killer, but here were Tom and Mac and the others all trying everything they had, and yet I put on this number fourteen Whirling Dun that I'd tied with medium-light starling wings, mole-fur body with two turns of gold tinsel around the hook at the end, glossy ginger-hackle legs, and just three whisks of it for the tail — "

I noticed that Mary was sitting in her usual attitude of rapt attention, with both elbows on the table and her fingers laced together like a hammock, and her chin resting on her fingers. She kept nodding silently, "Of course," and her eyes wandered over the table and around the room and up to the ceiling. I took another mouthful.

"Because you can say all you want about color," I insisted, gesturing emphatically with my fork, "but I, personally, think that trout must be aware of color, because otherwise how would they have distinguished my dark fly today and not paid any attention to Mac's or Tom's. It is my own personal theory — "

"John," said Mary suddenly, "do you like that stuffed trout over the mantel?"

I paused and looked at her in surprise. "Of course I like it," I said. "That's the first big rainbow I ever took out of the

Beaverkill. In fact, that trout is really an illustration of what I was saying just now about color." I resumed eating again. "I remember I just happened to have these few Royal Coachmen that I had bought in a little tackle store near Roscoe that morning, and it seems the old storekeeper must have had them lying in his window for years exposed to the sun, because the red was faded several shades lighter than the regular standard tie. . . ." I had a sudden cold premonition, and I set down my fork abruptly. "Mary."

"What is it, dear?"

"Mary," I said slowly, "why did you ask me just now whether I liked that stuffed trout?"

"I just wondered whether you liked it, that's all."

"What made you think maybe I wouldn't like it? Don't you like it?"

"Of course I like it, dear, only I wondered whether it might look all right somewhere else than over the mantel."

"What's the matter with it over the mantel? What else would you put over the mantel if you didn't have that trout?"

"Well," said Mary. "I thought maybe father's picture."

"Do you mean to imply," I almost shouted, "that you think your father is better-looking than a stuffed trout?"

Mary began to cry. "My father was a fisherman, too," she said, a little irrelevantly, I thought.

"We won't say anything more about it," I said firmly, and I continued to eat for several moments in silence. "That trout will remain over the mantel, of course." I took another mouthful. "I hope I don't have to mention it again."

Mary shook her head.

"We'll just drop the entire subject, Mary, if you don't mind."

"Yes, John," she said.

"I prefer not to discuss it further."

"No, dear."

I put down my fork again. Another thought had just struck me.

"As a matter of fact," I said, "how did you ever happen to think of moving that trout in the first place?"

"I don't know," said Mary. "I just thought of it."

"I mean, did anybody suggest it to you?"

She shook her head.

"Was your mother here today, by any chance?"

"No, John," she said.

"You mean to say you just thought of it by yourself?"

She nodded but didn't say anything.

I could feel a cold lump in the pit of my stomach.

"Mary," I said very slowly, "are you getting like that, too?"

"Like what too?" she asked, a little frightened.

"Like Herbert's wife."

"Who's Herbert?"

"Mary," I said, "I think we ought to understand each other very plainly about this whole thing."

"Eat your supper, dear," said Mary.

"Mary," I said, "I don't suppose you know what this sort of thing could lead to?"

"Dear, please eat your supper."

"I don't suppose you realize that it's just this sort of thing that has practically wrecked the Twitchells' home. I don't suppose you are aware how little things like this have turned the Twitchells' life into a veritable living hell — "

"Who are the Twitchells?" asked Mary.

So I told her about the Twitchells. . . .

The whole trouble with the Twitchells — as I tried to explain to Mary — was that Herbert's wife did not understand fishermen.

Herbert was a typical fisherman. That is, he had certain little traits and foibles that doubtless endear fishermen to their associates but are apt to set them more or less apart from other people, such as their wives. These traits date way back to prehistoric days when men used to live together in crude fishing camps and wring out their socks every night in the fireplace; and there is nothing whatsoever that can be done about them. Fishermen, for example, always throw matches on the floor. No matter how many ashtrays their wives set in front of them, their matches always end up on the floor. They track their muddy boots through the house, and when they take them off they scatter sand and pieces of sharp gravel on the rug beside the bed.

They drop their waders on the front porch; they knot their wading shoes together and drape them over the bannisters; they take off their wet pants in the kitchen and they hang their underclothes to dry in the parlor. They use the best linen guest towels to wipe their reels. They leave fishhooks in upholstered chairs. They demand their breakfast at dawn — "Isn't that coffee ready yet; here it is after four!" — and they are anywhere from two to six hours late for dinner. They are jumpy, irritable and moody over the winter, and during late February and March they are apt to break off abruptly in the midst of a conversation and sit staring into space for an hour. When they come home with a nice mess of trout they are insufferable, and when they come home without any fish at all they are unbearable. They always blame their wives for the weather.

Unfortunately, a wife who is married to a fisherman (and the same thing holds for golf wives, hunting wives, tennis wives, bowling wives, squash wives, skeet wives, badminton wives, and the wives of men who just sit all night and listen to the radio) never gets to see her husband often enough to learn to appreciate these tiny idiosyncrasies of his, and to make due allowance for them. An Antarctic explorer's wife, for example, sees her husband now and then between trips; even a flagpole-sitter's wife meets her husband while he is climbing down to change flagpoles; but a fisherman's wife only encounters her husband at odd moments, such as when he trips over her bed to turn off the alarm clock or bumps into her in the hall while carrying his tackle upstairs (for some reason, fishermen spend a great deal of time carrying their tackle upstairs and then carrying it down again), and his remarks on these occasions are limited to comments like "Where in the name of sweet gosh did you deliberately hide my socks with the red tops?" Sometimes, at the height of the season, he will encounter his wife on the street and stare at her for several minutes in an obvious effort to recall where he has seen her before, tip his hat politely, and walk on with a faintly puzzled expression.

The only thing a wife can do, under these circumstances, is to take into account the fact that her husband is under considerable emotional strain, and be careful not to heckle him with trifles such as household bills, the furnace, or the fact that his office phoned three times that day to find out where he had been. If a wife will make certain allowances for her husband like this, and in addition keep out of his way as much as possible during fishing season, I said to Mary, she could avoid to a very large extent the trouble the Twitchells were having.

The Twitchells were married about two years ago and everybody thought at the time that they would be very happy together. In fact, people referred to them as an ideal couple. "Herbert and Edith really make an ideal couple, don't you think?" they all said. Of course, Edith did not care anything about fishing; but Herbert assured us at the reception after the wedding that this was really a good thing. "For one thing, she'll never try to come along on a fishing trip," he laughed, putting his arm around her, "and fall out of the canoe or get her hook caught in a tree, or throw back a trout because the poor thing seemed to be suffering." He kissed her. "Will you, honey?"

"I really don't know the first thing about fishing," she confessed with a shy smile. "I wouldn't know one pole from another."

"Pole!" Herbert repeated, and nudged us with a wink. "She calls a rod a 'pole.' Gee, I get a kick out of that."

"I mean, I wouldn't even know how to work that little pulley thing that holds the string — "

"Pulley! String!" Herbert howled. "I ask you. Isn't that cute?"

We all assured him that it was very, very cute.

They went to Florida for their honeymoon — Herbert had always had an ambition to try some of that tarpon-fishing in the Gulf — and when they came back they settled down in a comfortable little house in the suburbs. Herbert put all his fishing tackle in a special den of his own, and never used the rest of the house except maybe to hang his rods in the kitchen while the varnish was drying, or to practice a little casting now and then in the parlor; and they seemed to be very happy together. To be sure, he began to act more and more absent-minded as April drew near, and occasionally that faraway look would come into his eyes and he would begin to hum to himself or finger the pages of a fishing catalog idly; and once Edith asked him rather sharply: "Herbert, what on earth are you moping about?" But Herbert merely rose in silence, and went upstairs to his den and shut the door, and the incident was soon forgotten. The first sign of a rift in the lute appeared when Herbert showed up at the Mayfly Club that spring.

"How's Edith?" we asked.

"She's all right, I guess," said Herbert without much enthusiasm.

"Is anything the matter?"

"Well," said Herbert, "I kind of wish she wouldn't keep calling my rod a pole, that's all."

"I thought you said that was cute."

"It is cute," said Herbert, "but it sort of gets on your nerves after a while. Like when I come downstairs all dressed in my fishing clothes, and carrying my waders and creel and rod case, I wish she wouldn't say: 'Are you going fishing?' "

"What's wrong with that?"

"Well, I suppose there's nothing exactly wrong with it," Herbert admitted, "but I wish she wouldn't ask me if I was sure I hadn't forgotten anything."

"She's probably just trying to be helpful."

"It's a little hard to explain," said Herbert. "But I wish at least she wouldn't tell me to be sure not to fall in and get wet. I guess I can fall in if I want to and get wet."

I looked at Mac, and Mac looked at me, but we did not say anything.

As a matter of fact, the first serious breach did not occur until late that fall, long after fishing season was over. Of course, Edith did not clean up his den on purpose. She did not plan it out ahead of time and deliberately wait her chance until he went away. She just yielded to that impulse which most women have to rearrange things. She said later that all she meant to do was just to straighten up a few things here and there. "I just happened to glance in the door and notice what a mess there was on the floor," she told her mother, when she was able to stop crying, "and I thought I'd try to fix it up for him as a little surprise. I thought he would be pleased."

Well, she got in there with her broom one morning, and she swept that floor as neat as a pin. She picked up a lot of stray flies, and old cleaning rags, and empty spools, and a leather glove with the fingers cut out, and some cigarette tins, and several odds and ends of silk thread, and she threw them all away. She took all his reels and put them in one drawer marked REELS. She took his tapered lines off the driers and rolled them up into a neat ball and put them in a drawer marked LINES. She took his rods out of their cases and wrapped them all together in a newspaper and put them on a shelf marked POLES. She took all his flies and emptied them out of the various little aluminum boxes and celluloid boxes and pillboxes where he kept them, and put them all in one big pasteboard box marked FLIES. She put away his boots in the bottom of the closet, and folded his shirts very carefully, and took everything out of the pockets of his fishing coat and hung it in the closet on a coat hanger. Last, but not least, she put a pink shade on the single bulb he had hanging over his workbench, and spread a rug on the floor, and hung a pair of bright print curtains in the window.

Herbert came home, and he went upstairs as usual to his den. Edith didn't say a word. She heard him open the door, and then she didn't hear anything else for a while. Then she said he called her just once — "Edith!" — in the strangest voice, as though he were choking. She went upstairs, and there he was standing stock-still in the center of his den, with perspiration on his forehead and his mouth going open and shut slowly. Edith said the expression on his face was something she would never forget to her dying day. He looked at her, and then he looked at the room, and then he took the drawer marked REELS and turned it upside down and emptied the contents on the floor. He took the drawer marked LINES and emptied it on top of the reels. He took the pasteboard box marked FLIES and dumped all the flies on the floor on top of the heap. Edith said she was too frightened even to scream. He took all his rods and threw them on the floor, and added his fishing coat, and shirts, and boots, and his cleaning outfit, and his line greaser, and his rod varnish, and slippers, and trout knife, and folding net and creel, and the pink lamp shade, and the print curtains, and he began to stir them around and around with an empty rod case.

"This," he said to Edith, in that same sort of choked voice, "is the way I like things. This is the way I know where they are instead of being put away somewhere. This is the way I always keep them."

He gathered up everything inside the rug, and knotted the corners of the rug together over the end of the rod case, and slung the whole thing over his shoulder.

"I am now going away," he announced to Edith. "I am going fishing in Jasper Park, and hunting in British Columbia and Alaska, and I am going to stay in the bush three months and sleep in my underwear, and grow a mustache. And when I come back I am going to have a look at this room, and if I find you have touched a single solitary thing I am going back into the bush again, and I am not coming out until I have grown a beard, too. I trust that I have made myself clear."

He didn't actually go away for three whole months, because Edith got hysterical and asked some of us to plead with him, and she promised on her word of honor never to tidy up his den again; but he did grow the mustache, and he wears it to this day. He told Edith it would serve to remind her now and then that he meant what he said.

From that time on, Herbert was really a changed man. Slowly but surely he began to revert to type. When he was first married to Edith, he always spruced up, and combed his hair, and put on a coat for dinner; but as the breach between them widened, and his domestic instincts began to yield to the old atavistic urge to hunt and fish once more, we noticed that Herbert seemed to slip back into his earlier habits again. He seldom shaved, and he would go without a haircut for weeks, and he often came to dinner with his boots unlaced and his shirt open at the neck. He picked up his chop bones in his fingers, and several times we saw him wiping his hands on his pants leg. He took up drinking again, and singing ribald songs — Herbert always carried an effective tenor — and he would play poker all night as long as anybody was willing to stay up with him. He spent more and more of his time at the Mayfly Club that spring, and we all observed that his visits home were growing shorter and shorter. His manner was becoming more savage, too.

"She objected to my fishing pipe today," he announced one night, when he returned to the Mayfly after a brief visit with his wife. He always referred to his wife as "she" these days.

"Now, Herbert," we said, "you don't want to let a little thing like that get you."

"A little thing!" Herbert exploded. "I've had that pipe for fifteen years. I've smoked it in fair weather and in foul. I've bitten through the stem, and patched the bowl with adhesive tape, and soaked it in rum to freshen it now and then, and I love that pipe like I love my own — " He broke off short. "When she has traveled as far with me as that pipe has, and remained as sweet, then maybe she can have a right to object. That's what I told her today."

We lowered our eyes. I guess we all could see it coming, by this time.

I shall never forget the day that Herbert arrived at the Mayfly wearing a new shirt. It was bright green, and he was smiling steadily as he drove up to the Club and waved his hand to us on the porch.

"She threw out my old fishing shirt," he called out rather cheerfully. His voice had a high hysterical quality, and his face was flushed.

"Never mind, Herbert," we tried to say casually, as though everything were all right. "You've still got the rest of your outfit."

Herbert shook his head triumphantly. "She gave away my old fishing pants, too. She found that old pair of corduroy pants I always wear, with both knees gone and patches in the seat, and she gave them to the man that takes care of our furnace. She said they were a positive disgrace."

We shifted in our chairs uncomfortably.

"I'm giving her one more chance," said Herbert, yanking his

old fishing hat down firmly over his ears. It was a battered felt hat, with grease stains all over it and the top crushed like a muffin and the hatband bristling with snelled flies like a half-plucked chicken. "One more chance, that's all. If she touches another single thing — "

We watched him in silence as he got in his car and drove on. . . .

Mary looked at me for a moment as I finished the story.

"Is that all?"

I nodded.

"And you haven't seen Herbert since?" she asked.

"We haven't heard a thing," I said.

Mary rose thoughtfully, and gathered up the supper dishes, and walked into the kitchen without a word.

It was just a week later, to the day, that I saw the story of the Twitchells' divorce in the papers. As I say, we had expected all along that it was coming, but it was pretty much of a shock just the same. We were very fond of Herbert, and I guess all of us had more or less secretly hoped that the thing would work itself out somehow. I know the thing knocked me pretty hard. After all, Herbert was a decent well-meaning chap, and he might just as well have married an understanding wife like Mary. It made a man realize how lucky he was, I thought to myself, as I walked home that night with the paper under my arm and sat down at the table and began to eat my supper in silence. Mary was unusually sweet and attentive; kept filling my plate, and offering me things she knew I liked, and she insisted on getting my pipe and matches when I was through. She even came and sat on the arm of my chair and lit my pipe for me.

"Something worrying you, honey?" she asked, fingering my bald spot.

I took a deep drag on my pipe. "You remember I was telling you about Herbert," I said.

I thought her face blanched at the word "Herbert."

"I don't suppose you've seen the papers," I said, handing her the newspaper.

She grabbed the paper, and her hands trembled so hard that

it rattled. Her face was deathly white. I thought it was strange that she should take Herbert's misfortune so hard. She set down the paper with a little cry. "Oh, John," she said.

"What's the matter?" I asked, somewhat startled.

"Oh, John," she said again in a stricken voice.

I noticed she was looking past my shoulder toward the mantel. I turned around and stared blankly at the mantel. The stuffed trout was gone. Her father's picture was hanging in its place.

I did not say anything. I just looked at her. I suppose it was the way I looked. Suddenly she sprang to her feet, pressed her knuckles against her mouth, screamed, "Don't you dare to strike me!" and rushed out of the room. I heard her run upstairs and slam the door of her room and slide the bolt in the door.

I sat for a long time gazing thoughtfully at the picture over the mantel. It was really the first time I had ever taken a good look at Mary's father. He had a long sad face, lined with care, with haggard cheeks and deep-sunken eyes. His eyes were the eyes of a man who had suffered. He seemed to be looking down at me now from the wall with a look of sympathy and understanding in his eyes.

After all, as Mary said, he had been a fisherman himself.

The Trout

Jesse Hill Ford

At the time Coy was eight he had been fishing with his grandfather five years—since he could first remember, when they fished for bream near Royal in the lily pad ponds belonging to old man Paris Austin. Later, after the dam at Muscle Shoals was built, they began journeying to a camp near Guntersville to fish in the backwaters of the Tennessee River. It was twenty miles from Royal, Alabama, where they lived, to the Tennessee River backwaters, and because Grandfather Rickman didn't drive, they would have to get someone to take them there in the car, with their yellow cane poles tied to the outside of it and the minnow buckets rattling inside. Usually Catherine, Coy's aunt, drove them to the fish camp on Goodluck Road, where they rented a boat and paddled out to the drowned trees where the white perch bedded, and there they would sit, with Catherine gone into Guntersville to visit friends for the day while Coy and Grandfather Rickman fished.

It was July, and the boat leaked, so that Coy took turns with the old man bailing out the boat with a pork and beans can, while they drifted and paddled among the trees the river had killed when the dam pushed it out of its banks. They had left the bank early that morning, and when Grandfather Rickman remarked that they had not got a fish and it was nine thirty, the paper label had come off the bean can and was sloshing in the water at Coy's feet. The water reminded him of summer leaves, and the snake doctors which lit on his cork or teetered now and then on the end of the yellow cane pole he held reminded him of airplanes. In the other end of the boat, Grandfather Rickman sat bent forward, looking intently at his own cork, floating beside a shattered gray stump. He seemed a very old and skinny man, hidden except for his face and hands by a long-sleeved shirt and cotton trousers and a felt hat which shaded his light-blue eyes.

Looking back at his own cork, Coy saw a remarkable thing, for it had gone down and under the surface in a swoop. He raised the tip of his pole at once and felt the tug of the fish for an instant before his line came up limp out of the water. The minnow's head was all that remained on the hook.

"I think I had a trout," he said.

"No," said his grandfather, who always spoke in a hushed voice for fear he would alarm the fish, "it was only a gar." And as though to prove the truth of what he said, Grandfather Rickman's pole bent suddenly and he raised the ugly fish to the surface before the hook came with the old man's minnow bitten in two. The gar thrashed the surface once before it faded back, slowly, like a sinking log.

"It felt like a big trout," Coy said.

"The garfish keep the other fish from biting," said his grandfather. "They're mean." He dipped his paddle in the water to move the boat on. "They'll get all our minnows," the old man said. "The scamps."

Coy took up the bean can and began to bail. The water which leaked in was pleasant and cool to his bare feet, and he wished he knew how to swim, for the sun was merciless and hot. He wore only a pair of shorts, and everywhere else he was brown.

He was always brown by the middle of June, lean and brown and growing, and Tennessee seemed far away, for his parents lived in Nashville and he went to school there and associated the city with wintertime. But he thought of Alabama as long summers and elm trees shading his grandmother's house and the smell of cow feed when his grandfather milked every morning and nightfall; of dew on the early-morning grass and of days when the rains flooded the streets of Royal, and the very air which blew and sifted through the rain made the cushions of a chair damp to sit on. And there were the long days, such as this, when they fished until the water turned brassy gold with the sun's decline and the honking of the car horn called them back to the bank.

Paddling back without fish on the stringer was a deep-hurting sense of defeat to Coy, a sensation of dying which his grandfather seemed not to feel, for to the old man, fishing did not have to mean catching fish. To the old man, fishing was a still and quiet patience, a hushed attitude of body, broken only by a laugh of pleasure when Coy pulled a fish out, or a cry of "Hey!" when the old man himself brought a white-sided perch up and into the boat. To Coy, paddling back with a full stringer of fish meant going back with a deep sense of victory in his breast.

"No," said Grandfather Rickman, when they had reached the new spot and were fishing again, near an old bleached tree which had fallen from the bank out into the river, "you'll know a trout if you ever feel one. It's like hooking the bottom, and all of a sudden the bottom begins to move, and then it goes wild, and that fish comes straight up out of the water. It makes a trout mad to hook him."

Coy remembered seeing one trout, a trout Mr. Vilous Lee had caught in one of Mr. Paris Austin's ponds. Mr. Vilous was a butcher, a vindictive fisherman who set out poles at several places along the bank trying to catch catfish, and he had seen the big trout the week before and had rigged an enormous pole with a minnow on the line nearly as long as his hand. Then he had crept far up the bank under the shade of a catalpa tree and waited. He had waited there all day from early morning until midafternoon, when Grandfather Rickman finally shouted, "Watch out, Vilous!" And with that the butcher had run down the long grassy stretch to the bank of the pond. The trout was already hung when he reached the big pole, and the butcher yanked the fish straight out of the water and, laughing in a wild, ugly way, he walked up the bank with the trout still dangling on the line. Coy's father, who was there that day, had said the fish was a large-mouth bass and that, mistakenly, the North Alabama fishermen called these fish trout. But the fish was still a trout to Coy, and to Grandfather Rickman, and to Mr. Vilous Lee. Far up the bank, the trout had struggled free of the hook and fallen to the grass, and the butcher had flung himself on the fish, reaching his rough fingers through its gills and raising it high in the air, making the creature writhe and bleed to be held so cruelly.

They had ridden back into town and weighed the trout on the scales at the grocery where the butcher worked — six pounds. It was the biggest fish Coy had ever seen caught, and he had dreamed afterward that someday he would catch a trout, but, having caught one, he would not feel such a cruel delight. The butcher's cruelty seemed somehow to be tied up with his taking a large spoonful of baking soda occasionally and gagging it down with water. Grandfather Rickman had said Vilous was ruining his stomach by the habit, and sure enough, only a few months before, the butcher had died. When Coy had come back to Royal from Nashville, at the summer's beginning, he had gone to the grocery store and seen a new butcher behind the counter. The new butcher had worked in Birmingham, he said. His name was Clisby, and he didn't fish.

"What happened to Mr. Vilous Lee?" Coy asked, dipping up a can of water from the bottom of the boat and pouring it quietly out into the river.

"Why, you know what happened," Grandfather Rickman said softly. "He died. They buried him."

"But why did Mr. Lee die?"

"They say it was his stomach. He had an operation in Birmingham. Then he came home and got all right, I thought. We went out to the ponds some last fall, before the weather got too cold."

"And then what?"

"Well, he had a spell this spring, and we only went fishing one time."

"Was he still taking soda, Grandpapa?"

"I think he had gone back to his bad habits. Yes," Grandfather Rickman said, after a pause, "I'm sure of it."

Coy thought of Mr. Vilous Lee dying, of a dark-red something in his stomach which the doctors had not been able to help, and he remembered the butcher's thick, freckled hands, and the strange sweet smell of his breath, and the wild, angry look of his eyes. Coy knew instinctively that the butcher *drank,* and that the smell was whisky, and he felt his grandfather's dispassionate disapproval of the habit.

"I didn't like him," Coy said. "He hurt my feelings."

Grandfather Rickman smiled. "You took his catfish off the line. He didn't like for anyone to touch his poles after he had set them out. He didn't think a fish was his unless he had taken it off the hook. You shouldn't dislike him for that." The old man spoke as though the butcher were still alive. "He gave us many a ride to the ponds," he said, after a moment.

"But I still didn't like him," Coy said.

"Well, Vilous never understood children," Grandfather Rickman said. "He didn't know what to say to them. He couldn't talk to a kid. But he was a good friend to me, Coy." Grandfather Rickman's voice had fallen now, for he had felt the butcher's death again, and his face was grave and sad.

Coy bailed the water out, scraping the can until the boat bottom was just barely damp. Then, while he watched, the water began seeping in again. It came in so slowly that he had no patience for it, and he shifted his pole to fish on the other side of the boat, away from the snags beside the old tree, out away from everything, away from the bank, where nothing would bite, where he knew the fish would not be. But he was bored.

Then the fish struck. Coy felt him before he realized the cork was gone under, and he lifted the pole in his trembling arms, fighting against the strength of the fish with his own strength, going so hard upward with the light pole that it bent sharply.

"Easy!" cried Grandfather Rickman. "Play him easy!"

But the pole broke just then, and Coy pulled in the broken

half and held it, his body frozen still by the sight of the trout coming out of the water and landing with a splash. The fish skittered sideways around the end of the boat toward the bank and went down deep again, moving back suddenly toward the river.

"Let him get tired," Grandfather Rickman cautioned. But Coy was already drawing in the broken pole. He reached the line and began frantically pulling the fish in toward the boat.

"No!" cried Grandfather Rickman. "You'll lose him! You'll lose him!"

And just as the old man yelled the second time, the fish came out of the water again, and this time, as he landed, the hook came loose and the line went sick and limp. The trout lay near the surface an instant, nearly exhausted, not realizing it was free. But then, with a flash of its green body, it was gone. Coy drew the hook out of the water and held it in his trembling fingers. It was bent straight. Then he looked at Grandfather Rickman.

"Why couldn't you listen to me?" Grandfather Rickman said. "That was a trout."

Coy could feel himself collapsing inside to an indrawn knot of sorrow in his stomach. Holding the broken cane pole across his lap, he began to weep. "A trout," he cried. "A trout!" There would never be such a victory so close again, and he felt the loss and the anguish slowly killing him.

"There," said Grandfather Rickman. "It's all right." The old man came cautiously forward to pick up the empty bean can. He sat down and began bailing out the boat. "You did the only thing you knew how to do. But if it happens again, don't try to pull him out of the water. Wear him down first."

Coy wiped his eyes on his arm, smelling the salt sweat and the sun in his skin. He nodded, struggling to recover. But he knew the trout would never strike again. It was gone back into the deep cool mystery of the green water, to remain there now, buried forever.